THE BAMPTON LECTURES, 1956

Christian Theology and Natural Science

SOME QUESTIONS
IN THEIR RELATIONS

E. L. Mascall

Student of Christ Church, Oxford
University Lecturer in the Philosophy of Religion
Priest of the Oratory of the Good Shepherd

Mala aurea in lectis argenteis qui loquitur verbum
in tempore suo

PROV. XXV. II.

LONGMANS, GREEN AND CO
LONDON · NEW YORK · TORONTO

LONGMANS, GREEN AND CO LTD
6 & 7 CLIFFORD STREET LONDON W I
BOSTON HOUSE STRAND STREET CAPE TOWN
605–611 LONSDALE STREET MELBOURNE C I

LONGMANS, GREEN AND CO INC
55 FIFTH AVENUE NEW YORK 3

LONGMANS, GREEN AND CO
20 CRANFIELD ROAD TORONTO 16

ORIENT LONGMANS PRIVATE LTD
CALCUTTA BOMBAY MADRAS
DELHI HYDERABAD DACCA

First Published 1956
Second impression (with minor corrections) 1957

PRINTED AND BOUND IN ENGLAND BY
HAZELL WATSON AND VINEY LTD
AYLESBURY AND LONDON

IN PIAM MEMORIAM

VIRI REVERENDI

JOHANNIS BAMPTON

Insignis Ecclesiae Sanctae Mariae

Sarisburensis

CANONICI

Cujus Animae Propitietur Deus

Mais priez Dieu que tous nous vueille absouldre.

Extract from
the Last Will and Testament of the late
REVEREND JOHN BAMPTON
Canon of Salisbury

"... I give and bequeath my Lands and Estates to the Chancellor, Masters, and Scholars of the University of Oxford for ever, to have and to hold all and singular the said Lands or Estates upon trust, and to the intents and purposes hereinafter mentioned; that is to say, I will and appoint that the Vice-Chancellor of the University of Oxford for the time being shall take and receive all the rents, issues, and profits thereof, and (after all taxes, reparations, and necessary deductions made) that he pay all the remainder to the endowment of eight Divinity Lecture Sermons, to be established for ever in the said University, and to be performed in the manner following:

"I direct and appoint, that, upon the first Tuesday in Easter Term, a Lecturer may be yearly chosen by the Heads of Colleges only, and by no others, in the room adjoining to the Printing-House, between the hours of ten in the morning and two in the afternoon, to preach eight Divinity Lecture Sermons, the year following, at St Mary's in Oxford, between the commencement of the last month in Lent Term, and the end of the third week in Act Term.

"Also I direct and appoint, that the eight Divinity Lecture Sermons shall be preached upon either of the following Subjects —to confirm and establish the Christian Faith, and to confute all heretics and schismatics—upon the divine authority of the holy Scriptures—upon the authority of the writings of the primitive Fathers, as to the faith and practice of the primitive Church—upon the Divinity of our Lord and Saviour Jesus Christ—upon the Divinity of the Holy Ghost—upon the Articles of the Christian Faith, as comprehended in the Apostles' and Nicene Creed.

"Also I direct, that thirty copies of the eight Divinity Lecture Sermons shall be always printed, within two months after they are preached; and one copy shall be given to the Chancellor of the University, and one copy to the Head of every College, and one copy to the Mayor of the City of Oxford, and one copy to be put into the Bodleian Library; and the expense of printing them shall be paid out of the revenue of the Land or Estates given for establishing the Divinity Lecture Sermons; and the Preacher shall not be paid, nor be entitled to the revenue, before they are printed.

"Also I direct and appoint, that no person shall be qualified to preach the Divinity Lecture Sermons, unless he hath taken the degree of Master of Arts at least, in one of the two Universities of Oxford or Cambridge; and that the same person shall never preach the Divinity Lecture Sermons twice."

ANALYTICAL TABLE OF CONTENTS

Chapter Two

THE NATURE OF SCIENTIFIC THEORIES

Chapter Three

COSMOLOGY AND CONTINGENCY

Chapter Four

CREATION IN THEOLOGY AND SCIENCE

Chapter Five

MODERN PHYSICS AND INDETERMINACY

Chapter Six

THE BODY AND THE SOUL

Chapter Seven

MAN'S ORIGIN AND ANCESTRY

Chapter Eight

THE PURPOSE OF CREATION

INTRODUCTION

TWO particular difficulties confront the man who is rash enough to write a book on the relations between Christian theology and natural science, and they both come from the scientific side. The former of these arises from the extraordinary rapidity with which, in the modern world, important scientific discoveries succeed one another and venerable scientific theories become antiquated and unfashionable; so that even textbooks by specialists are often obsolescent by the time that they are published. The second difficulty arises from the fact that, as time has gone on, the domain of science has grown wider and wider, while in any given field science has tended to become more and more specialised and technical; so that even a scientific worker, if he is questioned about a matter which falls in some region of science other than his own, may well find himself as much at a loss as someone else would be who was not a scientist at all. This being so, the task of the theologian who ventures into the scientific field is indeed perilous; where scientists themselves hardly dare to wander from their own back gardens, what hope is there for the poor outsider? Nevertheless, in a world in which the lives and outlooks of ordinary men and women have become dominated by the techniques, if not by the concepts, of science, the task of examining the relation of the traditional faith to the contemporary scientific situation is one which, however ephemeral its results are likely to be, urgently needs to be undertaken from time to time. It is of course true that in the last few years a number of books have appeared on the subject; and if they do not seem to me to be uniformly successful, this does not mean that I feel confident of doing any better than my predecessors. I have only felt it possible to make any attempt at this important, though transient, work of correlation by deciding to limit myself strictly to the small number of scientific questions of which I have anything more than the scrappiest knowledge. As the subtitle of this book indicates, I have simply tried to discuss *some* of the questions on the relations between Christian theology and natural science; but I think they are some of the most central and important ones. It would be idle for me to pretend to an exhaustive knowledge of even the small number of scientific matters on which I have touched; I am therefore glad to acknowledge unashamedly my debt to the large number of well-written and accurate semi-popular scientific books and periodicals which are available to the general reader to-day. Some of these will be found listed in the bibliography at the end of this book, but I would specially commend those admirable periodicals, the Penguin *Science News* and *New Biology*, *The Times Science Review* and, on a rather less popular level, *The British Journal for the Philosophy of Science*.[1] But, above all, I must express my gratitude to a number of scientific friends and colleagues who have patiently answered my questions and corrected some of my grosser misunderstandings; and in particular to Dr G. J. Whitrow, Dr A. C. Allison, Dr K. D. Bowers and Mr R. J. Robinson. They are in no way responsible for the errors that remain, but without their help those errors would have been more numerous and glaring than they are.

No one has the right to expect, or indeed to desire, anything less than the keenest and most unrelenting criticism of his writings, but anyone who writes about matters lying in the borderland of two highly technical disciplines may reasonably hope that that criticism will be sympathetic and constructive. Many of the most important intellectual issues at the present day lie in just such borderland realms, and there is little hope of solving them unless workers in each region are ready to help and be helped by those in the other and not merely to shoot them down. There are, for example, questions of the greatest moment and difficulty which lie in the region where physics and philosophy overlap and which need for their solution the most painstaking and generous collaboration of physicists and philosophers. Only too often, however, discussions between these two types of specialists are conducted in a way which reminds the spectator of an athletic contest. If a physicist falls into a type-fallacy, one point is scored to the philosophers; if a philosopher reveals his ignorance of the difference between energy and action, two points go to the physicists. This is great fun, but it is singularly un-

---

[1] Referred to in the footnotes by the initials *B.J.P.S.*

helpful. In the particular borderland where science overlaps with theology it is, I think, true for the most part that scientists and theologians treat each other with mutual respect and show readiness to understand each other's concerns. If this book does anything to increase that understanding, I shall feel it has been well worth writing.

I would end this introduction on a personal note. Ever since, as an undergraduate reading the Mathematical Tripos at Cambridge in the late nineteen-twenties under that great teacher George Birtwistle, I found myself getting more and more interested in the philosophical implications and associations of Relativity and Quantum Theory, I have hoped that I should one day write a book on the relations between Christian Theology and Natural Science. Now that, under the encouragement of the Electors to the Bampton Lecturership, that hope has been realised, the result is very different from anything that I could have foreseen. A mathematical training has both advantages and drawbacks as a preliminary to the study of theology, but I think it is useful for an occasional scholar to assume, in however un-Gregorian a sense, the motto "Not angles, but angels". When I look at this book now that I have finished it (for introductions, though they are printed first, are written last), I see that it does little to answer the questions that it raises. My chief purpose in writing it, however, has not been so much to answer specific questions as to show that there is a large domain of thought in which it is possible for theologians and scientists to engage in intelligent, good-humoured and fruitful conversation. This seems to me to be, in the long run, a more useful goal at which to aim than the improvisation of knock-down answers to awkward questions. For it is scientists and theologians that need to be brought together, not merely science and theology. And in any case, as Cardinal Gasquet remarked to Pope Pius XI, we are none of us infallible.

E. L. M.

Christ Church,
Oxford.
December, 1955

ACKNOWLEDGMENTS

My thanks are due to the following for permission to reproduce copyright material:

The Clarendon Press for Professor E. A. Milne's *Modern Cosmology and the Christian Idea of God* and Professor I. T. Ramsey's *Miracles*; the Cambridge University Press for Sir Arthur Eddington's *The Philosophy of Physical Science*, Dr Dingle's *The Sources of Eddington's Philosophy*, Professor Schrödinger's *What is Life?* and Professor R. B. Braithwaite's *Scientific Explanation*; the University of California Press for Dr Reichenbach's *Philosophic Foundations of Quantum Mechanics*; Sir Edmund Whittaker for his *From Euclid to Eddington* and (with Messrs Thomas Nelson & Sons) for his *Space and Spirit* and *A History of the Theories of Aether and Electricity*; Messrs Faber & Faber for Dr Martin Johnson's *Time, Knowledge and the Nebulae*; Messrs Hutchinson & Co. for Dr Whitrow's *The Structure of the Universe* and Dr Toulmin's *The Philosophy of Science*; Messrs C. A. Watts & Co. for Dr von Bertalanffy's *Problems of Life*; and Messrs Thomas Nelson & Sons for *The British Journal for the Philosophy of Science*.

E.L.M.

Chapter One

CONTACTS OF SCIENCE AND THEOLOGY

Et consilium pacis erit inter illos duos.—Zach. vi. 13.

I. CONTACT AND CONFLICT

IN his article on Psychotherapy in the twelfth edition of the *Encyclopaedia Britannica*, Dr E. D. Macnamara described in the following words the method of psychological analysis which is known as "time-association": "The patient places himself in a comfortable position and relaxes his attention to what is going on or to any particular line of thought so far as is possible. He is directed to listen to certain words pronounced by the analyst, and on hearing one forthwith to say the word which first arises in his mind. The time between the signal word and the reply is noted. . . . But the time element is in fact not the only one of importance in this test, since the character itself of the reply word is put to valuation."[1] I do not know whether the experiment has ever been tried of including the phrase "science and religion" in the list of signal words, but I strongly suspect that if this was done it would be found in a great many cases that the recumbent figure on the couch would utter with lightning rapidity the word "conflict".

It has, I think, become an implicit assumption in the minds of modern people that there is, at any rate, a *prima facie* antagonism between the outlook and discoveries of science on the one hand and the outlook and dogmas of orthodox religion on the other. In 1874 there appeared J. W. Draper's book, *The Conflict between Religion and Science*, in 1897 A. D. White's *A History of the Warfare of Science with Theology in Christendom* and in 1925 J. Y. Simpson's *Landmarks in the Struggle between Science and Religion*. "Conflict", "warfare", "struggle", these were the natural epithets to use; and if we are tempted to suppose that the assumption which they make is now a thing of the past, we ought perhaps to

[1] Vol. xxxii, p. 207.

remind ourselves that so recently as 1953 Professor H. H. Price gave to his Eddington Memorial Lecture the title, *Some Aspects of the Conflict between Science and Religion*. The present-day German Protestant theologian Julius Schniewind has told us that "the intrinsic incompatibility of Christology with the world view of modern science is a problem which must be taken very seriously",[1] and the celebrated theoretical physicist Erwin Schrödinger has written of "the natural enmity between science and religion".[2] Dr Dingle, reviewing two recent volumes on the relations between science and theology, has written as follows: "Professor Heim sees science not as a guide to truth but as a menace to be disarmed. *This is natural, if not inevitable, since he is first of all a theologian*."[3] In the face of all this, it may seem foolish and unrealistic to announce at the beginning of a discussion of the relations between Christian theology and natural science that one does not propose to conceive one's subject in the light of a warfare, a struggle or even a conflict. I am sorry to disappoint anyone who may be looking forward either to a spectacular rout of the devils of science (falsely so called) by the angels of orthodox theology or, on the other hand, to a sensational capitulation of the forces of superstition and reaction to the spirit of enlightenment and progress. I must, however, say that, so far as my own acquaintance with theology and science is concerned, I simply cannot see the question of their relations in that light. There are, I believe, a number of realms in which the two disciplines make contact with each other and in which important things about that contact can be said; but I do not believe that the contact is to be envisaged in terms of opposition. This is, I am aware, a provocative assertion and one which, made at the present day, needs justification. That justification can only be provided by concrete illustration, and to give this illustration will be the chief purpose of these lectures.

2. CONFLICTS WITHIN SCIENCE AND THEIR RESOLUTION

I do not, of course, wish to deny that there have on many occasions been conflicts, and sometimes very bitter conflicts, between officials and theologians of the Church on the one hand

---

[1] "A Reply to Bultmann", in *Kerygma and Myth*, p. 91.
[2] *Nature and the Greeks*, p. 9.   [3] *B.J.P.S.*, IV, p. 236 (italics mine).

and scientists on the other. Galileo before the Roman tribunals in the seventeenth century and Samuel Wilberforce at the British Association in 1860 are examples that spring immediately to the mind. Nor do I wish to deny that on particular questions at particular epochs theology and science may appear to hold inconsistent views. This should provide a field for friendly and fruitful discussion between theologians and scientists, but it gives no ground for conflict or antagonism. Between two different branches of science itself, or even within one and the same branch of science, it not infrequently happens that discussions of a question from different starting-points lead to apparently contradictory results, and it is the investigation of just such contradictions that can lead to the most notable advances in knowledge and in scientific theory. Two instances of this may be given. The first is the famous nineteenth-century argument about the age of the earth as a solid body. Geologists and biologists united in demanding for the past history of the earth a time-scale of thousands of millions of years. Nothing less, it appeared, would be adequate for the deposition of the material which forms the sedimentary rocks or—though this was more open to question—for the salinity of the ocean to have reached its present amount by the washing down of salt into the sea by the rivers. Again, nothing less would provide time for the evolution of the various types of terrestrial life, vegetable and animal. On the other hand, the physicists, led by Lord Kelvin, found it impossible to assign to the solid earth an age of much more than a hundred million years, and this for three reasons. The first reason, admittedly somewhat conjectural, was based upon the assumption that a fraction of the secular acceleration of the moon's longitude, otherwise unaccounted for, was due in fact to a steady diminution of the earth's angular velocity of rotation resulting from tidal friction; this would mean that before it solidified the earth was rotating appreciably faster than it is now, and, since the faster a liquid mass is rotating the smaller is its polar diameter in proportion to its equatorial diameter, the present flattening of the earth's figure, assumed to be identical with its flattening at the moment of solidification, would indicate how fast the earth was rotating when solidification occurred and would thus determine the date of that event. The second reason for the shorter time-scale was based upon Kelvin's calculation of the age of the sun, which is presumably not less than the age of the earth. The sun is radiating heat at a rate which is easily measured, and when all the known possible sources of solar energy were taken into account it seemed impossible for this process of radiation to have been going on for much more than a hundred million years without those sources being now exhausted. The third argument was based upon the rise in temperature which is observed when we penetrate beneath the surface of the earth. The magnitude of this temperature-gradient gives a measure of the rate at which the earth is losing heat and, since it is possible to estimate the temperature of the earth's rocks at the moment of solidification, the time that must have elapsed since solidification occurred could be calculated. The answer was that the earth could not have been solid for more than a hundred million years and possibly for not more than twenty-five million. There was thus a flat contradiction between the findings of different branches of science. Biology and, somewhat more hesitantly, geology demanded for the solid earth an age of at least a thousand million years; physics, on the other hand, could not allow more than a hundred million. The deadlock remained until the end of the last century; and when it was finally broken it was in consequence of a discovery which was totally beyond the purview of the earlier scientists, the discovery of hitherto unsuspected sources of energy within the atoms of matter themselves. The spontaneous disintegration of radio-active atoms, first observed in 1896, made it possible for the solid earth to have a vastly greater age than Kelvin could allow for it, without it having become any colder than we know it to be; the more recently discovered phenomena of nuclear fission and fusion have made it similarly possible to assign a greater age to the sun. The controversy was thus settled in favour of the long time-scale of the biologists and the geologists, but—and this is the important point—it was only in the light of knowledge that was altogether inaccessible in the days when the controversy arose; all that was then possible was to set the conflicting conclusions side by side in the hope, which was ultimately fulfilled, that a solution would one day be found.[1]

[1] A detailed discussion of the controversy is given by W. M. Smart, *The Origin of the Earth*, chs. vi–viii.

The other example which I shall give of an apparent contradiction within the field of science itself is more recent still. It is concerned with the nature of light. As far back as the end of the seventeenth century Newton had raised the question whether light was to be considered as consisting of trains of waves or of streams of particles, and, although he never committed himself very definitely to either alternative, he has been generally described as having favoured the corpuscular theory. His contemporary Huyghens explicitly advocated the undulatory theory, but the corpuscular theory was generally adopted and held its ground until the end of the next century, when the undulatory theory was definitely established as the result of the work of Young and Fresnel. From that time until quite recent years the view that light was a form of wave-motion remained unquestioned; it covered all the known phenomena and had culminated in the brilliant electro-magnetic theory of Clerk Maxwell. That light consisted of electro-magnetic waves was clear; that electro-magnetic waves were vibrations in an omnipresent impalpable medium seemed almost as certain, and the corpuscular theory seemed to have been irrevocably relegated to the lumber-room of discredited superstitions, with epicycles, homunculi and phlogiston. It came therefore as a considerable surprise when, in the year 1900, the German physicist Max Planck revived the corpuscular theory in a somewhat sophisticated form, in order to explain the fact that the energy emitted by a radiating body was distributed among the various wavelengths of the spectrum according to a law quite different from that predicted by the undulatory theory, and when shortly after this Planck's theory was found to explain a number of other phenomena as well. Its subsequent history will be the subject of later consideration; it blossomed into that remarkable efflorescence which, under the name of quantum theory, has revolutionised the whole of modern physics and has indeed produced a radically new view of the relation of physical theories to the universe which they describe. The significance of the matter for our present discussion lies in the fact that Planck's revival of the corpuscular view of radiation did not simply result in the abandonment of the undulatory view; the undulatory view had been far too successful for that, and it did in fact make sense of a large range of phenomena which the corpuscular view was powerless to explain. The fact was that whether you were to think of light as consisting of waves or of particles seemed to depend on what type of optical phenomena you were considering, while in some cases it seemed to be necessary to think of it as consisting of both at once.[1] The further discovery that electrons, which had shown every sign of being perfectly good particles, could also on occasion behave as waves —a discovery which has borne fruit in the electron-microscope— complicated the matter still further. The important point is that, for a quarter of a century or more, physicists found themselves in the position of having to work simultaneously with two views of the nature of radiation which seemed plainly irreconcilable. The reconciliation which was ultimately brought about by the later developments of the quantum theory was one which at the time could not even be dimly foreseen, and it has in fact required the adoption of a new view of the nature of such fundamental physical concepts as space, time and causality of so revolutionary a character as to make the celebrated paradoxes of relativity theory seem conventional in comparison. The importance of this example, as of the previous one, for our present purposes is its manifestation of the fact that, so far from science always present- ing a neatly unified and logically coherent picture of the universe, it frequently has to make shift with unreconciled contradictions, not of course in the sceptical assumption that the truth about the universe can actually contradict itself, but in the faith that there must be an ultimate reconciliation which we cannot yet see. The physicist has to get used to living with his contradictions; other- wise he will jettison one half of his facts in order to be consistent about the other half. And if we are ready to accept the existence of inconsistencies within science itself, we ought not to be worried about the occasional occurrence of inconsistencies between science and theology. For, in their different ways, neither the science nor the theology of any epoch can claim to be in a state of absolute finality.

---

[1] Cf. H. Margenau, *The Nature of Physical Reality*, p. 314 f.

3. CAUSES OF CONFLICT BETWEEN SCIENTISTS AND THEOLOGIANS

Several causes can, I think, be traced of the conflict between scientists and theologians which, however unnecessary and unjustified from the theoretical standpoint, has been a marked feature of the intellectual history of the last three hundred years, and has provided Dr A. D. White with material for nearly nine hundred large pages; they cast little credit upon either party to the dispute. The first is the quite overweening confidence which nineteenth-century scientists for the most part had in the finality of scientific theories. Newton, Dalton, Joule, Darwin and Maxwell had brought one department of the world after another under the dominion of the scientific method, and, although there were still a good many loose ends, there was little doubt that they would be tied up in due course without any substantial reweaving of the fabric. The equality of inertial and gravitational mass might still be a complete mystery, ether models might strain credulity by their complexity, and Darwinians and Lamarckians might dispute about the method of evolution; but little disagreement would have been felt with Laplace's dictum that Newton was not only the greatest genius that ever had existed but also the most fortunate, inasmuch as there is but one universe, and it can therefore happen to but one man in the world's history to be the interpreter of its laws.[1] As admirably written a popular account as H. W. Picton's *Story of Chemistry*, published in 1889, could sum up the later years of the reign of the phlogistic theory of combustion under the simple heading "The Conflict with Error" and the ultimate adoption of the oxygen theory under the heading "The Triumph of Truth". It is, of course, true that even in the nineteenth century there were scientists who felt no difficulty in being theists as well. The distinguished mathematical physicist Sir George Gabriel Stokes, who was an orthodox Christian, defended the possibility of miracles in his Gifford Lectures in 1891. "Admit the existence of a God, of a personal God", he wrote, "and the possibility of a miracle follows at once.

---

[1] Cf. Burtt, *Metaphysical Foundations of Modern Physical Science*, p. 18. A similar remark is attributed by Dampier to Lagrange (*A History of Science*, 3rd ed., p. 194).

If the laws of nature are carried on in accordance with his will, he who willed them may will their suspension. And if any difficulty should be felt as to their suspension, we are not even obliged to suppose that they have been suspended; it may be that the event which we call a miracle was brought about, not by any suspension of the laws in ordinary operation, but by the super-addition of something not ordinarily in operation, or if in operation, of such a nature that its operation is not perceived."[1] The impression was, however, for the most part overwhelming: science had laid bare the last secrets of the universe and practically nothing of importance remained to be discovered. And when the last secrets were laid bare, they contained no reference to God. Newton had triumphed, and in a way that he had never contemplated. "Magnificent, irrefutable achievements", writes E. A. Burtt, "gave Newton authority over the modern world, which, feeling itself to have become free from metaphysics through Newton the positivist, has become shackled and controlled by a very definite metaphysics through Newton the metaphysician."[2] In a way that he had never contemplated, I have said; for, as Burtt again has remarked, Newton himself believed that the laws which he had formulated were insufficient to maintain the stability of the universe and that frequent divine intervention was necessary to prevent its collapse; it was left to Laplace to show that Newton's laws were more adequate than he had thought and that therefore celestial mechanics had no need of the hypothesis of God.[3] And Newton's world, although it could not eliminate mind and purpose altogether, left them very little room. To quote Burtt once again, in Newton's system

> the world that people had thought themselves living in—a world rich with colour and sound, redolent with fragrance, filled with gladness, love and beauty, speaking everywhere of purposive harmony and creative ideals—was crowded now into minute corners in the brains of scattered organic beings. The really important world outside was a world hard, cold, colourless, silent, and dead: a world of quantity, a world of mathematically computable motions in mechanical regularity.[4]

[1] *Natural Theology*, p. 24.
[2] *Metaphysical Foundations of Modern Physical Science*, p. 227.
[3] Ibid., p. 294; cf. Dampier, *A History of Science*, 3rd ed., p. 188.
[4] Ibid., p. 236.

And again: "From being a realm of substances in qualitative and teleological relations the world of nature had definitely become a realm of bodies moving mechanically in space and time."[1] It is a small step from here to the view which conceives mind simply as an epiphenomenon of mechanical processes. In the words of Professor H. Butterfield:

> Newton felt that, though the system of Descartes necessitated a Creator who had set the clockwork into motion in the first place, it was in danger of making God superfluous once the universe had been given a start. And it is curious to note that, if earlier in the century religious men had hankered after a mathematically interlocking universe to justify the rationality and self-consistency of God, before the end of the century their successors were beginning to be nervous because they saw the mechanism becoming possibly too self-complete.[2]

It is, of course, true that even materialistic Victorian physicists and biologists managed in many cases to combine their materialism with a naïve acceptance of the doctrine of progress; neither their mechanistic physics nor their acceptance of the Second Law of Thermodynamics was strong enough to overcome the spirit of the age. And indeed, by a somewhat amusing enantiodromia, they saw the clearest manifestation of man's progress in his acceptance of a materialistic interpretation of the universe in place of a religious one. He had escaped from the degrading tyranny of gods and priests into the milder service of physical law. And of course their new allegiance, however complete in theory, was in practice not quite absolute. However sure the scientist might be that other people were only elaborate machines, his protocol contained an escape clause for himself.

I suggest then that, from the side of the scientists, one of the main reasons for the view that the relation between religion and science must be envisaged in terms of a conflict is provided by the last-century scientist's assumption of the virtual finality and immutability of the scientific notions of his day. Another reason is, I believe, to be found in the assumption that the concepts and theories of science provide the one true and literal description of the real nature of the world. What the world *really* consisted of

[1] *Metaphysical Foundations of Modern Physical Science,* p. 154.
[2] *The Origins of Modern Science,* p. 111.

was minute, unbreakable billiard-balls of about ninety different sizes, interacting in accordance with a few laws, such as Newton's laws of motion and gravitation and Hooke's law of elastic strain, which were of such a simple character that they could with little difficulty be taken as self-evident. If this picture needed supplementing by an omnipresent luminiferous ether, whose properties could be described in terms of cog-wheels, beer-froth, elastic strings and gyroscopes, no substantial difference was made. There was nothing metaphorical or symbolic about the ultimate entities of physics; they were the bricks out of which the world was made; they were more real than the objects of sight and touch, for the latter might be illusions, but the former could never be. Water might look and feel like a continuous mobile substance, but what it really *was* was an aggregate of an enormous number of tiny molecules, each of which consisted of two atoms of hydrogen and one larger atom of oxygen. Why our senses presented us with a coherent system of illusions might be something of a mystery, but of the fact there was no doubt. The entities of physical science—atoms, ether and the like—were the things of which the world consisted, and physical laws were descriptions of the way in which they behaved. The concepts and theories of science were not only to all intents and purposes final, they were also literally and ultimately true. Therefore any description which was inconsistent with them stood condemned on its own confession; there was no room for revision or compromise. How different from all this are the views of the nature of scientific concepts and theories which are held to-day will, I hope, appear in a subsequent lecture.[1] What I am concerned at the moment to make clear is that, from the side of the scientists, the main reason for the view that apparent inconsistencies between science and theology are to be interpreted by such concepts as conflict, struggle and warfare is the twofold assumption that the scientific views of a particular epoch are virtually final and are also literally true. And that is an assumption which ought not to be made without question.

If, however, the scientists are to be held largely to blame in this matter, the theologians can by no means escape unscathed. It is, of course, the easiest thing on earth to be wiser than one's fore-

[1] Cf. ch. ii, infra.

fathers, and we have no valid reason for self-complacency. If we had been in their situation we should in all probability have behaved as foolishly as, if not indeed more foolishly than, they. What our descendants in turn will think of us is a matter which is mercifully hidden from our eyes. The fact, however, remains that, when we look back upon the controversies between scientists and theologians in the past, we see the theologians only too often completely missing the real points at issue. How little theological discussion, in the strict sense, there seems to have been in either of the two great controversies of this kind, namely those concerned with the heliocentric system and with the theory of organic evolution respectively! The real questions which needed discussion were the questions of the relations which these new theories would have, if adopted, with the fundamental doctrines of Christianity about the nature and end of man, the fall and redemption. In fact, the main subject of argument in both cases was how, if at all, the new scientific theory could be reconciled with a literal interpretation of the early chapters of the book Genesis.[1] Now it is perfectly true that the adoption of certain conclusions of scientists might radically affect our views of the way in which the whole or certain parts of Holy Scripture are to be understood. But the Biblical question cannot be the ultimate one, if only for the reason that the Bible itself is of importance only for the doctrinal teaching which is embodied in it. If the Biblical question is considered as the primary one, the discussion between the scientist and the theologian is almost bound to appear as a contest between an impious biblioclast on the one hand and an ignorant and obscurantist bibliodule on the other. If, however, attention is concentrated upon the primarily theological issues, if, for example, questions are asked such as "How is man's centrality in the universe to be understood in terms of heliocentric cosmology?", "What is the relation between an evolutionary view of man's physical being and the Christian doctrines of fall and redemption?", or—and here we pass beyond the heliocentric doctrines of Copernicus and Galileo to the views of contemporary astrophysics—"How can Christian dogma be related to the possi-

[1] I use the term "literal interpretation" in its ordinary English sense. It corresponds to what Roman Catholic theologians would call not the literal but the natural interpretation.

bility that there are other rational beings than man in the physical universe?"; if questions such as these are asked, we shall not necessarily get conclusive and neatly worked-out answers, and indeed we have no right to expect them unless we are convinced that we know the last word in both science and theology, but we shall at least have deepened our understanding of the scope of Christian dogma and its power to make sense of the world which is God's creation, and we shall come back to the Bible with an enhanced grasp of the way in which it does, and of the ways in which it does not, reveal to us the truth of God.

It must furthermore be recognised—though here I am well aware that if I wish to avoid being hewn in pieces I must tread more delicately than Agag—that however firmly we are convinced of the uniqueness, finality and irreformability of the Christian revelation and of the Creeds in which the Church has expressed it, we cannot claim a like authority for the formulations of theologians or for the particular interpretations that have been put upon the revelation from time to time by the faithful. May I make it quite clear that I am not pleading in favour of that incoherent and undignified activity which is sometimes called "bringing the Christian Faith in line with modern thought"? The problem raised by the fact that the Second Person of the Holy Trinity became man in a particular place and at a particular time, for the sake of all men in all places and at all times, is far too intricate and profound to be disposed of by any such simple formula as that which I have just quoted. Dr L. S. Thornton has shown, in his book *Revelation and the Modern World*, how the theological movement which is commonly known as "Liberalism" broke down, through its fundamental assumption that the interior content of the Christian revelation can be detached without distortion or mutilation from the outward form in which it was originally given and can be inserted, again without distortion or mutilation, into the thought-forms of the modern age. Liberalism, says Dr Thornton, "set out to preserve the unchanging essence of the Biblical revelation; but it too easily, and even naïvely, identified that essence with the contemporary philosophic idealism of Western man. In doing so, it evaded the whole problem of historical religion, the problem as to how eternal truth can be manifested at all in the infinitely complex, slow-

moving yet ever-changing processes of time and space."[1] I believe that Dr Thornton is profoundly right on this point, and I
am firmly convinced that the paradigm for the interpretation of
the Christian revelation is to be found in the Bible itself and in
the liturgical and theological activity of the life of the Christian
Church, and not in the thought-forms of contemporary systems
of secular thought. Nevertheless the theologian is bound to be
influenced by the climate in which he lives, and as a matter of
historical fact the development of theological thought and expression bears upon itself the clear marks of the periods through
which it has passed. What can protect the theologian from serious
error as he performs his dangerous task is, I believe, not a rigid
determination to isolate himself from the world of his own day
and to think no thought that has not been thought before, but a
conscientious checking of all his speculations, especially those
that may have been derived preponderantly from non-Christian
sources, against the Biblical, liturgical and theological tradition
which he has inherited in his life as a member of the Church. He
may of course make mistakes, but, if he has common sense and
humility, they will, it is to be hoped, be corrected before their
consequences become serious. So long as he does his best to distinguish between his own speculations and the tradition of the
Church, he need not feel any hesitation about speculating. For
the only way to discover whether any new idea is fruitful or
sterile is to try it out; and speculations which turn out to be fruitful often find themselves incorporated subsequently in the
tradition. The Church's tradition is not a static deposit but a
living and developing organism. What was wrong with the
liberal theologians was not that they were ready to speculate, but
that they took as the criterion of their speculation not the tradition and life of the Christian Church but the climate of contemporary thought. On the other hand—and this is directly
relevant to our present concern—the theologians and Church
authorities who were most conscious of the sacredness of the
Christian revelation tended, when confronted with the new
scientific discoveries and theories, to reject and denounce them on
the basis of a narrow biblicism, instead of exploring their theological possibilities and testing out their capacity to contribute to

[1] Op. cit., p. 45.

and enrich the theological tradition. It is only right to add that, in so acting, they were frequently aided and abetted by the more conservative scientists of their day; the part, for example, that was played by the celebrated naturalist Sir Richard Owen in providing material for Bishop Wilberforce's attack upon Huxley is well known.[1] However the blame is to be distributed, the lesson is obvious. It is that theologians and scientists have nothing to fear from each other if they are conscious of their own limitations and of the necessarily provisional character of the state of their own studies at any particular time. There will, of course, be times when this happy symbiosis will be easier to achieve than at others, but the times when the *prima facie* divergences are most marked may well be the times when an honest attempt at mutual understanding will be most fruitful.

4. PAST SERVICES OF SCIENCE TO THEOLOGY

Even when we look back on the past, with its lamentable history of incomprehension, it is possible to pick out instances when the advance of science, so far from making the theological situation more difficult, has in fact removed embarrassments. One example of this is provided by the unification of sublunar and supralunar physics, which followed upon Newton's demonstration that the same laws can be formulated to describe both the motion of falling bodies on the earth and also the motions of the heavenly bodies in their orbits. For the ancient world the heavenly bodies were divine beings, which moved with steady speeds in circular paths because uniform circular motion was clearly the perfect type of motion. However irregularly things might go on in the sublunar world, beyond the sphere of the moon all was music and peace. It is true that when Christianity took over the ancient cosmology it interpreted it by a radically different metaphysical doctrine. St Thomas Aquinas, writing in the thirteenth century, is absolutely explicit that, however perfect circular motion may be, the ultimate reason why the celestial spheres revolve is because they are moved by God, and that when God's purposes are fulfilled, or, as he puts it, "when the number of the elect is complete", God will bring their motion to an end.[2]

[1] Cf. L. Huxley, *Life and Letters of Thomas Henry Huxley*, I, p. 183.
[2] Cf. *De Potentia*, v, 5.

Nevertheless, while denying that the celestial bodies are incorruptible absolutely, he affirms that they are incorruptible *secundum quid*.[1] The idea persisted that the supralunar world was endowed with a perfection that was lacking upon earth, and was governed by an entirely different set of laws; and the minds of respectable people were profoundly shocked when Tycho Brahe announced that the path of the comet of 1577 lay beyond the orbit of the moon and when Galileo in 1610 claimed to have observed spots on the sun. In spite of this reaction of sheer conservatism, it should be obvious that from the point of view of Christian theology the discovery that the same physical laws governed the sublunar and the supralunar universe should have been thoroughly welcome, for it removed the last vestiges of the pagan belief in the divinity of the heavens. In view of the actual history of the matter, M. Pierre Duhem may be going too far when he claims that this unification of the universe was the direct result of Christian theology,[2] but we can fully agree that it ought to have been.

A similar example is provided by the discrediting—for in view of the experience of recent years we can hardly say the demolition—of astrology. The people of antiquity were firmly convinced that the destinies of men and nations alike were governed by the influences of the heavenly bodies. The Christian Church did not deny outright this belief, which was after all part of the science of the time, but it claimed that Christian men had access to a benevolent power that was stronger than that of the stars. Neither *hypsōma* nor *bathos*, St Paul tells the Christians of Rome, neither the zenith nor the nadir of the stars, can separate them from the love of God which is in Christ the Lord.[3] The belief that influences from the stars were productive of effects on the earth continued, but merely as a physical theory. St Thomas admits this, but he is careful to add that they do not produce all their effects with certainty, since other agencies may intervene to prevent this; nor, except in an indirect and accidental and possibly ineffective way, can they be the causes of human acts.[4] Furthermore, "anyone who uses the consideration of the stars for the forecasting of future casual or fortuitous events or in order to know for certain the future actions of men" is alleged to be the

[1] *De Potentia*, iii, 17, *ad* 3.   [3] Rom. viii. 39.
[2] *Le Système du Monde*, II, p. 453.   [4] Cf. *S. Theol.*, I, cxv, 4 & 6.

victim of a "false and vain opinion", and his exploit is condemned as a superstitious and unlawful divination, in which the
devil will be involved; it is, however, added that there can be no
objection to anyone studying the stars to forecast purely physical
events such as the weather.[1] In spite of such weighty warnings as
these the belief in astrology continued well into the seventeenth
century among educated and thoughtful people; we may recall
the representation of the horoscope of Robert Burton on his
monument in Christ Church Cathedral in Oxford. Christian
people may thus well be grateful to science for having finally
delivered them from the baleful influence of the stars.

Not only is it true, however, that science has in the past performed services for which the theologian may well be grateful;
it is also possible to point to a number of instances in which the
scientific outlook of the present day is a good deal more congenial to Christian dogma than was the scientific outlook of the
nineteenth century. I propose to give three examples of this, but
before doing so I must once again emphasise that there is no
question of trying to justify Christian belief by its compatibility
with contemporary thought. It has been well remarked that to
marry the spirit of any age means to be a widow in the next and
I have no desire to qualify for this particular form of intellectual
bereavement. It may none the less be worth while to attend to
these examples, if for no other reason than the fact that many of
the cases in which it is commonly alleged that Christian beliefs
are inconsistent with the thought of to day turn out on examination to be cases in which, if they are inconsistent with anything,
it is in fact with the thought of the day before yesterday.

5. PRESENT-DAY RAPPROCHEMENTS BETWEEN SCIENCE AND THEOLOGY

First, then, I shall consider how modern views of the nature of
matter bear on the doctrine of the resurrection of the body. I am
not, of course, suggesting that there is any particular significance
for theism in the fact that contemporary physical science tends to
speak of matter in terms of electricity and energy, for there is
nothing particularly religious about either. That penetrating

[1] *S. Theol.*, II, II, xcv, 5.

Christian philosopher, W. H. V. Reade, in his posthumously published book *The Christian Challenge to Philosophy*, referred with well-merited scorn to "the naïve delight sometimes exhibited by friends of religion when they hear that the solidity of matter is being whittled away by modern physics, as though Materialism would at any rate be less dangerous if only matter could be made decently thin". "It makes", he pointed out, "not the slightest difference whether matter is as hard as adamant, as stodgy as suet, as volatile as gas, as agile as electricity, or as naked as a mathematical formula. The only relevant question is whether it is self-existent or created by God; and this, as we cannot too often remind ourselves, is a question upon which natural science has nothing to say."[1]

I shall have something to say later on about the implications of the Christian belief that a human being is not, as Platonic and Cartesian philosophy has held, a pure spirit temporarily inhabiting a material integument, but a psychophysical unity in which body and soul are intimately and mysteriously interlocked.[2] Here I am merely concerned with the fact that Christianity has held without intermission, if at times with some embarrassment, that the final condition of man is not simply spiritual immortality but physical resurrection: the life everlasting is the sequel to the resurrection of the body. The cosmic implications of this fact are indeed profound. Because we are by our nature physical beings linked by our bodily metabolism both with one another and with the rest of the material world ("Whatever Miss T. eats", Mr de la Mare has reminded us, "turns into Miss T."), our resurrection will involve nothing less than the transformation of the whole material order. This is, in fact, what orthodox Christian theology, following the teaching of the Bible, has always held. The resurrection of the body is intimately linked with the ultimate transfiguration of matter as such.

Now there have always been problems about the nature of the identity between the bodies which we now have and the bodies in which we shall rise. St Paul recognised the question, "How are the dead raised, and with what manner of body do they come?",[3] and his own reply was simply to point to the continuity between a seed that is sown in the ground and the plant that arises from it.

---

[1] Op. cit., p. 130.   [2] Cf. chs. vi, vii, infra.   [3] I Cor. xv. 35.

The question cannot be evaded, and its difficulty has been largely responsible for the neglect into which, during the liberal period of theology, the doctrine of the resurrection of the body fell. Shall I have the same body as I have now or a different one? And if the same one, in what will its identity consist?

Even the question of the continuous identity of my body throughout my earthly life is a puzzling one. My body certainly does not consist of the same atoms that composed it when I was six months old; nor is it recognisably similar in appearance, except in certain very general respects. It may perhaps be said that this is purely a verbal question; it all depends on what you mean by "same". If by "same" you mean "composed of the numerically identical particles", then I have not the same body that I had forty years, or even half an hour, ago. But I have the same body if you define sameness in terms of continuity of spatial extension and of association with a continuous mental life, a continuity which it is no doubt difficult to specify precisely, owing to its complexity, but which is perfectly familiar to all of us. In fact, it will be said, we all know what I mean if I say that I have the same body now that I had in childhood; and I do not mean that it consists of the same material particles.

Now such an answer may be satisfactory if we are concerned simply with the identity of our bodies during the course of our earthly life, for in this case the continuity is obvious and recognisable. It will be equally satisfactory if we are concerned with the question whether our Lord rose on the first Easter morning with the same body as that in which he was crucified. For, on the orthodox doctrine of the resurrection, although Christ's risen body was in many respects strikingly different from the body that suffered and died on the Cross, it was spatially and causally continuous with it. The tomb was empty on Easter morning because the body which had been laid in it was risen and glorified.

When, however, we are concerned with the general resurrection at the Last Day the question is nothing like so simple. It would be hardly orthodox to say that we shall *not* rise up in the bodies which we have now; yet bodies do decay after death, and, in view of the vicissitudes which their material particles then undergo, what precisely can we mean if we say that they will be the *same*? Do we mean that the resurrection body will consist of numerically the same particles which went to make it up at the moment of death? If so, what happens to the man who has lost an arm in an accident? Will he be armless for all eternity? And what happens to that favourite exhibit of the sceptics, the man who has been eaten by cannibals? In any case, will not our bodies be vastly different after the resurrection? Did not Origen suggest that they will be spherical? And what sort of redistribution of matter would that remarkable metamorphosis involve?

St Augustine of Hippo, in the admirable little Latin treatise on the elements of the Christian Faith which he wrote in A.D. 421 and which is known as the *Enchiridion*, faces the question courageously but not altogether successfully. By the power of God, he says, the matter will return to the souls which originally animated it; but God will exercise his power to exclude unseemly excess or defect. Fat men will not necessarily rise fat, or thin men thin; the case of Siamese twins and other monstrosities is not forgotten; but God will see to it that "the bodies of the saints will rise again free from defect, free from deformity, free from any corruption or burden or difficulty".[1] St Thomas Aquinas, writing in the thirteenth century, adopts substantially the outlook of the great African father. He insists quite uncompromisingly that it is numerically the *same* body that the soul resumes, since otherwise "it would not be called a resurrection but rather the assumption of a new body",[2] but he shows a certain vagueness whether the material particles (*pulveres*) will return to the parts of the body from which they came.[3] And when he asks whether everything that was materially in a man's members will be raised up, he contents himself with saying that "everything that is in the man will rise, if by everything we mean the totality of the species [i.e. everything that is necessary to constitute human nature], but not if we mean the totality of the matter".[4] Again, in dealing with the problem of pathological dwarfs and giants, the Angelic Doctor quite unconcernedly remarks that "what is superfluous or lacking in a man, the divine power will cut off or supply". "If", he says, "on account of some defect the formative power could not produce the right quantity which the species requires, the power of God will supply what is lacking in the resurrection."[5]

---

[1] *Enchiridion*, chs. 84–91.   [2] *S. Theol.*, suppl. lxxix, 1.   [3] Ibid., 3.
[4] Ibid., lxxx, 5.   [5] Ibid., lxxxi, 2.

He does, it is true, seem to believe that it will be possible to trace the history of every portion of matter that the world contains at the Last Day, but he also seems to be quite clear that in the last resort what makes the body the *same* body is the fact that it is united to the same soul, as matter to its form.[1]

St Thomas does not in fact seem to be very much concerned with the question of the re-aggregation of the precise material particles; his line seems to be that there is plenty of matter about anyhow, and that God can always produce more if it is needed, but that other things being equal, matter may as well belong where it belonged before. He is much more interested in what the resurrection-bodies will be like; and he devotes much space to expounding their impassibility, their subtlety, their agility and their clarity.[2] There is no particular reason why we should follow him here, and I imagine he would be the first to admit the speculative character of some of his particular conclusions. What is important is his emphasis upon two points: First, that the resurrection of the body involves its transformation into a state vastly different from that in which it was before; secondly, that in spite of this transformation it remains fully and totally human. "Whatever belongs to the wholeness of human nature will rise again whole in us who rise."[3] And it is important, though it is not always easy, to remember that for St Thomas matter did not mean the hard, eternal, minute billiard-balls of the nineteenth-century physicists, but the metaphysical partner of the Aristotelian "form"; however he may have envisaged the re-integration of our bodies in the resurrection, he certainly did not think of it as simply the sorting out and re-assembling of tiny material components.

I have thought it worth while briefly to sketch St Thomas's discussion of this question, not because I think it can be very directly related to present-day scientific notions, but because I think it provides a useful example of the difficulties which the question presented to a Christian thinker of the highest intellectual power. Those difficulties were certainly not lessened with the supersession of scholasticism by the outlook of nineteenth-century physics and chemistry. At the present day, I suspect that a good deal of our difficulty arises from our tendency to remain

---

[1] *S. Theol.*, lxxix, 1 *ad* 4.   [2] Ibid., lxxxii–lxxxv.   [3] Ibid., lxxx, 3.

unconsciously under the dominion of the nineteenth-century scientific concepts even when we are most conscious that they have been superseded. I do not, of course, propose that we should tie up Christian dogma with the scientific concepts of our own time in order to get it free from its embarrassment by those of the period immediately past, for we have no reason to suppose that present-day scientists are in possession of final and ultimate truth any more than their predecessors were. Nevertheless, it may assist us in the disentangling process if we recall how radically the nineteenth-century view of matter has been abandoned by the science of to-day. It is true that physical events are observed —flashes on a fluorescent screen, for example, or clicks in a loud-speaker, or streaks on a photographic plate—which can be interpreted as the effects of individual electrons, protons, neutrons or mesons, but very few physicists would commit themselves to the view that electrons, protons, neutrons, or mesons are persisting substantial entities which can be assigned a local habitation and a name in the intervals between our observations. And in any case, it is just the occurrence of these individual observable events—the disintegration of *this* particular radium atom, the quantum-jump of *this* particular electron—that falls outside the scope of physics.

For almost all physical scientists to-day would hold that the laws of physics—and it has now been realised that this was as true of classical as it is of quantum physics, though the classical physicists for the most part failed to see it[1]—are entirely concerned with the behaviour of aggregates consisting of immense numbers of the elementary entities; as regards the behaviour of any individual elementary entity, they specify nothing but probabilities, which is as much as to say that, as to what any particular elementary entity will do on any particular occasion, they can tell us nothing at all. (Similarly, the statistics of the street-accidents in Oxford for the year do not tell you whether in fact I shall be run over if I cross Carfax at noon to-morrow, though they may tell you how likely this is to happen.) Indeed, the very identity of the elementary entities becomes tenuous in the extreme when we recall that not only have we only probable

---

[1] See, e.g., K. R. Popper, "Indeterminism in Quantum Physics and in Classical Physics", *B.J.P.S.*, I, Nos. 1 & 2 (1950). Cf. ch. v, infra.

knowledge as to what any particular elementary entity will do, but also have only probable knowledge as to which elementary entity we are considering. (It should be remembered here that the word "probable", as used by scientists, does not necessarily imply a high degree of probability. It is contrasted with "certain", not with "improbable", and covers events which would ordinarily be described as very improbable indeed.)

The picture which many of us have derived from popular scientific writings, of the atom as a kind of miniature solar system consisting of electrons revolving in elliptical orbits round a massive positively charged nucleus, may be useful for certain limited purposes, but we have no reason to suppose that it is a literal description of the ultimate reality; the Victorian physicists' billiard-ball picture also had its limited uses. And if we are tempted to suppose that any conceptual picture which gives the observed results is thereby proved to have physical reality we may well reflect on an amusing example given by Sir Edmund Whittaker. "The vibrations of a membrane which has the shape of an ellipse", he tells us,

> can be calculated by means of a differential equation known as Mathieu's equation: but this same equation is also arrived at when we study the dynamics of a circus performer, who holds an assistant balanced on a pole while he himself stands on a spherical ball rolling on the ground. If now we imagine an observer who discovers that the future course of a certain phenomenon can be predicted by Mathieu's equation, but who is unable for some reason to perceive the system which generates the phenomenon, then evidently he would be unable to tell whether the system in question is an elliptic membrane or a variety artiste.[1]

We should notice further that not only are physical models misleading if taken as more than useful aids to the imagination, but that also it is becoming more and more plain that the ultimate laws of physics are not capable of interpretation in terms of physical models at all. The present-day physicist does not think of space as his nineteenth-century predecessor did, as filled with invisible and impalpable cog-wheels, gyroscopes, elastic strings,

---

[1] *The Beginning and End of the World*, p. 17.

beer-froth and paraffin wax; he writes down a differential equation and tries to keep his imagination in check.

When therefore we ask the present-day physicist of what the material world ultimately consists, we are unlikely to get any other reply than Eddington's famous dictum: "Something unknown is doing we don't know what." That the material world has substantial reality we can hardly deny; for a great deal is in fact going on in it. But that its reality is that of minute eternal hard elastic particles colliding with one another in three-dimensional Euclidean space there is no reason whatever to suppose, and any objections to the resurrection of the body that are based on such an assumption are hardly worth while answering to-day. Indeed, if we were going to give the last word on the question to contemporary physics, the difficulty would not be that matter is so fixed in its nature and so regular in its behaviour that it could not manifest the flexibility that the resurrection would require; the difficulty would rather be that matter is so fluid in its nature and so unpredictable in its behaviour that it would hardly have sufficient permanence. Certainly nothing in the theories of contemporary science would suggest that the resurrection of the body depends upon the possibility of re-assembling dispersed but permanently identifiable material particles.

We can only dimly imagine what the transformation of matter at the last day will involve, but it will presumably be of so radical a nature as to make it quite impossible to say of any portion of it, "Ah! yes, that bit used to be *there*." It is through our bodies that our life as human beings consists; through our bodies we live in fellowship with one another and in unity with the rest of the material world. And the Son of God took to himself a body of the substance of our bodies, so that we might be incorporated into him and adopted into his sonship. The resurrection of our bodies might well seem called for on general grounds, when we consider what sort of being a human being is; but its guarantee is the incarnation and resurrection of Christ.

For the resurrection of the body is the resurrection of the Mystical Body, the resurrection of Christians into the glorified human body of the risen Christ. We may let St Augustine have the last word here: "We have said, 'Remember that we are dust', but out of the dust he made man, and to dust he gave life, and in

Christ he hath brought this dust to the kingdom of heaven, he who made heaven and earth."[1]

The second example which I shall give of a question in which, as it seems to me, the outlook of the science of to-day ought to be welcomed by Christians is concerned with the nature of space. Once again, we must delve a little into the history of Christian thought. The cosmological scheme which the Church inherited from Judaism was that picture of a flat earth covered with a hemispherical firmament which in our own day has caused so much excitement to Dr Bultmann and his friends. "The cosmology of the New Testament", he writes, "is essentially mythical in character. The world is viewed as a three-storied structure, with the earth in the centre, the heaven above, and the underworld beneath. Heaven is the abode of God and of celestial beings—the angels. The underworld is hell, the place of torment."[2] Very different was the cosmology of the Greek and Latin world into which Christianity leapt from its Syriac and Semitic cradle soon after the middle of the first century. It is true that the Greek cosmology, like the Semitic, was for the most part geocentric. The heliocentrism of Aristarchus of Samos, formulated in the third century B.C., had not established itself, and the main features of Aristotle's system, with occasional modifications such as those suggested by Eudoxus, commanded general assent. Nor was the matter fundamentally changed by the work of the Alexandrian astronomer Ptolemy in the middle of the second century A.D., animated as the controversy between the Aristotelians and the Ptolemeans afterwards became. Whereas the Semitic earth was a flat surface covered by a hemispherical dome, this latter being surrounded by water, the Greek earth was a spherical body, round which rotated a number of spherical shells, each bearing one of the planets on its course. Those who suppose that the Church never had to make terms with an unfamiliar cosmology until the time of Copernicus and Galileo altogether underestimate the magnitude of the challenge which confronted it in the first century. What is surprising is that the Church seemed so little concerned at the matter, and that it made the necessary adjust-

---

[1] Quoted by Alfred Noyes, *The Unknown God*, p. 251.
[2] *Kerygma and Myth*, p. 1.

ments with so little fuss. How ready Christian theologians were
to accept the cosmological scheme of contemporary Greek
science, and at the same time how little they thought it necessary
to work out more than a sketchy and somewhat casual reconciliation between it and the imagery of the Bible, can be seen from the
rather quaint discussions in the *Hexaëmeron* of the fourth-century
father, Basil of Cappadocia. Even on the question of the shape of
the earth statements tend to be ambiguous. The sixth-century
geographer Cosmas Indicopleustes vehemently maintained that
the earth was not only flat but also oblong, and there were others
who followed his view. The opinions of many writers are difficult
to interpret, partly owing to a frequent vagueness as to the
difference between a sphere and a circular disc; opinions vary as
to how far belief in a spherical earth was common in the early
Middle Ages. By the eighth century, however, this belief becomes
general,[1] and by the beginning of the fourteenth century the
geocentric cosmology reaches its final Christian form in the
great system of the *Divine Comedy* of Dante. Dr A. D. White
describes it as follows:

> The earth is no longer a flat plain inclosed by four walls and
> solidly vaulted above, as theologians of previous centuries had be-
> lieved it, under the inspiration of Cosmas; it is no longer a mere flat
> disc, with sun, moon, and stars hung up to give it light, as the earlier
> cathedral sculptors had figured it; it has become a globe at the centre
> of the universe. Encompassing it are successive transparent spheres,
> rotated by angels about the earth, and each carrying one or more of
> the heavenly bodies with it: that nearest the earth carrying the moon;
> the next, Mercury; the next, Venus; the next, the sun; the next
> three, Mars, Jupiter, and Saturn; the eighth carrying the fixed stars.
> The ninth was the *primum mobile*, and inclosing all was the tenth
> heaven—the Empyrean. This was immovable—the boundary be-
> tween creation and the great outer void; and here, in a light which
> no one can enter, the Triune God sat enthroned, the "music of the
> spheres" rising to him as they moved. Thus was the old heathen
> doctrine of the spheres made Christian.
>
> In attendance upon the Divine Majesty, thus enthroned, are vast
> hosts of angels, who are divided into three hierarchies, one serving
> in the empyrean, one in the heavens, between the empyrean and the
> earth, and one on the earth. . . .

[1] Cf. G. H. T. Kimble, *Geography in the Middle Ages*, ch. ii.

Below the earth is hell. This is tenanted by the angels who re-belled under the lead of Lucifer, prince of the seraphim—the former favourite of the Trinity; but, of these rebellious angels, some still rove among the planetary spheres, and give trouble to the good angels; others pervade the atmosphere about the earth, carrying lightning, storm, drought, and hail; others infest earthly society, tempting men to sin. . . .[1]

Such was the medieval picture of the universe, with the earth in the centre and God at the top of the circumference, a local earth with a local heaven. And yet I think we may be misled if we suppose that for the medievals the difference between earth and heaven was simply a matter of geometrical separation, of spatial extension. As Professor Butterfield has reminded us, there was for them not merely a quantitative distance but also a qualitative difference between the different regions of the universe. "Though the earth itself was thought to be composed of four elements . . ., everything in the skies—the spheres and the heavenly bodies —was considered to consist of a different kind of matter, a fifth essence, a peculiarly perfect kind of material. While everything on the earth was subject to change and decay, the material that formed the skies was unchanging and incorruptible."[2] And if there was such a radical change on crossing the orbit of the moon, how much greater must have been the change on entering into the empyrean, the very home of God. Dr C. S. Lewis has remarked that the New Testament writers managed to combine the idea of a heaven above their heads and the idea of the mode of life of the ever-blessed God without difficulty or confusion, and that the real and pernicious period of literalism came only in the Middle Ages and the seventeenth century.[3] I am inclined to think that the greatest of the medievals kept the synthesis him-self; and that, for Dante, as one moved away from the abode of

---

[1] *History of the Warfare of Science with Theology*, I, p. 118.

[2] "Dante's View of the Universe", in the broadcast symposium *The History of Science*, p. 22.

[3] *Miracles*, p. 188. Cf. E. Bevan, *Symbolism and Belief*, p. 44 f. In the chapter on "Religious Language" in his book *Authority and Freedom*, Dr R. H. Thouless has pertinently pointed out that "realisation of the difference between the meta-phorical and the literal uses of language was not a discovery of the nineteenth century" (p. 68) and that metaphor has always been part of the stock in trade of Christian writers. While this is true, I do not think that, any more than Bultmann's own solution in terms of "demythologising", it meets all Bultmann's difficulties.

men to the abode of God, spatial separation counted for less and less, and qualitative distinction for more and more, until the distinction between different regions of an extended universe had given way to the distinction between creatures and their Creator. Be this as it may, the displacement of the earth from the centre of the universe by Copernicus and Galileo, and still more the unification of the sublunar and the supralunar world by Newton's discovery of universal gravitation, abolished all qualitative differences between different regions of space. Henceforth one had either to locate God and his angels and saints in heaven, in the same sense as Nelson's Column is located in Trafalgar Square, or else to deny the legitimacy of applying spatial terms to them in any sense whatever. And once the alternative is stated in those terms the answer is inevitable. Heaven becomes a purely spiritual state, the Ascension of Christ becomes a destruction of Christ's human nature, and our future condition becomes an enjoyment of immortality in which neither the body nor anything analogous to bodily experience can have any part.

It was with the publication of Newton's *Principia* in 1687 that a clear statement was given of the doctrine of the nature of space that was to dominate physical science for more than three centuries. In contrast to his great contemporary Leibnitz, for whom space was essentially a system of relations between bodies, Newton drew a sharp distinction between absolute and relative space and attributed objective reality to the former, to the extent of describing it as "the sensorium of God". "Absolute space, in its own nature", he wrote in a famous Scholium to the *Principia*, "without relation to anything external, remains always similar and immovable."[1] Space was for Newton an infinitely extended uniform Euclidean receptacle, in which material bodies were immersed without their presence making any difference to space itself. All sorts of things could happen *in* space, but nothing whatever could happen *to* space. The conclusion inevitably followed—though it would perhaps be too much to say that it can be derived with absolute cogency from Newton's principles —that any spatial or quasi-spatial experience whatever must be located somewhere in Newton's physical universe. All the space that there is or ever can be must be part of this one infinite uniform

[1] Ed. of 1729 (tr. Motte), I, p. 9.

Euclidean continuum. Thus if, for example, the enjoyment of heaven involves any sort of spatial experience, heaven must be simply a limited volume of our physical universe; and even if increased understanding of the scattering of light makes it inaccurate to describe it as being "above the bright blue sky", nevertheless its location relative to the earth at any moment is in principle specifiable in spherical-polar co-ordinates in the same way as the location of the great nebula in Andromeda. When such a way of thinking had come to prevail, it was almost inevitable that, for educated people, the application of any kind of spatial language to religious realities should seem altogether ridiculous and barbaric. One of the results was that complacent doctrine that "heaven and hell are states, not places", which has done so much to deviscerate modern religion.

It is thus important to notice that, with the advent of the Theory of Relativity and still more with that of the Quantum Theory, the Newtonian conception of space has become altogether discredited. We ought not, of course, to take too seriously some of the vivid metaphors in which the new conceptions have been expounded by their great popularisers, for example, Eddington's agreeable picture of the standard metre-rod taking up a length which is in a fixed proportion to the radius of curvature of space-time wherever it may be, because "it wants to do just what it did before", or the picturesque description of matter as being nothing but puckers in the four-dimensional continuum. I shall discuss in the next lecture the relation between the language of scientific theories and the phenomena with which they are concerned; at the moment I merely wish to point out how completely the Newtonian view of space as a receptacle has been abandoned by modern physics. I hope it will be clear that I am not saying anything so naïve as that "science has now shown that space is curved, and so heaven is somewhere in the fourth dimension". What I do maintain is that, once the Newtonian view of space is abandoned, it is no longer necessary to hold that all experiences which involve spatial characteristics must be linked together in one unified extensional spatial continuum. On some forms of modern cosmological theory, this is true even within the realm of purely physical processes, as with the famous "bursting of the bubble" in Eddington's "expanding universe."[1] All I want to point out is that, if Christian theology finds it necessary to describe the mode of existence of the ascended Christ, or of the angels and saints in heaven, or of the blessed after the resurrection, in spatial terms—and this is a question which need not be decided here—modern science puts no difficulties in the way. There may be theological difficulties in the language of the so-called Black Rubric when it says that "the natural Body and Blood of our Saviour Christ are in Heaven and not here", but they are theological difficulties and not scientific ones. In Dante's universe, the localisation of heaven was compensated, so to speak, by a radical *qualitative* difference between the different regions of the universe; from the standpoint of modern physics it could be compensated by an absence of spatial connectivity between the heavenly realm and this. It was the view of Newton, coming between these, that left only the alternatives of a purely spiritual heaven and of a realm that merely replicates, somewhere among the stars, the conditions of our present existence; for, having unified the sublunar and the supralunar regions of the physical universe by his law of universal gravitation, he then, by means of his receptacle theory of space, left no room for spatial experience elsewhere. Once again, I am not trying to demonstrate the existence of a spatial heaven from the theories of modern science; I am only anxious to point out that present-day science leaves a good deal more elbow-room than the science of yesterday left for theological speculation.

The third example which I shall take is rather more loosely knit than the former two, but I think it will also be illuminating. It is concerned with the nature of time. Newtonian physics had, along with its receptacle theory of space, a very similar view of time. "Absolute, True and Mathematical Time", wrote Newton, "of it self, and from its own nature, flows equably without regard to anything external, and by another name is called Duration: Relative, Apparent and Common Time is some sensible and external (whether accurate or unequable) measure of duration by the means of motion, which is commonly used instead of True time: such as an Hour, a Day, a Month, a Year."[2] And again: "All motions may be accelerated or retarded, but the True, or equable

---

[1] Cf. A. S. Eddington, *The Expanding Universe*, ch. iii.
[2] Op. cit., I, p. 9.

progress, of Absolute time is liable to no change.''[1] Now relativity theory has called into question the notion of absolute time, no less than that of absolute space; though it must be added that certain forms of General Relativity, and in particular Einstein's, have restored absolute time (and indeed a kind of absolute space) to the universe as a whole, as distinct from its parts.[2] It is also true that, even in the heyday of Newtonian physics, there were philosophers who drew the distinction between the measured mathematical time of physics and the subjective time, the *durée* or *temps vécu*, of human experience.[3] Nevertheless, in spite of the protests of such writers as Bergson, the general impression held that it was the measured mathematical time of physics that was the real time by which the development of the world was to be measured, and that any deviations from it on the part of individual experients represented aberrations of no real significance. Now, relativity theory has not, of course, admitted as equally valid for scientific purposes all subjective impressions of the passage of events; but it has abolished the notion of one rigid self-sustaining time-process which is the unrelenting standard by which all that happens in heaven and earth is to be judged. We have returned to something much more like St Augustine's doctrine of a world existing not *in tempore* but *cum tempore*, whether or not we take St Augustine's further step of attributing the world's existence to God. In fact, the notion that time is the mode under which created beings exist, rather than a pre-existent and self-existent stream in which they are immersed, was general in Christian thought down to the seventeenth century. It is involved in the truth which, in spite of its difficulties for the human imagination, Christian theology has consistently affirmed, that God, the Creator of everything other than himself, does not exist in time at all. St Thomas Aquinas is really only repeating St Augustine when he writes: *simul cum tempore caelum et terra creata sunt;*[4] we ought not to be misled when he tells us elsewhere that time, like place, is extrinsic to things (*extrinsecum a re*),[5] for by this he

---

[1] Op. cit., I, p. 11.

[2] See, e.g., the discussion of this by G. J. Whitrow, *The Structure of the Universe*, p. 79.

[3] Cf. H. Bergson, *L'Évolution Créatrice*, ch. i.

[4] *S. Theol.* I, xlvi, 3 *ad* 1.

[5] *De Pot.*, iii, 17c.

simply means that the heavenly bodies rotate by the power of God and not, as the Greeks thought, in virtue of their own inherent divinity. Neither St Thomas nor any other Christian theologian, so far as I know, had arrived at the notion which was the peculiar contribution of Special Relativity, that the actual numerical time-scales used by different observers might vary from one to another; it is therefore all the more significant that, in spite of his belief that one time-scale applied to the whole universe, he persisted in holding that time was created with things and was not a pre-existent stream into which things were launched when created. But in this he was in line with the consistent tradition of Christendom. It was left for Newton to impose upon English thought the doctrine of creation *in tempore*; and it is natural that, just as his receptacle theory of space led him to view space as the sensorium of God, so what we might describe as his escalator theory[1] of time led him to view time as the mode under which God himself experiences events. For if space and time exist antecedently to, and independently of, creatures, where and how can they exist except as attributes of God? Newton's view on this question is expressed quite unambiguously in the General Scholium which he added to the second edition of the *Principia* in 1713:

> [God] is Eternal and Infinite, Omnipotent and Omniscient; that is, his duration reaches from Eternity to Eternity; his presence from Infinity to Infinity; he governs all things, and knows all things that are or can be done. He is not Eternity or Infinity, but Eternal and Infinite; he is not Duration or Space, but he endures and is present ...; and by existing always and every where, he constitutes duration and space.[2]

How little, in spite of his own warnings, had Newton avoided the snares of metaphysics!

On three different questions, then, the nature of matter, the nature of space and the nature of time, we have seen science quite recently abandoning the views which had prevailed for more than three hundred years and adopting a standpoint more congenial to the outlook of Christian theology. The significance

[1] The point is that the escalator is moving before you step on to it.
[2] Op. cit., II, p. 389.

of this fact ought not to be exaggerated, but it is perhaps of interest, and not least for the reason that, when people declare themselves unable to accept the Christian religion because of the outlook of science, the science involved very frequently turns out to be the now largely abandoned science of the nineteenth century.

6. EVOLUTION AND PRE-HUMAN EVIL

I shall add to the previous examples a slightly different one, different, that is, in that it is concerned not with scientific theories that have quite recently displaced their forerunners, but with one that, although formulated in the last century, still, with some modifications of detail, keeps its place. I mean the general theory of organic evolution, including the evolution of man. I shall be concerned with other aspects of it later; here I shall refer to it mainly in its relation to the problem of the existence of pre-human evil.

The teaching of the Christian Church about the origin and nature of evil in this world has been steadily based upon the story of the Fall of Man related in the third chapter of the book Genesis. There has of course been a great amount of discussion as to the extent to which certain details of the story should be understood metaphorically, and the Dutch sect which is alleged to have taught as the *articulus stantis vel cadentis Ecclesiae* that the serpent spoke to Eve in Hebrew is not representative of the main body of Christendom. Nevertheless, it was until recent years almost universally held that all the evils, both moral and physical, which afflict this earth are in some way or another derived from the first act by which a bodily creature endowed with reason deliberately set itself against what it knew to be the will of God, while, in accordance with the Hebrew tradition which identified the serpent of the Genesis-story with the devil,[1] it has also been held that, in so rebelling, man was giving way to the prompting of an incorporeal being who had already revolted against God in the spiritual realm.

Some of the difficulties which the theory of evolution has been alleged to place in the way of the traditional account need not at

[1] Cf. Wisdom, ii. 24.

the moment delay us very long. From the side of ecclesiastics and theologians the tendency, upon which I have previously remarked, to take the question as primarily a test-case for Biblical inspiration rather than to discuss the real theological issues involved, has been notorious. Some of the discussions which took place in the Roman Church on the question round about the beginning of this century now make somewhat amusing reading;[1] but it is notable that the Papal encyclical *Humani Generis* of August 1950, while explicitly tolerating the doctrine of the physical descent of man from other living creatures, condemns, as inconsistent with the doctrine of original sin, all theories which do not affirm the descent of the whole human race from one pair of ancestors. This passing of judgment by ecclesiastical authority upon the purely scientific issue seems to me to be unfortunate, even though the predominant view among anthropologists to-day seems to be that all existing human races are descended from the same common human stock. Common descent from one ancestor is not the only way of explaining and understanding the relation of all men to the Fall; it is perfectly conceivable that God might have made a number of independent human races with such a common metaphysical and moral unity that the sin of one would involve all in that mysterious predicament which we describe as original sin.[2] It is not immediately evident that original sin can be transmitted only by physical generation; it needs to be remembered that, however terrible its effects may be, original sin is not so much a positive entity as an absence of original righteousness; and no physical mechanism is needed to transmit the absence of something. Precisely how original righteousness would have been communicated from one member of the human race to another it is difficult to suggest, for the very reason why it is not communicated is that the means of communication is no longer there; it is never easy to examine something which is absent. But even in the Roman Church itself the opinion can be found strongly represented that original righteousness itself would not have required the existence of some quasi-physical mechanism for its transmission but merely the "positive will of

[1] Cf. H. J. T. Johnson, "The Unity of the Human Race" and "The Bible, the Church and the Formation of Eve", *Downside Review*, LXVIII, LXIX (1950–1).
[2] Cf. p. 286 f., infra.

God, *libera Dei ordinatio*, to bestow original grace as a collective gift (and in this sense as a natural gift) to the whole of humanity so long as it remained innocent or until its first serious fault: this first fault would cause *ipso facto* that universal falling away which is hereditary [i.e., original] sin".[1] Certainly we need not consider original sin as inherited like any physical characteristic; the priest-biologist in Soviet Russia who is said to have announced that he had located on one of the human chromosomes the gene which carried original sin, and that he was hoping to produce a mutation in it which would make it possible to breed a human stock free from both concupiscence and original guilt, must, if he existed at all, be pronounced to be something of a theological oddity.

Furthermore, it must be emphasised that the essence of the Fall is moral and not intellectual. It was, of course, natural that, in the days before evolutionary theory had been thought of, the state of the first man should be envisaged as one of virtual omniscience. Dr Robert South in a well-known sermon assured his hearers that "an Aristotle was but the rubbish of an Adam, and Athens but the rudiments of Paradise",[2] but it is surely more reasonable to suppose that primordial man was mentally far more like a small child than like a brilliant scientist or philosopher. The Garden of Eden does not mean that man was at an advanced stage of development; he was more probably at the beginning of his path. But he was *on* the path and going in the right direction, whereas ever since, except in so far as the healing grace of God has restored him, he has lost his way.

It is further to be noticed that the special gifts which the tradition of Catholic theology has attributed to Adam—a certain immunity from concupiscence, ignorance, suffering and even death—are quite explicitly asserted to be preternatural gifts and in no sense part of man's natural physical endowment. Transposed into the setting of evolution, the assertion of man's primordial immortality does not in any way deny that man has in-

---

[1] A. Verrièle, *Le Surnaturel en nous et le Péché originel*, p. 222. Cf. p. 135: "The generic unity of the human species and the transmission of human nature by generation were in no wise a sufficient condition by themselves for a propagation of original righteousness—or of its privation—by the mere fact of generation. There was needed for that *an entirely free positive disposition by God.*"

[2] *Sermons*, I, ii.

herited from his animal ancestry that liability to physical death which is common to all but the lowest types of living creatures. The immunity to death which was bestowed upon man—and which in fact he lost before he had time to enjoy it—was a super-added gift which would have elevated man's nature to a super-natural condition, in which, it has been generally believed, he would have been transformed, *expleto terrestris vitae cursu*, into a condition analogous to that of Christ's human nature after the Ascension.[1]

I have, however, digressed from my main point, which is concerned with the question of pre-human evil. Knowing what we now do about the past history of this earth, it seems difficult to suppose that nothing that happened upon it in any way contravened the will of God until the commission of the first human sin. We ought not, of course, to exaggerate the suffering of sub-human animals. As Dr C. E. Raven has pointed out, even intense physical discomfort involves little in the way of anguish if it is entirely unaccompanied by recollections of similar experience in the past or anticipations of its continuance or repetition in the future. Even the most horrible twinge would be bearable in the specious present if we had not only no expectation, but also no conception, that it could occur again. And there is every reason to believe that the experiences of even the higher animals are entirely or almost entirely confined to the specious present, for the investigations of brain-physiologists have revealed that the exercise of imagination in the recollection of past, and the anticipation of future, events is closely connected with the possession not only of an elaborate nervous system but also of a highly developed frontal cerebral cortex, the very thing that physically distinguishes man most clearly from the brutes. "Pain", Dr Raven writes, "does not take a major part in the experience of any organisms below the human level; and . . . the life of wild creatures far from being spent in constant fear is active, rhythmic and, if such a word be allowed, joyous."[2]

It is also well known that the trouble with microbes and viruses is not that they exist, but that human beings are not entirely im-

[1] Cf. with the above discussion, chs. vii, viii, infra.
[2] *Natural Religion and Christian Theology*, II, p. 116. Cf. ch. viii, p. 296, infra.

mune to their attacks.[1] Be this as it may, it is difficult to feel, when we consider the course that evolution has taken on this earth, that, even before man appeared, everything was going precisely as God ideally intended it to go. It is therefore interesting to recall that the Church has held from the beginning that, before the creation of man, sin had already occurred in the angelic realm, and that a firmly based tradition ascribes to the angels, among other occupations, that of tending the material world. If there is any truth in such ideas, if the world in God's intention was to be one in which the realms of matter and of spirit were to be linked together in intimate union (as they are, in microcosm, most conspicuously linked in each individual human being), and if the lower levels of this cosmos were to be under the surveillance and loving care of the higher, it seems reasonable to suppose that defection and rebellion in the angelic realm will drastically disorder the material world, and that, while its development in accordance with God's purpose will not be entirely frustrated, it will be grievously hampered and distorted. The way in which this notion has been worked out in the novels of Dr C. S. Lewis is too well known to need more than passing reference; and indeed the notion is one whose possibilities are perhaps more satisfactorily exhibited in the idiom of imaginative narrative than in more severely academic forms. I shall have something more to say about it at a later stage.[2]

7. AN EXAMPLE OF THEOLOGICAL SPECULATION

The final point which I wish to illustrate, in concluding the present lecture, is that the discoveries and theories of modern science, so far from giving the orthodox theologian grounds for despondency and alarm, frequently provide him with scope for a highly interesting and stimulating application of his theological principles. I shall give one instance of this at the moment, and, if the discussion ends up somewhat inconclusively, this apparent irresponsibility may perhaps be pardoned in the last pages of an already somewhat over-long discussion. The question will be that of the uniqueness of the Incarnation.

At the end of his book *Modern Cosmology and the Christian*

[1] Cf. F. M. Burnet, *Viruses and Man*, passim.   [2] See ch. viii, infra.

Idea of God, Professor E. A. Milne has raised an interesting question for dogmatic theology. He states it as follows:

> God's most notable intervention in the actual historical process, according to the Christian outlook, was the Incarnation. Was this a unique event, or has it been re-enacted on each of a countless number of planets? The Christian would recoil in horror from such a conclusion. We cannot imagine the Son of God suffering vicariously on each of a myriad of planets. The Christian would avoid this conclusion by the definite supposition that our planet is in fact unique. What then of the possible denizens of other planets, if the Incarnation occurred only on our own?[1]

As Milne himself remarks, "we are in deep waters here, in a sea of great mysteries. But", he continues, "the way out is not fantastically improbable"; and he goes on to suggest a solution.

> Everyone has heard of the new subject of radio-astronomy, which has discovered the reception by ourselves of radio-signals apparently issuing from sources in the Milky Way. It is not outside the bounds of possibility that these are genuine signals from intelligent beings on other "planets", and that in principle, in the unending future vistas of time, communication may be set up with these distant beings. . . If that is so, there is no prima facie impossibility in the expectation that first of all the whole solar system, secondly our own group of galaxies, [may we perhaps interpolate "lastly, the whole intergalactic universe"?] may by intercommunication become one system. In that case there would be no difficulty in the uniqueness of the historical event of the Incarnation. For knowledge of it would be capable of being transmitted by signals to other planets and the re-enactment of the tragedy of the crucifixion in other planets would be unnecessary.[2]

Before discussing the question in detail, it seems to be desirable to point to certain phrases which, in spite of the brevity of his statements, seem to indicate clearly that there was, from the standpoint of Christian theology, a deficiency in Milne's understanding of the Atonement. Whatever he may have considered to be the inner significance of the Passion of Christ considered in itself, it appears that for Milne the necessary and sufficient condition for

---

[1] Op. cit., p. 153.   [2] Ibid.

it to be effective for the salvation of God's creatures is that they should *know about it*. Whatever may be the biological character of such corporeal rational beings as the universe may contain, if they can be given the good news that the Son of God became incarnate in the human species and that, living a life of perfect love and obedience, he gave himself to the extreme extent of suffering death on the Cross, this may be expected to evoke a response of gratitude which will break down any barrier of sin that is separating these creatures from God. Such would seem to be the view of redemption that underlies Milne's suggestion. It is in sharp contrast with the attitude of the great classical tradition of Christian thought. For the latter, the essence of redemption lies in the fact that the Son of God has hypostatically united to himself the nature of the species that he has come to redeem and, by offering himself to God the Father in their nature, has offered them to God the Father in him; and, although of course it would not be maintained that this redemption operates, as it were, automatically in all the members of the human race by the mere fact that the Son of God has lived and died as man, it would be maintained that it operates in them by their incorporation into that human nature in its risen and ascended glory and by their co-operation with the grace that this incorporation brings. By dying and rising again in human nature, Christ has reunited human nature to God; and in so far as we are partakers of his human nature we are restored in him. The Son of God became man in order that, in him, men might become the sons of God; that is the Christian message as we find it in the New Testament and the Fathers, and as the great tradition of Christendom has held it. On it depends the whole doctrine of the Church as the Body of Christ, and of the Sacraments as Christ's acts in his Body. Admittedly it has commonly been held that the ultimate effects of redemption extend beyond the human race to the material creation as a whole; but this is because man has been generally looked upon as the only corporeal rational being in the universe, to whom in the beginning the rest of creation was subjected as to God's vice-gerent, and to whom it is once again subjected in the assumption of manhood by the Son of God.[1] It would be difficult to hold that the assumption by the Son of the nature of one

[1] Cf. Heb. ii, 5–18.

rational corporeal species involved the restoration of other rational corporeal species (if any such exist) if these latter were not hierarchically graded beneath the first but were co-ordinate with it. Christ, the Son of God made man, is indeed, by the fact that he has been made man, the Saviour of the world, if "world" is taken to mean the world of man and man's relationships; but does the fact that he has been made man make him the Saviour of the world of non-human corporeal rational beings as well? This seems to me to be doubtful; I shall return to this point later on.

There is a second remark of Milne's which suggests a deficiency in his view of the Atonement, namely his remark about "the tragedy of the crucifixion". His suggestion seems to be that the notion of the crucifixion of the Son of God is so horrible that, while we can just manage to bring ourselves to stomach the fact of its having happened once on Calvary, the thought of its repetition elsewhere in the universe is altogether impossible to entertain. I find this suggestion extremely difficult to understand. There is, of course, an aspect of the crucifixion which is ghastly beyond words, and I do not wish to belittle it. But the whole message of Christianity is that the supreme horror of the crucifixion of God incarnate has been transformed by his resurrection into the supreme glory of the redemption of the human race. If the crucifixion is sheer unrelieved horror, how can we tolerate the notion of it happening even once? If the horror is not unrelieved but is changed into victory and glory, why cannot the change happen again and elsewhere? Indeed, the very phrase "the tragedy of the crucifixion" is one which a Christian theologian would employ only with considerable reservations. *Regnavit a ligno Deus*. The tragedy of the Cross, it has been well said, is the tragedy not of God but of man; and we may add, it is the mystery of man's redemption. For Christianity, the history of the world is not a tragedy but, to borrow a name from Dante's epic, the Divine Comedy. Milne's remark about the tragedy of the crucifixion confirms the suspicion that he appears to have looked upon redemption as consisting simply in the response of God's creatures to the news of God's love, rather than in the incorporation of them into God's redeeming activity; it would only be natural on such a view to emphasise the horror of the crucifixion, in order to stimulate the soul to penitence and amendment of life.

The suggestion which I wish to make, with all the tentativeness that is proper to a matter about which we are in almost complete ignorance, is that there are no conclusive *theological* reasons for rejecting the notion that, if there are, in some other part or parts of the universe than our own, rational corporeal beings who have sinned and are in need of redemption, for those beings and for their salvation the Son of God has united (or one day will unite) to his divine Person their nature, as he has united to it ours, and has done (or will do) in it whatever is necessary for their restoration to fellowship with God, as he has done what is necessary for ours. I am, of course, aware that this possibility has not been seriously entertained by the great Christian theologians of the past, but that is surely because they have never seriously considered the possibility that the universe may contain corporeal rational beings other than man. Their failure to do so, however, seems to me to rest not primarily upon theological but on scientific grounds; so long as the science of their day saw no grounds for assuming the existence of non-human rational inhabitants of the material universe, we can hardly wonder that the theologians saw no grounds for assuming it either. It is unfortunate that when the possibility of a plurality of rational species has been taken into account by theologians in recent years, it has generally been by theologians whose Christological and soteriological outlook was very far from that of Christian tradition.[1] The only conclusive theological objection that I can imagine is one that would arise from a view of the Incarnation which, although it has enjoyed a brief period of popularity, represents a complete departure from Christian tradition and is now very much on the decline; I mean the extreme kenotic view. If, in accordance with this view, we held that between his incarnation and his ascension the Son of God temporarily abandoned, to a greater or less degree, his divine attributes, and that during that period his divine nature was, as it were, scaled down to the limits of manhood, it would certainly be difficult to hold that an incarnation could take place *simultaneously* in two different parts of the universe. For, if incarnation means limitation to a particular place, all other places are *ipso facto* excluded; the Son

[1] Cf. E. W. Barnes, *Scientific Theory and Religion*, pp. 323 f., 401 f.

of God could no more be in two places at once than any of us can. Moreover, it would seem to be just as difficult to conceive of incarnations taking place in different parts of the universe at *different* times. For even the most extreme kenoticist would hold that, after the Ascension, the Son is permanently established in his heavenly glory; and this would make any further incarnation, conceived on the kenotic model, altogether impossible. These objections, conclusive as they are on a kenotic view, seem, however, to have no force for a traditional orthodox Christology. If the Incarnation of the divine Word involves no change in the Godhead, if the transcendence of the Creator over his creation is such that he can assume a finite nature to himself and in it can live a creaturely life without any abandonment of his divine activity and attributes, if, in short, in the words of the *Quicunque vult*, the Incarnation takes place not by the conversion of the Godhead into flesh but by the taking up of manhood into God, there seems to be no fundamental reason why, in addition to human nature being hypostatically united to the Person of the divine Word, other finite rational natures should not be united to that Person too. If finite and infinite natures are compatible in the Person of the Word, there seems to be no reason why several finite natures should not be equally compatible. To suggest this possibility is, it must be emphasised, totally different from suggesting that God might become incarnate on more than one occasion in the *same* rational nature, that, for instance, Socrates and Gautama Buddha might, equally with Jesus of Nazareth, be incarnations of the divine Word. The Word became man by assuming a human nature which had no personal individuality of its own and, in assuming it, he conferred his personal individuality upon it; if *per impossible* he assumed, and conferred his personal individuality upon human nature twice over, there would not after all be two individuals but only one; which is simply a paradoxical way of saying that in fact human nature could not be assumed by the divine Word more than once, since it is individualised in his Person and that Person is numerically one. We may make the point less metaphysically in the following way. The divine Word assumed human nature in order to renew and restore it, and, having renewed and restored it, he offers renewal and restoration to every member of the human race by incorporation into him. There is nothing that a second incarnation in human nature could achieve that has not been achieved by the first. All men are called to become members of Christ's Body by being incorporated, as men, into his manhood and, being so incorporated, are offered as one Man to the Father. But the very possibility of this incorporation depends upon the fact that they are *men* and Christ is *man*, that he has taken upon himself their nature. It will not in the least degree follow that rational beings of a *non-human* species can be incorporated into his manhood. If redeemed men are all one man in the Word-made-man, we may expect that redeemed Martians (if there are Martians and they are not human)[1] will be all one Martian in the Word-made-Martian; and this would seem to require an incarnation of the Word in Martian nature as its foundation. But all this is, of course, speculative in the extreme, since we know nothing about the nature of such beings, nor even whether they exist.

It is, of course, quite possible that human beings are the only rational beings within the material realm (we know, of course, that there are non-human rational beings in the realm of pure spirits). In 1928 the late Sir Arthur Eddington was prepared to admit that there might be "a few rival earths dotted here and there about the universe", but felt "inclined to claim that *at the present time* our race is supreme".[2] Whether in fact we consider the conditions which have made the earth a possible home for living creatures to be unique or not will largely depend on whether we consider the earth's formation as being, from the point of view of physics, a freak occurrence or not; and this is extremely difficult to determine in view of the multitude of competing theories of the earth's origin. Dr W. M. Smart, in his recent book *The Origin of the Earth*, lists no less than nine alternative views of the formation of the Solar System, none of which is exempt from serious criticism, and more recently still much favour has been given to an entirely new theory propounded by

[1] I have taken the hypothetical inhabitants of Mars as an example, since we have a convenient word by which to denote them, but very few astronomers would admit the possibility of the higher forms of life on any of the planets or satellites of the Solar System (see, e.g., W. M. Smart, *The Origin of the Earth*, ch. iv). If there are inhabited bodies they are probably to be found in other parts of the galactic system, or in the extra-galactic nebulae.

[2] *The Nature of the Physical World*, p. 178.

Professor Urey.[1] However, when we reflect that about a hundred million extra-galactic nebulae are accessible to observation[2] and that our local nebula, of which the sun is a member, has been estimated to contain something of the order of a hundred thousand million stars,[3] it would perhaps be unwise to be too dogmatic about the matter. Nevertheless, if we are inclined to be intimidated by the mere size of the universe, it is well to remember that on certain modern cosmological theories there is a direct connection between the quantity of matter in the universe and the conditions in any limited portion of it, so that in fact it may be necessary for the universe to have the enormous size and complexity which modern astronomy has revealed, in order for the earth to be a possible habitation for living beings.[4] It will thus be well for us to keep a perfectly open mind on the question of the existence in the universe of rational corporeal beings other than man.

Furthermore, even if such beings exist, man may, for all we know, be the only corporeal creature who has fallen and needs redemption; Dr C. S. Lewis has made play with this notion in his novel *Perelandra*. Again, if they have fallen, the conditions both of fall and of redemption may be radically different from those that apply in the case of man. Even in man the relation between the individual and the species is highly mysterious; the fact of original sin is undeniable, but its adequate formulation is the despair of theologians. In order to produce a really tidy theory of both man's fallenness and his redemption, it would be necessary not merely to know, as we do, that the human race is a

[1] This is the theory of the formation of planets by accumulation of cosmic dust at comparatively low temperatures. Cf. H. C. Urey, *The Planets*, and the remarks of J. B. S. Haldane in *New Biology 16*, p. 31 (1954).

The latest theory of all at the time of writing appears to be that developed by H. Alfvén in his book *On the Origin of the Solar System*. It is a variant of the nebular theory of Kant and Laplace in which ionisation phenomena are given a vital role.

Hoyle, who has abandoned his earlier view that the planets came into existence as the result of a supernova explosion of a companion of the sun for the view that the sun was born in a whole shower of stars and that the supernova or supernovae belonged to the shower, believes that there might be as many as a hundred thousand million planetary systems in our own galaxy alone (*Frontiers of Astronomy*, p. 83 f.).

[2] Cf. G. J. Whitrow, *The Structure of the Universe*, p. 127.

[3] Ibid., p. 24. Smart, op. cit., suggests about 50,000 million.

[4] I am indebted for this point to an unpublished paper by Dr G. J. Whitrow.

metaphysical unity but also (as we do not) what precise sort of metaphysical unity it is, and precisely how the individual man is related to the universal manhood which is particularised in him. If even our knowledge of man is so limited and obscure, how much more limited and obscure must be our knowledge of other rational species. But at least we have no reason to suppose that the relation of the individual to the species in a non-human rational corporeal being will be exactly the same as that relation is in man; the solidarity of Martians, both in fall and redemption, may be very different from that of men. It may or may not be such as to require an incarnation of the Son of God in Martian nature. It may be well to remember that St Thomas Aquinas held that, even in the case of man, God *might* have worked redemption in some other way, though he held that the method of the Incarnation was by far the most suitable one.[1] There may or may not be somewhere in the universe rational beings other than man. If there are, they may or may not have fallen. If they have fallen, their redemption may or may not require that the Son of God should become incarnate in their nature. God may or may not have some other way of restoring them to fellowship with himself; he may perhaps have an even more wonderful way, of which we cannot form the remotest conception. Whatever may be the truth about this, I would at any rate repeat my suggestion, that I cannot see any conclusive theological objection to the view that the divine Word may have become incarnate in other rational species than our own. There is, however, one final point on which some comment is needed.

Both St Paul and the author of the Epistle to the Hebrews lay great stress upon the fact that, by his incarnation, the divine Word has, not only as God but also as man, acquired supremacy over the creation of God. God, says the Epistle to the Ephesians, made Christ to sit at his right hand in the heavenly places, far above all rule, and authority, and power, and dominion, and every name that is named, not only in this age, but also in that which is to come.[2] By the incarnation of the Son of God, the Epistle to the Hebrews tells us, man has received the fulfilment of God's promise, the promise that man should be set over the works of God's hands and that all things should be put in subjection under

---

[1] *S. Theol.*, III, i, 2.   [2] Eph. i. 20, 21.

man's feet.[1] Is this teaching compatible with the view that an incarnation of the Son is possible in any other rational species than man? There is, it must be admitted, a difficulty here, but it is perhaps relevant to observe that the argument of both Ephesians and Hebrews rests upon the unquestioned, but also unformulated, assumption that there are no corporeal rational beings in the universe other than man. Is this assumption to be taken as being part of the deposit of faith or not? I find it very difficult to give a confident answer to this question. If, for the sake of argument, we can assume that the essential point is not the subjection of the material world to man as such, but its subjection to whatever rational corporeal creatures there may be (remembering that it has been commonly held that it is precisely by his possession of rationality that man bears upon himself the image of God and has been given dominion over the lower creation on this earth), it might well be held that the restoration of the true ordering of the universe involves the personal union of the divine Word with *all* rational corporeal natures that exist, and not only with the nature of man. Is it, in fact, man alone or a whole family of rational creatures that is to rule over God's world as God's vicegerent? This is the underlying question and, on whichever side our personal preferences may lie, I do not see that we are in a position to answer it with certainty.

This has been a highly inconclusive discussion, but I do not think it has been altogether pointless. It has perhaps shown how wide is the liberty that Christian orthodoxy leaves to intellectual speculation, and how many are the avenues that it opens up. Theological principles tend to become torpid for lack of exercise, and there is much to be said for giving them now and then a scamper in a field where the paths are few and the boundaries undefined; they do their day-by-day work all the better for an occasional outing in the country. Outings, however, are outings and work is work, and it is very important not to confuse them with each other.

8. CONCLUSION

The discussion in this lecture has inevitably manifested a somewhat rambling and even scrappy character, for its main pur-

[1] Heb. ii. 7, 8.

pose has been to show, by taking a number of typical examples, how loosely knit the relations between theology and natural science are. I began by denying that their attitudes to each other ought to be thought of in terms of conflict; but I also tried to make it plain that we ought not to expect that they will harmonise at every point nor to be disappointed if they fail to do so. Neither the science nor the theology of any epoch can lay claim to absolute finality; it was the assumption that either or both of them could that, as I have tried to show, was mainly responsible for the sense of conflict. Nevertheless, it is interesting to note—and I have tried to show this by taking some concrete instances—that present-day scientific notions are a good deal more favourable to the outlook of orthodox theology than were the scientific notions of the last century or those of the last three centuries taken as a whole. Whether or not it was necessary to liberalise theology in order to meet the demands of science yesterday, it is certainly not necessary to do so to-day. How long this happy situation will continue it is impossible to tell; nor, as I have said, does it ultimately matter. There is room enough in the world for the theologian and the scientist to live together, if each of them understands his scope; and, like Zerubbabel and Joshua, the priest and the prince in the book of the Prophet Zechariah, each may wear his golden crown without jealousy of the other, and the counsel of peace shall be between them both.

Chapter Two

THE NATURE OF SCIENTIFIC THEORIES

Animadvertet parabolam et interpretationem, verba
sapientium et aenigmata eorum.—Prov. i. 6.

I. SCIENTIFIC THEORIES AND THE PHYSICAL WORLD

THE statements which scientists make are of widely different types, varying from simple straightforward registrations of individual sensible phenomena, couched in the language of ordinary speech, such as "That white powder which you gave me exploded when I heated it", to very general and abstract formulations, expressed in highly technical terminology, such as "An electron in an *s*-state always has a spherically symmetrical electron cloud with $(n - 1)$ spherical nodes, where n is the principal quantum number".[1] And there are a variety of statements of intermediate types, such as "Bees are blind to red, but have a range of colour-vision extending into the ultra-violet"[2] and "A phenomenon exactly similar to Faraday's magnetic rotation of the plane of polarisation of light can be observed when rays of radiant heat are made to pass through rock-salt in a strong magnetic field".[3] The type of statement with which we shall be mainly concerned is that which expresses a physical hypothesis or theory, and, since in the minds both of scientists and of the general public the difference between statements of this kind and ordinary descriptions of sensible phenomena is frequently ignored or misunderstood, it will be important to devote a little time to discussing the peculiar kind of relation which they have to the latter.

We must, however, recognise that there are certain scientific theories the expression of which differs very little in logical type from generalisations from sensible experience. For example, the

---

[1] W. Hume-Rothery, *Atomic Theory for Students of Metallurgy*, p. 75.
[2] Hugh B. Cott, in *Evolution as a Process*, p. 50.
[3] E. Whittaker, *History of the Theories of Aether and Electricity*, I, p. 190.

theory of human evolution, expressed in some such sentence as "Human beings are descended from ape-like ancestors" is of very much the same kind as the statement "Swedish people have fair hair", though its verification is of necessity more hazardous and indirect. The terms which occur in it are all such as might occur in a sentence of common speech. Such statements of theories are, however, rare in science. Almost invariably, scientific theories need for their expression technical terms, such as "nucleon", "entropy", "allelomorph", "displacement-current", and so on, whose definition in terms of sense-observations is extremely complicated and remote. However, for many purposes it is convenient and fruitful to think of these words as if they denoted objects comparable with those which we see and touch, and indeed most physicists feel unhappy unless they can form such a picture. The consequence is that once they have found such a fruitful representation they tend to feel and to say that the representation is what the phenomenon under consideration *really is*. Matter is *really* made of neutrons, protons and electrons, hereditary characters are *really* located at specifiable points on the chromosome, electricity is *really* a flow of electrons or alternatively a set of elastic strains in the ether, and so on. One of the most famous examples of this tendency is provided by Eddington's two tables, which Professor Stebbing castigated so drastically, and perhaps not entirely fairly,[1] in her book *Philosophy and the Physicists*. One of the tables was the extended, coloured, substantial, solid table of everyday life; the other was the physicist's table, composed mostly of empty space, in which enormous numbers of tiny electric charges were rushing about with immense speed. "I need not tell you", Eddington wrote with conscious humour, "that modern physics has by delicate test and remorseless logic assured me that my second scientific table is the only one which is really there—wherever 'there' may be."[2] For no one knew better than Eddington that the hypostatisation of scientific concepts was a thing of the past, unsuccessful as was his own attempt to find a substitute for it in his doctrine of "selective

[1] A penetrating criticism of Miss Stebbing's discussion is given by Mr W. R. F. Hardie in his article "Ordinary Language and Perception" in the *Philosophical Quarterly*, V, p. 98 f. (1955).

[2] *The Nature of the Physical World*, p. xiv.

subjectivism".[1] "Until recently," he wrote, "the physicist used to borrow the raw material of his world from the familiar world, but he does so no longer. . . . There is a familiar table parallel to the scientific table, but there is no familiar electron, quantum or potential parallel to the scientific electron, quantum or potential."[2] "Science", he added, "aims at constructing a world which shall be symbolic of the world of commonplace experience."[3]

The tendency to hypostatise the concepts of science was the besetting sin of the Victorian physicist. Matter was explained away as consisting of invisible atoms and impalpable ether, though with remarkable inconsistency the atoms and the ether themselves were felt to be unexplained until they could be provided with the fundamental properties of geometrical extension, inertia, elasticity and the like. Gyroscopes and indiarubber and wax and beer-froth were made of matter, and matter was made of ether. But when we enquired what ether was made of, it turned out to be gyroscopes, indiarubber, wax and beer-froth on an ultra-microscopic scale, or at any rate something with properties very like theirs. The heroic lengths to which mathematical physicists were prepared to go in order to recover in the ether the properties of which they had previously divested large-scale matter can be seen by reading the chapter on "Models of the Aether" in Sir Edmund Whittaker's *History of the Theories of Aether and Electricity*. Here, for example, is his description of the ether-model proposed by Fitzgerald in 1885:

> This was constituted of a number of wheels, free to rotate on axes fixed perpendicularly in a plane board; the axes were fixed at the intersections of two systems of perpendicular lines; and each wheel was geared to each of its four neighbours by an indiarubber band. Thus all the wheels could rotate without any straining of the system, provided they all had the same angular velocity; but if some of the wheels were revolving faster than others, the indiarubber bands would become strained.[4]

Whether physicists believed in their heart of hearts that the

---

[1] Cf. *The Philosophy of Physical Science*, passim.
[2] *The Nature of the Physical World*, p. xv.   [3] Ibid.
[4] Op. cit., I, p. 292. Cf. C. F. von Weizsäcker: "The physical world view of the nineteenth century . . . thought that a process which was not perceptible to the senses had been understood only after it had been reduced to a model after the pattern of the perceptible" (*The World View of Physics*, p. 31).

ether "really consisted" of elements such as these may seriously be doubted; the fact remains that most of them seemed to be unable to believe that any system of mathematical equations could describe a physical phenomenon until they had mentally constructed a model to correspond to it. And there is no doubt that this conceptual model-building acted as a most powerful stimulus to research. Perhaps this is partly due to the extent to which in this country physical research was dominated by the great model-builders Clerk Maxwell and Kelvin; Whittaker remarks of the latter that no one has ever excelled him "in that power to which Gauss attached so much importance, of devising dynamical models and analogies for obscure physical phenomena", and points out that this power has always been cultivated by the "Cambridge school" of natural philosophers.[1] However, by the end of the nineteenth century the attempt to find mechanical models for optical and electro-magnetic phenomena began to be abandoned, largely under the influence of Sir Joseph Larmor, who urged that "we should not be tempted towards explaining the simple group of relations which have been found to define the activity of the aether by treating them as mechanical consequences of concealed structure in that medium; we should rather rest satisfied with having attained to their exact dynamical correlation, just as geometry explores or correlates, without explaining, the descriptive and metric properties of space."[2] Even to-day, however, I doubt whether physicists are quite happy if they are deprived of a familiar representation of their phenomena. Few of them, for example, think naturally in terms of relativity theory; for most of them it simply involves putting into their equations a term representing the increase of mass with velocity and then going on thinking, in the old "classical" way, of Euclidean space and Newtonian time.[3] Of the physicist, no less

[1] Op. cit., I, p. 241. Maxwell himself, however, appears to have understood that the models of physical theory ought not to be taken too literally; cf. Joseph Turner, "Maxwell on the Method of Physical Analogy", *B.J.P.S.*, VI, p. 226 f. (1955).

[2] Quoted by Whittaker, ibid., I, p. 303.

[3] Cf. these remarks of Dr H. Dingle: "To the average mathematical physicist, relativity simply consists in substituting the Lorentz for the Galilean transformation of space and time measurements. The 'relativity correction' is a commonly used expression, as though it were simply a matter of putting in some small term that had previously been overlooked. But that is a very superficial view" (*The Sources of Eddington's Philosophy*, p. 5).

than of man in general, it is true that *mens convertit se ad phantas-mata*. And in the lay mind the popular scientific journals, with their pictures of neutrons like tennis balls and electrons like marbles, accompanied by zig-zag and wavy lines as the only true and authentic representation of gamma-radiation, must have firmly implanted the notion that the entities of which physics talks are the real bricks out of which the universe is constructed. and indeed it has only been under the sheer brute force of quantum phenomena that physicists have been brought to recognise the essentially pragmatic character of the language of physical theory. Even at the present day there are physicists who are reluctant to accept as final the indeterminist interpretation of the formulae of quantum physics; Einstein held out for a quarter of a century and he has quite recently been joined, though with some reluctance, by M. Louis De Broglie.[1]

I propose now to expound and comment upon some of the views that are held at the present day as to the relation of physical theories to the world which they describe, and it may be well at this stage to make it clear what this discussion has to do with the subject of these lectures. The point is simply this, that it was widely held until comparatively recently that physical statements professed to give a literal description of the constitution and behaviour of the world. If these statements were sufficiently general in their scope and had been verified by observation and experiment, they were raised to the rank of physical theories. Furthermore, the theories that were accepted were of a determinist type, and, as they were alleged to apply to processes in the human body no less than in the realm of lifeless matter, it was widely alleged that human freedom was an illusion, a claim that was obviously unwelcome to religious belief. I shall give attention later to the latter part of this position, that which is concerned with the issue of determinism. At the moment I shall merely discuss the former question, that of the relation of scientific statements to the world in which we live.

Until the discoveries of recent years brought about a radical re-examination of the whole basis of physical theory, it was commonly assumed that the difference between rival theories in the same field was simply the difference between falsehood and truth.

[1] Cf. L. De Broglie, *The Revolution in Physics*, p. 220 f.

I gave in the last lecture an example from a well-written popular work, in which the decline of the phlogistic theory of combustion was described as "the Conflict with Error" and the ultimate adoption of the oxygen theory as "the Triumph of Truth". One theory had been proved to be false and another had been proved to be true; it was as simple as that. Similarly, it was believed that Ptolemaic cosmology was wrong and Copernican cosmology was right, *tout court. Paiens ont droit et chrestiens ont tort.* It is true that in 1883 Ernst Mach caused something of a sensation by maintaining, in Sir William Dampier's words, that "science does but construct a model of what our senses tell us about Nature, and that mechanics, far from being the ultimate truth about Nature as some believe it to be, is but one aspect from which that model may be regarded". But, as the same writer points out, "his work was ignored by some, slighted as fanciful by others, and overestimated for originality by the few who studied and appreciated it".[1] It is thus interesting to notice that in 1917 Einstein, in developing his gravitational field theory, explicitly adopted one of Mach's fundamental principles.[2] It is also interesting that Mach was far more of a reactionary than he or anyone else realised. To quote Dampier again, "Most of Mach's ideas may be found in the writings of the older philosophers, but they came quite fresh to the unphilosophic men of science of the late nineteenth century".[3] In fact, in antiquity itself and throughout the Middle Ages, the relation of scientific theories to actual fact had been an open and disputed question, in particular in relation to astronomy. The matter has been exhaustively studied by M. Pierre Duhem in his great work *Le Système du Monde* and more briefly in his *Essai sur la notion de Théorie physique de Platon à Galilée.* In our modern celebration of the victory of Copernicus and Galileo over Aristotle and Ptolemy we often overlook the fact that throughout the Middle Ages there was a spirited contest between the two geocentric systems of Aristotle and Ptolemy themselves. Briefly, the difference was that Aristotle, on theoretical grounds, insisted on representing the motions of the planets by combina-

---

[1] *History of Science,* 3rd ed., pp. 316–17.

[2] Whittaker, *History of Theories of Aether and Electricity,* II, p. 167 f. Dr G. J. Whitrow has pointed out that Mach was anticipated by Berkeley a century and a half before; cf. "Berkeley's Philosophy of Motion", *B.J.P.S.,* IV, p. 43 (1953).

[3] Loc. cit.

tions of rotating concentric spheres, fifty-five in all being needed;
while Ptolemy, without abandoning the principle of reducing all
the motions to combinations of circular motions, complicated
the picture and destroyed its aesthetic perfection by epicycles,
eccentrics and equants.[1] There were even attempts in the fifteenth
and sixteenth centuries to combine the two methods.[2] Now the
difficulty was that Aristotle's system of concentric spheres, while
it manifested admirably that symmetry and uniformity which was
felt to be proper to the quintessential supralunar realm, was very
unsuccessful in predicting the positions in which the heavenly
bodies were actually to be found; while the Ptolemaic system,
which was almost entirely satisfactory from the standpoint of
prediction, within the limits of observational error of the time,
was highly untidy and intricate. (There was in fact one glaring
anomaly, from the observational point of view, even in the
Ptolemaic system, as Copernicus did not hesitate to point out, in
connection with the apparent diameter of the moon; but nothing
could be done about this.)[3] In Duhem's words, "the Averroists
[i.e. the medieval Aristotelians who based their understanding of
Aristotle on the work of the famous twelfth-century Arab com-
mentator Ibn Roschd] adopted hypotheses physically acceptable,
but they could not 'save the phenomena'; the Ptolemeans save

---

[1] The distinction between eccentrics and epicycles is not fundamental. Anything that can be done by the one can be done by the other, and there was a
controversy in the ancient world as to which representation was the more
correct; cf. Duhem, *Système du Monde*, I, p. 434.

[2] Cf. F. Sherwood Taylor, *The Attitude of St Thomas to Natural Science*,
p. 8 f.

[3] Ptolemy, *Almagest*, V. The centre of the moon's eccentric had to be placed
so far from the earth in order to get the moon's orbital motion right, that the distance between the earth and the moon, which was carried upon an epicycle of
considerable size, varied enormously from time to time, producing a correspondingly vast variation in the moon's apparent diameter. A note in the translation of the first five books of the Almagest published by the Encyclopaedia
Britannica Company reads as follows:

"From this theory of eccentricity it follows that the moon's distance from the
earth varies by as much as 34 to 65, or nearly 1 to 2. And since, for small angles,
the tangents are nearly proportional to the angles, the size of the moon's diameter
(as Copernicus points out in Chapter 2 of Book IV, *On the Revolutions of the
Heavenly Spheres*) will vary as 1 to 2. But, by observation, this is not true. The
diameter varies very nearly as 55 to 65, just as the epicyclic theory without the
eccentric theory allows. Hence at this point the Ptolemaic theory, in saving
the appearances of the angular distances, is unable to save the appearances of the
diameter's variations." (p. 148.)

the appearances fairly accurately, but their suppositions contradict the science of nature".[1] For to the medievals, the "science of nature" did not mean, as it would to us, a science based upon experiment and observation but one derived from the *a priori* reasoning of Aristotle. The common way of reconciling theory with observation was by the reflection that we who live in this fallen sublunar world cannot expect to know the truth about the incorruptible realm of the planets and stars. St Thomas Aquinas appears to have accepted Aristotle's arguments as providing the ultimate physical truth about the celestial bodies and their operations;[2] but he was perfectly ready to accept the Ptolemaic system as a calculus for practical purposes, or indeed any other system which would perform that function with equal or superior efficiency. "There are two kinds of way", he writes, "in which a reason may be given for anything. The first is for proving some principle satisfactorily, as for example in natural science a sufficient reason is brought forward for proving that the motion of the heavens is always of uniform velocity. In the other way a reason is brought forward, which does not satisfactorily prove a principle but which shows that the effects which follow agree with the principle already propounded, as for example in astronomy [*astrologia* is the Latin word!] the explanation by eccentrics and epicycles is propounded because, when this position has been adopted, the sensible appearances of the heavenly motions can be accounted for (*possunt salvari apparentia sensibilia*); nevertheless this explanation is not a conclusive proof, because the appearances might perhaps be accounted for by adopting a different position."[3] It was not therefore a new and ingenious dodge when, in the preface which Osiander wrote to Copernicus's *De Revolutionibus* (and which was at the time believed to be by Copernicus himself) the heliocentric system was represented as being a mere hypothesis, or when Bellarmine in 1615, while expressing grave

[1] *Essai*, p. 73. Cf. A. R. Hall, *The Scientific Revolution*, p. 52.

[2] Fr. F. C. Copleston would dissent (*Aquinas*, p. 72). How different was St Thomas's *metaphysical* understanding of the physical universe from Aristotle's can be seen in J. de Tonquédec's, *Questions de Cosmologie et de Physique chez Aristote et Saint Thomas*, p. 28 f.

[3] *S. Theol.*, I, xxxii, 1 *ad* 2. ("Sensible" here, as elsewhere in this chapter, means, of course, "pertaining to the senses" and not, as in modern speech, "reasonable"). Cf. Philipp Frank, "Metaphysical Interpretations of Science", *B.J.P.S.*, I, p. 68 f. (1950).

doubts as to the compatibility of geocentrism with Holy Scripture, saw no objection to using it for explaining the phenomena. Indeed, as Dr A. C. Crombie has remarked, the Copernican hypothesis had actually been used as the basis of the Gregorian reform of the calendar in 1582, thirty-four years before the condemnation of Galileo.[1] It is amusing to notice, as Professor Butterfield has pointed out, that Copernicus seems to have propounded his system as much on *a priori* as on purely observational grounds. "Copernicus's own system was so far from answering to the phenomena in the case of Mars that Galileo in his main work on this subject praises him for clinging to his new theory though it contradicted observation",[2] namely observation of the variations in the brightness of that planet. "Of Copernicus", writes Dr G. J. Whitrow, "we find that the high-priest of modern empiricism, Francis Bacon, complained that 'Copernicus was a man who did not care what fictions he introduced into nature provided his calculations answer'", and again he remarks that "[Galileo's] scholastic opponents . . . were continually appealing to simple and plain observations of actual concrete phenomena; they were, in short, the positivists of their day".[3] What finally discredited the Ptolemaic theory was the observation of the phases of the planet Venus. On the Ptolemaic theory Venus can never be seen larger than the half-moon shape, but Galileo's telescope easily exhibited its gibbous phase.[4] However, though this was sufficient to discredit Ptolemy, it was not in fact sufficient to establish Copernicus; the new phenomenon could be saved just as well by the system of Tycho Brahe, which gave precisely the same relative motions for the celestial bodies as were given by the Copernican system in its original form and could have been elaborated in the same way in which the Copernican system had to be elaborated.[5] As Sir James Jeans observed, the reason why Tycho's system plays no part in the history of science is simply that all

---

[1] Cf. A. C. Crombie, *Augustine to Galileo*, p. 325 f.

[2] H. Butterfield, *The Origins of Modern Science*, p. 23.

[3] "On the Foundations of Dynamics", *B.J.P.S.*, I, p. 93 (1950).

[4] See, e.g., H. Spencer Jones, *General Astronomy*, p. 233.

[5] Tycho's system is in fact what the simple Copernican system becomes if we superpose on the latter a revolution equal and opposite to that of the earth round the sun. The earth then comes to rest, with the moon and the sun revolving round it, while all the other planets are revolving round the sun.

later developments in astronomy were made by people who believed in the Copernican system.[1] What ultimately established the ascendancy of the Copernican system was the work of Kepler and Newton. Copernicus had managed to reduce the number of circles needed to save the appearances of the heavens from about eighty to thirty-four;[2] Kepler, by abandoning the requirement of circles and of uniform velocity, replaced these by five ellipses with the sun in one of the foci of each. (The moon, of course, remains as a satellite of the earth, the earth's only salvage from the wreck of Ptolemy's system.) This is Kepler's famous first law, and he added two others which described the variation of velocity at different points of a planet's orbit, and the relations between the orbital times of different planets. It was Newton's achievement to display Kepler's laws as being simply a special case of a more general set of laws, which could be applied no less to the fall of apples on the earth than to the motions of the planets in deep heaven. Newton's three laws of motion and his inverse-square law of universal gravitation finally abolished the idea of a qualitative difference between the various parts of the universe and achieved the final secularisation of the quintessential supra-lunar realm. Only in our use of the term "heavens" for the sky and of the phrase "celestial mechanics" for the science that deals with the motion of its contents, there survives the last vestige of the august divine dignity which the stars and the planets enjoyed in the estimation of the ancient world.[3] Their aura of deity had not however been annihilated; it had merely transferred itself to Newton's Laws. Deistic pietism might indeed see the spacious firmament on high and all the blue ethereal sky and spangled heavens, a shining frame, proclaiming their great Original. The working formula of the eighteenth century might, as Whitehead says, see the Newtonian forces as nothing less than the imposed conditions provided by a God who made his appearance in religion under the frigid title of the First Cause and was appro-

---

[1] *The Growth of Physical Science*, p. 136.
[2] A. C. Crombie, op. cit., p. 313. Cf. also H. Dingle, *The Scientific Adventure*, ch. iii, "Nicolaus Copernicus (1473–1543)". Cf. the diagram in A. R. Hall, *The Scientific Revolution*, p. 62.
[3] The names of the planets might be quoted as another instance, but for the fact that the Olympian deities were really supermen rather than gods in the philosophical sense.

priately worshipped in whitewashed churches.[1] But the natural
end was that which Collingwood saw in eighteenth- and nineteenth-century materialism. "It denies God," he wrote, "but only
because it has transferred the attributes of God to matter, and
being the offspring of a monotheistic tradition thinks one God
quite enough. The phenomenon is so uniform that in a general
way we can recognise a materialist author by his habit of using
the traditional forms of Christian piety in speaking about the
material world."[2]

The success of post-Newtonian physics in correlating and
predicting the occurrences of nature was such as to render the
view that the function of scientific hypotheses is merely to "save
the appearances" psychologically untenable, even though its
logical possibility remained untouched. Subsequent years seemed
but to confirm the estimate of Newton made by his contemporary
Alexander Pope:

> Nature and Nature's laws lay hid in night:
> God said, *Let Newton be!* and all was light,

though, as time went on, there seemed to be less and less room
for God in the universe whose secrets Newton had discovered.
By the end of the nineteenth century, in spite of the occasional
protests of nonconformists like Mach, one view of the nature of
scientific theories has come to dominate the scene, the view that
they describe, or at any rate profess to describe, the world as it
really is. In forming a hypothesis in any field of science, the
scientist is making a guess at the real nature of the invisible
machinery that is responsible for the phenomena under investigation; he works out as many of the consequences of his guess as
he can, and devises experiments to see whether its predictions are
in fact realised. If they are, then his hypothesis has been confirmed; and a sufficient number of successful predictions will re-

[1] *Adventures of Ideas*, p. 157.
[2] *The Idea of Nature*, p. 104. Cf. the following passage, written by Clerk
Maxwell in 1873, quoted by H. Dingle in his lecture on "The Scientific Attitude
in 1851 and in 1951" (*B.J.P.S.*, II, p. 93 (1951)):
"Though in the course of ages catastrophes have occurred and may yet occur
in the heavens, though ancient systems may be dissolved and new systems evolved
out of their ruins, the molecules out of which these systems are built—the foundation stones of the material universe—remain unbroken and unworn."

move any reasonable suspicion that the initial confirmations were due to chance. The hypothesis is then raised to the rank of a theory, and the invisible machinery which it postulated is accepted as really present, in the same sense of "really" as is involved when, for example, we say that the Arc de Triomphe is really in the Place de l'Étoile. Thus, for example, the phenomena of interference were held to show that light really consisted of waves and not corpuscles, and, as the waves were believed to be real ones, a real medium had to be postulated for their transmission. The further discovery that the waves were almost certainly electro-magnetic ones made no difference; that merely meant that electro-magnetic phenomena also were really disturbances in this medium. Thus was developed the doctrine of the omnipresent ether, which reached its final efflorescence in the ether-models to which I have already referred, before it was swept away by the advent of Relativity. A typical expression of this attitude is provided by the following quotation from the colossal work of J. W. Mellor bearing the appropriate title *A Comprehensive Treatise on Inorganic and Theoretical Chemistry*, which was published as late as 1922. The author is referring to the atomic theory of matter.

> The vitality of this time-honoured theory is remarkable; it is ever assimilating new facts and ever enticing the chemist to fresh fields and pastures new. Innumerable prophecies based on the atomic hypothesis have been completely verified, so that the atomic theory is now regarded as a pyramid of truth. Consequently, although no one has ever seen an atom, A. R. A. Smith (1884) could say: We believe in atoms because, so far as we can see, nature uses them. *The greater the number of facts consistently explained by one and the same theory, the greater the probability of its being true.* The overwhelming mass of circumstantial evidence, direct and indirect, which modern chemistry and physics offer, has justified the faith of Dalton and almost, but not quite, demonstrated the real existence of tangible atoms.[1]

"The real existence of tangible atoms": that is how the chemist had come to think about his world. Relativity-physics, for all its

---

[1] Op. cit., I, p. 113. The words in italics above are in heavy type in the original.

revolutionary character, tended rather to strengthen than to weaken this realistic attitude to physical theory; for relativity-physics lends itself extremely well to geometrical representation as soon as the imagination has surmounted the initial difficulties of assimilating time to space by multiplying its measures by the square root of minus one and then coalescing it with the three dimensions of space in a four-dimensional non-Euclidean continuum. Thus we get the vivid picture of matter as being nothing but a pucker in space-time which was used to such effect in the brilliant popular expositions of Sir Arthur Eddington.[1] It was only with the advent of the quantum theory that it became more and more evident that no sort of physical or geometrical picture of the phenomena was ultimately sufficient; and when no such picture exists there is obviously no further danger of identifying it with the "real" nature of the phenomena. Quantum theory has in fact forced upon the consideration of physicists a fact which ought to have been recognised long before, that the concepts of physical theory may be perfectly successful in "saving the appearances" without themselves having the same kind of physical reality as the phenomena. In consequence, philosophers of science have recently been led into a thorough re-examination of the logical and epistemological status of physical theories.

Professor I. T. Ramsey, in a course of unpublished lectures, has pointed out that a scientific theory, in any developed science, can never be shown to be simply "false" and therefore *a fortiori* can never be abandoned on that account. What happens is that it has to be made more and more complicated in order to cover newly discovered phenomena, and ultimately its retention is more trouble than it is worth. The process of increasing complication may in fact go on for a long time, if there is no other theory in the field. If, however, a simpler theory is devised which covers the phenomena with equal or greater adequacy and has equal or greater predictive power, the ultimate supersession of the earlier theory is only a matter of time. The precise instant at which this supersession will occur is to some extent arbitrary, and there is certainly never a critical point when something or other happens which "proves" a theory false. There will be a tendency to hold on to the earlier theory as long as possible, for even scientists are

[1] Cf. *The Nature of the Physical World*, ch. vi.

conservative in their outlook, and it is always more pleasant to work with concepts that have become familiar than to learn to handle a new, and at first sight outlandish, set. What in fact happens in the end is not that the older theory is proved to be false but that it is abandoned as useless; and this is the reason why there is frequently a transition-period during which different scientists of equal competence are working with different theories and neither can prove that the other is wrong. The example by which Professor Ramsey illustrated his thesis was that of the replacement of the phlogistic theory of combustion by the oxygen theory. Another example has been given by Dr M. Polanyi[1] who remarks that Arrhenius's theory of electrolytes maintained its place in the text-books for over thirty years in the teeth of conflicting evidence, by the simple device of describing the phenomena of strong electrolytes as "anomalous". In this connection it is perhaps worth while observing that there may sometimes be alternative lines of advance and that in following one line there may be loss as well as gain. The phlogistic theory asserted that when a combustible body was burnt it lost a material component, which was known as phlogiston; Lavoisier in the 1770s asserted that it gained a material component, which he called oxygen and identified with the "dephlogisticated air" discovered by Priestley. Since bodies when burnt increased in weight, provided the products of combustion were not allowed to escape, there were obvious advantages in Lavoisier's theory, though the older view could still be defended by the supplementary hypothesis that phlogiston had negative weight. From the point of view of chemistry the oxygen theory had the merit of simplicity, and in addition it covered a large range of phenomena whose explanation by the older theory was intolerably complicated. Nevertheless, its adoption diverted attention from the fact that combustion is attended by rise in temperature; and it may well be that, if phlogiston, instead of being totally discredited, had been identified with what later on was to be known as thermal energy, we should not have had to wait until 1824 for Sadi Carnot to lay the foundations of the science of thermodynamics.

[1] *B.J.P.S.*, III, p. 228 (1952).

2. SCIENTIFIC THEORIES AND "MAPS"

The status of scientific descriptions and theories has recently been investigated in some detail by both Dr Stephen Toulmin and Professor R. B. Braithwaite, and it will be useful for our present purposes to pay some attention to their discussions. Dr Toulmin, in his book *The Philosophy of Science*, asserts with emphasis that such famous popularisers as Jeans and Eddington badly mystified their readers by devoting a great deal of space to expounding the concepts and models used by the physicists in their theories, while saying very little about the function that those concepts and models were designed to perform. "Jeans, for instance," he writes, "relied on finding a happy analogy which would by itself bring home to his readers the chief features of the General Theory of Relativity. And how did he invite them to think of the universe? As the three-dimensional surface of a four-dimensional balloon. The poor layman, who had been brought up to use the word 'surface' for two-dimensional things alone, now found himself instructed to visualise what for him was a self-contradiction, so it was no wonder if he agreed to Jeans' calling the universe a mysterious one."[1] I am reminded of a passage from a philosopher with a very different background from that of Dr Toulmin, namely the distinguished French scholastic, M. Étienne Gilson. "In 1930 . . .", he writes, "Sir James Jeans decided to deal with philosophical problems in the light of contemporary science. The upshot was his most popular book: *The Mysterious Universe*. Now, if the universe of science is mysterious, what is not? We do not need science to tell us that the universe is indeed mysterious. Men have known that since the very beginning of the human race. The true and proper function of science is, on the contrary, to make as much of the universe as possible grow less and less mysterious to us. Science does it, and she does it magnificently. . . . How is it then", M. Gilson asks, "that a scientist can feel well founded in calling this universe a 'mysterious universe'?" And he answers: "The true reason why this universe appears to some scientists as mysterious is that, mistaking existential, that is metaphysical, questions for scientific ones, they ask science to answer them. Naturally, they get no

[1] Op. cit., p. 12.

answers. Then they are puzzled, and they say that the universe is mysterious."[1]

Gilson's answer is clearly different from Toulmin's, but it does not follow that they may not both, from their different angles, be correct. I am myself a little inclined to doubt whether the layman is as mystified as Toulmin suggests. I suspect that, when he is told that the universe is the three-dimensional surface of a four-dimensional balloon, he manages to combine the comfortable feeling produced by the homely associations of the familiar word "balloon" with the pleasant sense of initiation into a mystery that goes with the use of the occult term "four-dimensional". But that the layman is in danger of being seriously misled I fully agree.

Toulmin introduces his own view of the nature of scientific descriptions by considering the Principle of the Rectilinear Propagation of Light. He points out that, when we say "Light travels in straight lines", we are clearly not using the words "light" and "travels" in their ordinary sense, for we should continue to accept the statement as true even if we were confronted by a sunlit prospect in which everything was at rest. What, in fact, the statement does is to provide us with a model which, if we use it in accordance with certain principles of inference, enables us to correlate and predict a large variety of optical phenomena, for example the length of the shadow cast by a wall of known height when the sun is at a specified angular elevation. He goes on to remind us that it is only in the simpler cases that the model is a geometrical or physical one. "Only in a very few branches of physics", he writes,

does the drawing of diagrams play a logically central part. In most branches the logical role played in geometrical optics by diagrammatic techniques is taken over by other less primitive kinds of mathematics; and these are often of a complexity and sophistication far greater than could ever be handled diagrammatically. Yet however sophisticated and complex these may become, they play a part comparable to that of picture-drawing in geometrical optics: they serve, that is to say, as *techniques of inference-drawing*. In dynamics, for example, the counterparts of our geometrical diagram are the equations of motion of the system of bodies under investigation.[2]

[1] *God and Philosophy*, p. 122 f.   [2] Ibid., p. 32 (italics mine).

And he goes on to point out that the really useful models are those that are capable of wide "deployment", that is to say, those which suggest further questions than those which they were originally devised to answer and which cover a range of phenomena wider than that which they were originally devised to correlate and predict. He makes the penetrating suggestion that it was just this unlimited deployability of physical theories which Planck and Einstein had in mind when they insisted that electrons and gravitational fields were as "real" as tables, chairs and omnibuses. For, in spite of the obvious difference of the scientific concepts from the objects of everyday experience, their applicability is in principle unlimited.

Toulmin makes some interesting observations about the attitude of Ernst Mach. Mach himself insisted that the sole justification of theories and models was their success in correlating and predicting the results of observation and experiment, but he thought they were simply condensed descriptions of the observational and experimental facts and nothing more. Toulmin, while agreeing with the first part of this assertion, has little difficulty in showing the falsity of the second part; for it is clearly impossible to derive an observation-report like "The shadow was ten feet six inches deep" by logical inference from theoretical statements like "Light travels in straight lines". The theoretical statements are not just logical constructions from the observation-reports; hence, although the observation-statements can be derived from the theoretical statements, they are not logical consequences of them. The method of derivation is a complicated one, whose application involves not only the laws of logical inference, but also certain principles of application, which are as much a part of the theory as the model itself is. In connection with the example which Toulmin used to illustrate his point, it is interesting to notice in passing that, as long ago as 1927, Dr P. W. Bridgman, in his book *The Logic of Modern Physics*, which expounds a radically "operational" view of physical theory, protested against the identification of light with a "thing travelling" and alleged that this identification had caused unnecessary complications. "From the point of view of operations," he wrote, "light means nothing more than *things lighted*."[1] And again:

[1] Op. cit., p. 151.

It seems to me that it is very questionable whether Einstein, and all the rest of modern physics, for that matter, have not paid too high a price for simplicity and mathematical tractability in choosing to treat light as a thing that travels. Physically it is the essence of light that it is *not* a thing that travels, and in choosing to treat it as a thing that does, I do not see how we can expect to avoid the most serious difficulties.[1]

In developing positively his view of the nature of scientific theories, Toulmin makes great use of the analogy of a map. He remarks how natural it is for us to speak of "finding our way around" a range of phenomena with the help of a law of nature, or "recognising where on the map" a particular object of study belongs.[2] Information about the country can be obtained from the map, but not by a process of logical deduction; we need to know how the map is meant to be used. And one sort of map will give us information of one kind, and another sort of map will give us information of another. The parallel is obvious. "Jeans and Eddington", writes Toulmin,

> were both primarily mathematicians, and in their popularisations of physics gave prominence to the mathematical side of the subject, but the results were in certain respects misleading: the physics is not in the formulae, as they suggested and as we are often inclined to suppose, any more than being able to find your way about is part of a map. The problem of *applying* the theoretical calculus remains in physics the central problem, for a science is nothing if its laws are never used to explain or predict anything.[3]

Toulmin points out that frequently one scientific theory will explain all and more than another scientific theory explains, and will also show why the latter theory breaks down if it is pressed beyond its proper limits; he gives the example of physical and geometrical optics; another example would be provided by quantum and classical dynamics. In like manner, a detailed physical map will give all the information, and more, that is given by a simple road map and will explain why the latter becomes misleading if we use it for the acquisition of information that it is not in fact meant to give; if for example we assume that, because the road map denotes towns by circular blobs, the towns are really circular.

[1] *The Logic of Modern Physics*, p. 164. [2] Op. cit., p. 105. [3] Ibid., p. 108.

Toulmin takes care to remark that the comparison of physical theories with maps breaks down if pushed too far. For, he asks, what in the map corresponds to the laws of nature in physics? It could, he replies, only be the laws of projection according to which any particular map is produced. But, although there is a certain parallel between laws of nature and laws of projection, there is this great difference between them, that the cartographer knows before he starts to draw his map what his laws of projection are going to be, while the laws of nature have to be *discovered* in the course of the task.[1] In fact, Toulmin observes, there is no way of saying beforehand what techniques of explanation will be appropriate in any given field of study. He goes on to note that, in trying out a theory, physicists prefer to make a small number of observations over a large range of circumstances, rather than a large number over a small range, and that this shows that they are not in fact investigating the *truth* of the theory but its *scope*. For the concepts which the statements of the theory mention are not the objects of observation, but only refer to the latter in a highly indirect way via the principles of interpretation of the theory; the statements of the theory are therefore not the sort of things that could be true or false, but they are either usefully applicable in a given sphere or not. To illustrate the point by a parallel of my own, we could hardly ask whether Dickens's presentation of Mr Micawber as an attractive ne'er-do-well is true or not, but we could significantly ask whether it was intended as a portrait of the author's father and, if so, whether it was an accurate one.

In the final chapter of his book, Toulmin discusses the uniformity of nature and the question of determinism. I shall say something about these matters later on; at the moment I wish to put side by side with Toulmin's account of scientific theories that given by Professor R. B. Braithwaite in his book *Scientific Explanation*.

3. SCIENTIFIC THEORIES AND "MODELS"

For Braithwaite, a scientific law is simply a generalisation, that is, a proposition expressing a constant conjunction between

[1] *Philosophy of Science*, p. 109.

properties;[1] and "scientific hypotheses, which, if true, are scientific laws, will then . . . be taken as equivalent to generalisations of unrestricted range in space and time of greater or less degrees of complexity and generality".[2] "A scientific system consists of a set of hypotheses which form a deductive system; that is, which is arranged in such a way that from some of the hypotheses as premises all the other hypotheses logically follow."[3] He points out that the hypotheses may be considered as arranged in an order of levels, those on the highest level occurring only as premises of deductions and those on the lowest level occurring only as conclusions of deductions, while those on the intermediate levels occur as conclusions of some deductions and as premises of others. As an example of a simple system he gives the system which was established by Galileo's investigation of the behaviour of massive bodies falling near the surface of the earth. This system has three levels, with one hypothesis on each of the first two and an indefinite number on the third. The top-level hypothesis asserts that every body freely falling near the earth falls with an acceleration of 32 feet per second per second. From this there follows deductively the second-level hypothesis which asserts that every body starting from rest and falling freely towards the earth falls $16t^2$ feet in t seconds, whatever number t may be. From this there follow an infinite number of third-level hypotheses of which typical examples are that every body starting from rest and falling freely for 1 second towards the earth falls a distance of 16 feet, that every body starting from rest and falling freely for 2 seconds towards the earth falls a distance of 64 feet, and so on. As we descend from one level to another we come to propositions of successively diminishing generality. The establishment of a system as a set of true propositions depends on the establishment of its lowest-level hypotheses. The empirical verification of one or more (but not all) of the lowest-level hypotheses *confirms* the higher-level hypothesis from which it is deductively derived, but nothing less than the verification of *all* the lowest-level hypotheses would be sufficient to *prove* it; on the other hand, the empirical falsification of any one of the lowest-level hypotheses will be sufficient to *refute* it.

Braithwaite's next point is that, in general, scientific systems

[1] Op. cit., p. 9 f.   [2] Ibid., p. 12.   [3] Ibid.

are more complicated than the example just given, in that the top level usually consists of not one but several hypotheses. In such a case it is likely that any particular lowest-level hypothesis will be the logical consequence not of any one but of a conjunction of several highest-level hypotheses. If this lowest-level hypothesis should be empirically refuted, it will follow that at least one of these highest-level hypotheses is false, but which particular ones will not be indicated. And in many cases it is possible to maintain the truth of any one of them that we like, if we are prepared to modify the others sufficiently drastically. (Similarly, we may observe, if a number of witnesses disagree, we can usually save the face of any one of them if we are prepared to condemn all the others as liars.) Thus, Braithwaite remarks,

> Ptolemy was able to save the geocentric hypothesis by supposing that the planets moved in complicated orbits round the earth. But at some time a point is reached at which the modifications in a system required to save a hypothesis become more unplausible than the rejection of the hypothesis; and then the hypothesis is rejected.[1]

The supersession of the phlogistic theory by the oxygen theory would provide another example of this. He also points out—and this is a point which was also made by Professor Ramsey—that

> generally speaking, a hypothesis was not rejected until an alternative hypothesis was available to take its place. Long before Einstein propounded his theory of gravitation it was known that Newton's theory could not account by itself for the observed motion of Mercury's perihelion. But Newton's theory was not dethroned until Einstein's theory was available to take its place. The process of refuting a scientific hypothesis is thus more complicated than it appears to be at first sight.[2]

There is, in fact, no simple Conflict with Error and no simple Triumph of Truth.

Having laid this foundation Braithwaite next goes on to discuss calculi and their interpretations. A calculus, considered simply in itself and apart from any interpretation of it, is, in Braithwaite's phrase, "a game for one player", in which, starting from certain given written formulae, we derive other formulae

---

[1] *Scientific Explanation*, p. 20.   [2] Ibid.

from them by manipulating them in accordance with certain rules. The calculus is thus defined by its initial formulae and its rules. In itself a calculus has no meaning whatever, but it is often possible to interpret a calculus as a representation of a deductive system, and indeed many calculi can be given more than one interpretation. The first calculus which Braithwaite constructs has three initial formulae and five rules of play, and he derives forty-two formulae from it. The whole game can be interpreted in various ways. For example, it can be interpreted as the deduction of forty-two propositions about the relations of three classes from three contingent propositions about the composition of the classes concerned. Alternatively it can be interpreted as the deduction of forty-two propositions about highest common factors from three logically necessary propositions about the highest common factors of three particular numbers taken in pairs. The relevant difference between these two interpretations is that in the first case all the propositions of the deductive system are contingent (an *impure* deductive system), while in the second case they are all logically necessary (a *pure* deductive system). Braithwaite then constructs a second calculus, which differs from the first calculus in having three additional initial formulae but only two rules of play; what it gains on the formula-swings it loses on the rule-roundabouts. By interpreting the three additional initial formulae as certain logically necessary propositions and also giving an appropriate interpretation to the two rules, it is possible to interpret the second calculus as a *mixed* deductive system (i.e. a deductive system in which some of the propositions are contingent and some logically necessary), in which the impure deductive system which was the first interpretation of the first calculus is included. That is to say, in this new mixed system the contingent propositions are exactly the same and are deduced in exactly the same order as in the old impure system. The mixed system in fact falls into two parts, a pure part consisting of logically necessary propositions and an impure part consisting of contingent propositions; and the importance of this lies in the fact that, whereas the propositions of the impure part cannot be deduced without making use of propositions in the pure part, all the propositions of the pure part can be deduced without making use of any of the propositions in the impure part. The pure part thus forms a pure deductive system on its own. The advantage of this from the point of view of the scientist is that it enables him to leave all the heavy deductive work to the mathematician, for the theorems of the pure part can be deduced by pure mathematicians, operating an algebraic calculus, without any concern for possible empirical applications. All that the scientist need do is to apply the final fruits of the mathematician's labour to whatever purpose he wishes. On the other hand, from the logician's point of view the impure system is much better than the mixed one, for in it all the propositions are contingent and all the logic lies in the deductive principles. In fact any mixed system can be transformed into an equivalent impure system by substituting additional deductive principles for its logically necessary initial propositions.

Braithwaite finally remarks the fortunate fact that physicists have nearly always found that the mathematics which they needed for their theoretical systems had already been worked out by the pure mathematicians. "Thus Einstein, in developing general relativity (1916), had Riemann's non-Euclidean geometry (1854) and Ricci's tensor calculus (1887) ready to hand; and the non-commutative multiplication used in quantum mechanics (1925–7) had been worked out in connection with Cayley's matrices (1858) and with operational methods for handling differential equations (Boole, 1844). Modern biologists", he adds, "have not been so fortunate, and have had for the most part to work out for themselves the statistical mathematics they required."[1] We ought, however, perhaps to remember that Newton had to devise the theory of fluxions in order to deal with the complexities of his own mechanics.

After this brilliant exposition of the logical structure of deductive systems in science, Braithwaite now proceeds to enquire into the status of the theoretical terms which a science employs. What is actually the meaning of such terms as "electron" and "proton"? Nothing at all, Braithwaite replies, apart from their context, and their context is a calculus. "They are used as symbols in a calculus which is to be interpreted as an applied deductive system; they are not understood as having any meaning apart from their place in such a calculus."[2] We do not attach direct

[1] Op. cit., p. 48. [2] Ibid., p. 51.

meanings to all the formulae of the calculus, but only to those
which we can interpret as propositions about empirical observations; the other formulae have only an indirect meaning via their
relation in the calculus to these. How then are the theoretical
terms related to experience? They must be related to it somehow, or else we should be doing pure mathematics and not
physics at all. Many philosophers of science, such as Mach and
Karl Pearson, have given the answer that was formulated by Lord
Russell, that theoretical concepts are simply logical constructions
out of empirical data; that, for example, we cannot define an
electron as being some kind of empirically observable entity, but
we can explicitly define the word "electron" in terms of empirical
observations. So we can in principle translate every sentence
containing the word "electron" without loss of meaning into a
sentence in which there occur only words denoting entities that
are directly observable. However, Braithwaite, following F. P.
Ramsey, constructs a simple example of a theory in which there
occur theoretical terms that are not definable in this way; and so
the question remains. What is the status of theoretical concepts if
they are not logical constructions out of empirical data? What do
we mean by an electron? Ramsey gave an answer which Braithwaite states in the following words:

> There is a property E (called "being an electron") which is such
> that certain higher-level propositions about this property E are true.
> From these higher-level propositions there follow certain lowest-
> level propositions which are empirically testable. Nothing is as-
> serted about the "nature" of this property E; all that is asserted is
> that the property E exists, i.e. that there are instances of E, namely,
> electrons.[1]

However, for Braithwaite there is something unsatisfactory about
these unobservable entities of which we can only say that they
exist and that their existence has certain consequences. And the
work of symbolic logicians since Ramsey's death in 1930 seems
to him to make a better answer possible. He proposes to by-pass
the question of the existence of electrons altogether, and to consider instead simply the way in which the *word* "electron" occurs
in the calculus. All that is important is that we shall understand

[1] *Scientific Explanation*, p. 79.

the function of the theoretical terms in the calculus which we use, and our answer to the question "Do electrons really exist?" is simply to explain the functions of the words and other symbols used for electrons in the calculus which is interpreted as the deductive system of contemporary atomic physics. As an example of a symbol which he believes every atomic physicist would agree in interpreting in this way he gives the ψ-function of Schrödinger, but he also asserts that the same situation occurs in the use of such a commonplace sentence as "Every cat eats fish". For this sentence does not attribute the property of ichthyophagy to one particular thing called "Every cat"; there is no such thing. Nor does it attribute it to the class of cats, for classes cannot eat anything. The statement is simply a formula in a calculus, and from it, by applying the rules of the calculus, we can derive sentences which do describe observable events, such as the sentence "Drake eats fish", where "Drake" is the name of a particular cat. But in spite of this Braithwaite affirms, in opposition to such philosophers as Schlick and Ramsey, that general hypotheses are better described as propositions than as rules.

The final stage in this part of Braithwaite's discussion consists of an exposition of the part played by models in scientific explanation. Starting from the fact, already established, that, given any calculus, it is frequently possible to find more than one deductive theory that will function as an interpretation of it, Braithwaite goes on to distinguish between two kinds of interpretation. In both kinds, of course, the higher-level hypotheses are *logically* prior to the lower-level ones; that is inherent in the very nature of a deductive system. But in one kind the interpretation of the initial formulae containing the theoretical terms is also *epistemologically* prior to the interpretation of the derived formulae not containing these terms; in the other kind it is epistemologically posterior. In such a case, the first interpretation is said to be related to the second as *model* to *theory*. Both have the same formal structure, and there is a one-one correlation between the propositions of the theory and those of the model; but they have different epistemological structures. In the model, the logically prior premises determine the meaning of the terms occurring in the representation in the calculus of the conclusions; in the theory, the logically posterior consequences determine the meaning of the theoretical terms occurring in the representation in the calculus of the premises. To use a model is to use a quite straight-forward interpretation of the calculus, in which the logical and the epistemological movement is in the same direction, and to think about a model is frequently the most convenient way of thinking about the structure of the theory. There are, however, serious dangers in using models, and scientists have not in-frequently fallen into them.

The first of these dangers to which Braithwaite points is that of identifying the theory with a model for it, so that the theoretical concepts will be taken as being the objects of the model. This was, of course, the besetting sin of the nineteenth-century physicists. It led to the notion that gases were "really" made up of minute billiard-balls, that space was "really" filled with an imperceptible elastic solid of extreme rigidity but at the same time perfectly penetrable by solid bodies, and so on. It has somewhat lost its hold over physicists of to-day, though one sometimes suspects that, if they could find an excuse, they would be glad to slip back into it. The second danger is much more subtle; it consists, in Braithwaite's words, of "transferring the logical necessity of some of the features of the chosen model on to the theory, and thus of supposing, wrongly, that the theory, or parts of the theory, have a logical necessity which is in fact fictitious".[1] Braithwaite em-phasises that "if it is possible to construct a pure mathematical model for a scientific theory there are many advantages in doing so".[2] It often makes it possible to utilise existing mathematical theory, and also to extend the theory upwards, so that more fundamental mathematical concepts can be introduced. Again, he points out that there are advantages in constructing a model in which some, but not all, of the initial propositions are logically necessary, in the case when we wish to consider together various scientific theories which have some, but not all, of their highest-level hypotheses in common. "Nevertheless," he adds, "however

---

[1] Op. cit., p. 94. Margenau has made substantially this point in commenting on Reichenbach's application of multi-valued logic to quantum physics: "So far as measurement is concerned, an electron is either present within a given volume or it is not. The fact that one may not draw the usual inferences concerning the electron's fate from such an observation is the responsibility of the laws of nature and not the laws of logic" (*Nature of Physical Reality*, p. 462).

[2] Op. cit., p. 108.

convenient and mathematically elegant it might be to use a model with logically necessary propositions, unless such a model corresponds to the theory with its empirically testable consequences, it will not serve as a model for the theory."[1] His final conclusion is as follows:

> The upshot of this somewhat involved discussion is that no consideration as to the logically necessary or contingent status of the highest-level propositions of a model for a theory is any reason for supposing that any highest-level hypothesis in the scientific theory itself is logically necessary. . . . It is frequently possible to construct a theory with no Campbellian initial hypotheses [i.e. with no hypotheses which are only about theoretical concepts] which is empirically equivalent to a theory containing Campbellian hypotheses in the sense that in each theory there can be deduced exactly the same empirical generalisations about observable properties.[2]

The relevance of these conclusions to certain assertions of Sir Arthur Eddington will, I think, be sufficiently obvious, and Braithwaite in fact makes mention of it.[3] I shall say something about it myself in a later lecture; Braithwaite's own remark upon the point at issue is as follows:

> Many philosophers, reluctant to admit that the necessity of a scientific law consists simply in its being a true generalisation associating the occurrence of one empirical property with that of another, have sought for a necessity in scientific laws which is either logical necessity or is closely akin to it. Some of them have found support for their position in the features of logical necessity which are involved in the representation of the hypotheses of a scientific theory by means of formulae or other modes of expression which appear naturally to represent a deductive system containing logically necessary propositions.[4]

Braithwaite goes on to assert that "it is essential to disentangle the genuine elements of logical necessity involved in scientific deductive systems and in the models which it is natural to use in thinking about them".[5] That he has done this task and has done

[1] *Scientific Explanation*, p. 109.
[2] Ibid., p. 110. As Margenau points out, there are "connections which are formal according to one and epistemic according to another theory" (*Nature of Physical Reality*, p. 85).
[3] Op. cit., p. 109.   [4] Ibid., p. 96.   [5] Ibid.

it magnificently must, I think, be admitted, but I am less happy about the reason which he has given for embarking upon this undertaking. It is, he tells us, "in order to reject (as I wish to do) the view that there is anything objective in causal necessity over and above constant conjunction".[1] He nowhere, however, shows that this positivistic doctrine is the only alternative to the doctrine of logical necessitation which he has refuted. Many, among whom I should number myself, would hold that the way is now open for a rehabilitation of the view that there are real causes operating in nature, the view which historically has provided the basis for one of the most impressive approaches to belief in a Creator. In two of the later chapters of his book, Braithwaite explicitly discusses causality and teleology, and he does this with his usual analytical brilliance. He has little difficulty in showing that, so far as the registration of purely sensory data is concerned, it is perfectly possible to reduce the notion of causality to that of constant conjunction, and the notion of teleology to that of the attainment of one and the same final state under a variety of different environmental circumstances. What is the ultimate significance of such constant conjunction and of such uniform attainment Braithwaite nowhere permits himself to enquire, and there is good reason for this. These are metaphysical questions, and Braithwaite is not writing metaphysics. Nor am I at the moment, though I have tried to discuss the metaphysical foundations of Christian theism elsewhere.[2] What I wish to do is to indicate as clearly as I can at this point the significance for our present subject of the somewhat protracted discussion in which I have indulged concerning the books of Toulmin and Braithwaite on a subject which might not seem to bear very directly on the interests of a Bampton Lecturer. The point is simply this: that for something like three centuries, from the time of Newton almost to the present day, the picture of the world with which science has worked, and under which our contemporary civilisation has moulded itself, has been that of a self-operating mechanism governed by determinist laws. In Burtt's words, "from being a realm of substances in qualitative and teleological relations the

---

[1] *Scientific Explanation.*

[2] Cf. my two books, *He Who is: a Study in Traditional Theism* and *Existence and Analogy.*

world of nature had definitely become a realm of bodies moving mechanically in space and time".[1] Or, as a Victorian minor poet put it:

> When science from creation's face enchantment's veil withdraws,
> What lovely visions yield their place to cold material laws!

It was in vain that the infants of the Foundling Hospital praised the Lord who had made laws which never shall be broken for the guidance of the worlds that had obeyed his mighty voice. It was in vain that Erasmus Darwin, in his poem *The Economy of Vegetation*, got in in 1791 five years ahead of Laplace:

> "Let there be light!" proclaimed the Almighty Lord,
> Astounded Chaos heard the potent word;
> Through all his realms the kindling Ether runs,
> And the mass starts into a million suns;
> Earths round each sun with quick explosions burst;
> And second planets issue from the first;
> Bend, as they journey, with projectile force,
> In bright ellipses their reluctant course.

And when attempts were made, as by Marx and Spencer, to restore to the world the purposiveness of which post-Newtonian physics had deprived it, it was only by locating that purposiveness in matter itself. Not that, in any case, that made much difference to the scientists. Philosophers might be Kantians or Hegelians, Faraday might even to the middle of the nineteenth century retain his Sandemanianism, but the future was with the heroic agnosticism of Thomas Huxley, draping with the last sombre vestures of Calvinism a grim and unrelenting world. Of the failure of the theologians of the time to comprehend the truth of the situation it is, I think, as St Benedict said of the gyrovagues and the sarabites, better to be silent than to speak. It is, thus, difficult to exaggerate the importance of the change that has been made in this situation in recent years, though, as yet, it has penetrated very little into those deeper levels of the soul which, often independently of the conscious mind or even in opposition to it, control the way men feel, behave and—if they do it at all—worship. The importance of analysis like that of Toulmin and Braithwaite

[1] *Metaphysical Foundations of Modern Physical Science*, p. 154.

is the witness that it bears to the abandonment of the almost universal post-Newtonian assumption that physical theories, in so far as they are valid, are literal descriptions of the real constitution of the world. Neither Toulmin's nor Braithwaite's exposition is necessarily final;[1] nor, I think, does Toulmin's analogy of the map agree in all points with Braithwaite's doctrine of the model. Nor is it of the first importance if relativity and quantum physics are more congenial to religion than classical physics; I think that is probably true, but it is secondary and may only represent a temporary phase. Far more important than any revolution in scientific theories themselves is the revolution in the view of what a scientific theory is. In principle, of course, this latter revolution might have taken place even if there had been no notable change in the scientific theories themselves. In actual fact, however, it was the ultimate inability of Galilean and Newtonian physics to co-ordinate the observational and experimental facts that led to the invention of relativity and quantum physics. And relativity and quantum physics—especially the latter—refuse to fit in, or only fit in very uncomfortably, with the old idea of what a scientific theory is and what it is intended to do. Thus there has come about a thorough overhaul of the whole doctrine of the relation of physical theories to the world which they describe, which has made most of the last-century objections to theism inapplicable. I do not think we ought to worry too much about the somewhat positivistic flavour which both Toulmin and Braithwaite give to their discussions; that may represent only a temporary occupancy of the swept and garnished house which was formerly inhabited by scientific materialism, and may in time give way to a more metaphysical tenancy. The really significant thing is the ejection of the former occupant by the side-door of the philosophy of science after three centuries of intermittent assault upon the physical front door had failed to dislodge him.

[1] F. A. Hayek has interestingly argued that in biology and certain branches of applied physics "much of the undoubtedly theoretical work does not aim at the discovery of new laws and at their confirmation, but at the elaboration from accepted premisses of deductive patterns of argument which will account for complex observed facts. If in these instances we can speak of hypotheses which require to be tested, they must be sought in the assertion that this or that pattern fits an observable situation, and not in the conditional statements of which the explanatory pattern itself consists and which is assumed to be true" ("Degrees of Explanation", in *B.J.P.S.*, VI, p. 213 (1955)).

4. SCIENTIFIC THEORIES AND "REALITY"

There is, however, one further aspect of the question which I think it will be well to discuss briefly. It may be felt that such views as Toulmin's and Braithwaite's go too far in the extent to which they deprive scientific theories of their former status as literal descriptions of the real world. It may be admitted that some such view is necessary when one is discussing theories that profess to deal with what goes on at the sub-atomic level, where the classical notions of continuous space and time become incapable of systematising the experimental facts; but so long as we keep at the level of molecules or do not go too far below, surely, it will be said, the theories which we use seem to describe objects which are extended in space and time in the same sense as chairs and tables are extended in space and time, and describe them in the same way. The new highly sophisticated doctrines may be all very well if you are trying to solve the perplexities of nuclear physicists or low-temperature thermodynamicians, but the old-fashioned view is perfectly satisfactory for organic chemistry and many other branches of science and we should be lost without it. Take for example this sentence, where the reference is to textile chemistry:

It is found that in addition to the simple cross-linking previously described, the methylolamides, the ethylene oxides, and ethylene imines also polymerise in the fabric to give coherent polymer chains in the interstices of the fibre which impart a further rigidity to the whole, as these interstitial polymers are linked by pendent reactive groups to the fibre chains.[1]

Or this, in relation to radiomimetic drugs (i.e. those drugs which produce effects on living cells similar to those produced by X-rays or gamma-rays):

The resemblance in general form between these polymeric structures is quite marked. The most important feature which they have

[1] *Science News 31*, p. 77 (1954). Cf. No. 20, p. 9 f. (1951); No. 32, p. 43 f. (1954), and the article "Chemistry" by R. C. Cahn in *Chambers's Encyclopaedia World Survey*, p. 88 f. (1954).

in common is that the distance between two adjacent reactive groups along the 'backbone' is in all cases about 3·7 Å, though in the case of (d) a molecular model is required to see this clearly as it is caused by a three-dimensional spiral arrangement of reactive groups.[1]

Or take again the following passage from Sir Charles Sherrington:

> In wool-keratin the molecule has an extensible backbone which lengthwise pull unfolds to a more open zig-zag. Hence the wool's reversible extensibility. Again, the immense significance of muscle to life rests on its property of changing length and lengthwise tension. This, it is claimed, is due to a protein-molecule of folding and unfolding type.[2]

Does it not seem perverse to deny that the whole explicative force of such statements as these depends on their being understood as describing the way in which the molecules are literally extended in space? If a structure attributed on purely chemical grounds is found to give a convincing reason for some purely physical property (as, for example, the peculiar physical properties of plastics are explained by the twisting together of their extremely long molecules), if, that is, a picture devised to explain one property is found also to explain another property of quite different kind, is that not strong *prima facie* evidence that the reality is "like" the picture in the common or garden sense of "like"? Or take the fact that unobservable entities initially postulated for the explanation of large-scale phenomena often become, by an improvement of the observational technique, to all intents and purposes observable. Does not the Brownian movement, for example, manifest to our sight the behaviour of individual molecules? Now that we have improved our chemical technique so as to make monster molecules, and our optical technique so as to see objects far more minute than any we could see before, we can photograph through an electron-microscope single molecules of substances like hemocyanin. And if we see that the large molecules exist, can we doubt that much smaller ones exist, whether we shall ever be able to see them or not? Again, take the case of the chromosomes in the cells of living creatures. Purely by the statistical study of the results of breeding

---

[1] *Science News* 31, p. 78.   [2] *Man on his Nature*, p. 101.

experiments, it has been possible to assign the genes which are associated with various inheritable characters to definite positions on the chromosomes and to explain certain remarkable cases by hypotheses about chromosomes "crossing over" and "looping"; then when we photograph the giant chromosomes in the salivary glands of Drosophila under the microscope, we see these processes actually occurring. Is not this good evidence that chromosomes "really" cross-over and loop? Again, would anyone in his senses deny that tubercle bacilli exist in the same sense in which cats exist, and say instead that the hypothesis of their existence merely provides a successful model for the visual phenomena that certain biologists see when they look down their microscopes and for the sufferings of people with tuberculosis? What are we to say about the fact that the threshold of observability has been steadily lowered until we have now in many cases reached the point at which the complications of quantum phenomena come in? Did chromosomes and tubercle bacilli not exist until microscopes were good enough for us to see them? Perhaps it will be said that we do not really *see* them even now, because we have to look through the optical system of a microscope. (Just so, Galileo's opponents alleged that the moons of Jupiter were really produced by his telescope.) But is there any relevant difference between seeing something through a microscope and seeing it through your spectacles? Or, for that matter, between seeing it through your spectacles and seeing it through the lens of your eye? Of course, microscopes and spectacles may mislead you if they are out of order, but then so may your eyes if you have been taking alcohol or santonin. We must either believe that our instruments, when properly adjusted, show us things as they really are, or else cease to believe that we know anything at all about the external world. As Dr Mary B. Hesse has written:

> We do not doubt the object-like-ness of viruses and large organic molecules which just come into view in highly magnifying microscopes, and it is natural to extrapolate to a hierarchy of particles of decreasing size and increasing unlikeness to ordinary objects: atoms, nuclei, protons, electrons. It is difficult to see how a rigid ontological distinction can be made anywhere in this hierarchy, that is, we cannot find grounds for saying the particles greater than, say, two Ångstroms in diameter are objects in the external world,

and those less than two Ångstroms are only mathematical constructions.[1]

These are the kind of objections to doctrines like that of Braithwaite that are, I think, likely to come to the minds of a good many chemists and biologists, and I do not think they will abandon them because of the difficulties with which physicists frequently, and they themselves occasionally, are faced at the quantum level. I confess that I sympathise with this reaction, but I think that we may be somewhat misled by the generally positivist tone of Braithwaite's writing into misunderstanding the real bearing of his argument. What he has shown, supposing that his reasoning is correct, is that a scientific theory and a mathematical or physical model for it will both have the same logical structure, since they are both interpretations of the same calculus. This may very well seem at first sight to imply that, if we adopt the model, we are henceforth not thinking about the theory at all but only about the model, since the theory and the model have no direct relation to each other but are merely related indirectly in virtue of the fact that they are both of them interpretations of the calculus. However, Braithwaite explicitly says that "to think in terms of the model is . . . frequently the most convenient way of thinking about the structure of the theory", and I think what enables him to say this is the fact that the logical similarity between the theory and the model is a direct one into which the calculus does not come at all. For the calculus has no *logical* similarity to either the theory or the model; it has in fact no logical structure at all, it is a sheer game, whose elements are formulae related by rules, not propositions related by implication. To develop the matter further would involve the adumbration of a metaphysical and epistemological doctrine, in the course of which my divergences from Braithwaite would become fairly marked. I should want to suggest, for example, that the model plays in our knowledge of the world around us a part similar to that which the sensible species plays in the Thomist doctrine of perception; it is an *objectum quo*, through knowing which we are enabled to know

---

[1] *Science and the Human Imagination*, p. 151. It is considerations similar to these that make me feel that there is something inadequate about the sharp distinction between scientific and everyday descriptions drawn by Professor Gilbert Ryle in *Dilemmas*, ch. v.

under one or other of its aspects the *objectum quod* which is the real world.[1] And I should follow out the parallel to the point of affirming that the real world does not simply replicate the features, or some of the features, of the model any more than the Thomist *ens reale* simply replicates the features, or some of the features, of the sensible species.[2] To suppose that it does would be to take as one's parallel the representative doctrine of perception, which, beginning with Descartes, was propped up in an amputated condition by Locke and died an ignominious death at the hands of Berkeley. I should affirm that the real world is an intelligible world and can therefore be known by our minds, though they know it only through the mediation of the senses. Being an intelligible world, it has an intelligible structure and so is the proper object of mathematical physics. The mistake of the post-Newtonian scientists was to assume that the intelligible structure of the world must simply reduplicate the structure of our sensible experience, with the so-called secondary qualities left out and a few mysterious non-sensible qualities, such as mass and electric charge, brought in. However much it might have to be complicated in order to cover one range after another of phenomena, the intelligible world was essentially a sensible world, even if paradoxically we never sensed it. So we were told that apparently solid matter was really composed of atoms, and then that atoms were the genuine solid matter; that apparently empty space was really full of ether, and then that ether was another kind of matter, though one with a very strange combination of properties. The world that we sensed was not the real world, though somehow or other we sensed it; while the real world was also a world

---

[1] Sir W. Russell Brain seems to get very near to this view; cf. the following phrases: "a table as an object which continues to exist when you are not aware of it and which is other than the sensory elements by means of which you perceive it"; "our sensory experiences of objects other than ourselves reach consciousness already stamped with externality"; "we do not need to infer that our experiences refer to the external world"; "a visual sensation may enable us to have a glimpse without itself being the appropriate object of a glimpse" (*Mind, Perception and Science*, pp. 73, 76, 82). However, he speaks of both perception and physics as "symbolical representations" of the world (ibid., pp. 59, 79), and never gets quite free from the idea that the perceptual and the physical world are different kinds of "copy" of the real world. His criticisms of Ryle seem to be mainly justified (ibid., p. 80 f.).

[2] It is perhaps as well to repeat that the word "sensible" as used here simply means "pertaining to the senses" and has not its meaning in common speech.

of sensible qualities, though for some reason or other we never sensed it. This highly peculiar doctrine was, I should suggest, simply a translation into the cosmological realm of the Lockean view of perception as nothing more than a refined version of sensation. If all perception is really sensation, then all that is perceived must be really sensible; and so, if the real world is perceptible, it must really be made up of sensible objects, even if they are not the ones which in fact we sense. All our theories of the world have thus in the last resort to be reduced to sensible shapes; and the criterion of a good theory is not that we shall be able to *understand* it but that we shall be able to *imagine* it.

The inevitable consequence of this attitude was that, when it came to be realised that the world which we perceive could not be explained in sensible terms—that is, roughly, with the advent of relativity and quantum theory—the world as something with real existence in itself had to go. If reality and sensibility are identical, then if sensibility goes reality goes with it. The world thus becomes a system of sense-data, and physical objects are complexes of sense-data and nothing more; this is what we find in the earlier philosophy of Lord Russell. Finally, when explanation in terms of sense-data is found to raise its own problems, there is nothing left for philosophers of science to do but discuss the language-habits of physicists; and this brings us to the present day.

I would maintain, however, that intelligibility is something with a wider range than sensibility. The world does not lose its claim to reality by ceasing to be imaginable as an infinite uniform Euclidean receptacle, populated by tiny rapidly moving massive lumps drifting uniformly down the stream of time, and only recover that claim by becoming imaginable as a four-dimensional non-Euclidean space-time continuum, in which what used to be thought of as material objects are now seen to be wrinkles or puckers. Just as the essence of perception is not sensing objects but apprehending them, even if we can only apprehend them through the mediation of sense, so the paradigm of a real world is not its sensible imaginability but its intelligible apprehensibility.[1]

[1] It may be interesting, in the light of the doctrine stated above, to see what interpretation is to be given of the perceptual experiences undergone by consumers of mescalin (the active principle of peyotl), which have been described by Mr Aldous Huxley with such enthusiasm in his small book *The Doors of Perception*, and discussed by Professor R. C. Zaehner in *Blackfriars*, XXXV, p. 310

I do not mean by this that anything which can be conceived by the intellect is thereby shown to exist, but I do mean that anything which concretely exists can be grasped by the intellect in its concrete existence. If therefore the universe of modern physics is one in which all attempts to make it intelligible by models of sensory type fail and which requires for its systematisation the kind of concepts that are used by quantum physics, this does not in the least imply that it is unreal or subjective. It simply means that the formulae of quantum physics express the kind of intelligibility that it has.[1] If we adopt some such view as this, I do

(1954). The physiological effect of mescalin is to inhibit the production of the enzymes that control the supply of glucose to the brain, so that the sugar-content of the brain is reduced; the psychological effects are an intense heightening of sensations, especially visual ones, and a marked reduction of will-power and moral responsibility. Huxley describes the experience by saying that "the eye recovers some of the perceptual innocence of childhood, when the sensum was not immediately and automatically subordinated to the concept" (p. 18), and that "the percept had swallowed up the concept" (p. 42). It would, I think, be truer to say that perception had been reduced almost entirely to sensation, so that the sense-datum had become the ultimate object of the perceptual act. The experient had apparently become incapable of passing through the sense-datum to the intelligible object, and still more of apprehending the intelligible object as the creature of a transcendent first cause. All the value that properly belongs to either the intelligible object or to its Creator had become attributed to the mere sense-datum, which had lost any function as an *objectum quo*, and appeared to be pure *objectum quod*. It is therefore not surprising that Huxley identifies his experience with the Beatific Vision (p. 12), though elsewhere (p. 58) he denies this. He accepts (p. 16) a suggestion of Dr C. D. Broad that the normal function of the brain is to eliminate the greater part of reality from our experience (a view which has been worked out in some detail by Mr M. M. Moncrieff in his book *The Clairvoyant Theory of Perception*) and suggests that mescalin inhibits this restrictive activity. It seems to me to be far more probable that mescalin itself restricts the brain's power to know reality, by eliminating everything that lies on the far side of the sense-datum.

[1] It will be seen that I am asserting that we have an intellectual apprehension of the singular existent; in view of what I have written elsewhere, some of my readers may be surprised to find me holding such an apparently "un-Thomist" position. I do not think that St Thomas is unambiguous on the matter, and I am not sure that Dom Illtyd Trethowan, when he puts forward a similar view in his *Essay in Christian Philosophy*, is really being as un-Thomist as he thinks. Strictly speaking, of course, it is neither the sense that senses nor the intellect that understands, but the composite human being who senses by his senses and understands by his intellect; as strict a Thomist as M. Gilson has firmly maintained this in his *Réalisme Thomiste et Critique de la Connaissance*. All I am really concerned to assert in the text is that the intellect, *as the faculty whose object is the real existent*, is involved, together with the senses, in the perceptual act. And, in any case, like St Thomas, I am not concerned to say what is Thomist but what is true.

not think there is anything to disconcert us in the brilliant analysis of Braithwaite. Models and theories alike are *objecta quibus*, by the consideration of which we can deepen our understanding of the intelligible universe which is the *objectum quod*. They have their exits and their entrances, and one model in its time plays many parts. They have their varied uses and their various degrees of usefulness; it is the great merit of Braithwaite's discussion to show what those uses and that usefulness are. He has, I think, luminously shown that they are not and cannot be simply images of the real world, though they can at times approximate to that status. There are models and models. If you set out to make a full-scale model of a railway engine which is correct in every detail, you will find, if you achieve your design, that you have not made a model at all, but another railway engine. It is impossible to attain to this point with the conceptual or imaginal models of physics, for there is and can only be one universe. Nevertheless, one model differs from another in glory; there are also models terrestrial and models celestial. Each of them has its own function, which is to help us to grasp, under some particular aspect, the real and intelligible universe in which *ens et verum convertuntur*.[1]

It will, I think, be useful at this point to insert some remarks about the discussion contained in the later chapters of Dr Mary B. Hesse's admirable book *Science and the Human Imagination*, although it was unfortunately written too early to contain any

---

It may be worth while to note at this point that, in spite of its very different terminology and mode of exposition, Dr Henry Margenau's book *The Nature of Physical Reality* (which incidentally contains one of the most lucid accounts available of modern physical theories) adopts substantially Braithwaite's view of the relation of physical theory as such to the empirical world. And it, too, makes the fatal identification of perception with sensation which I have criticised in the text; thus Margenau says explicitly, "The term *perception*, when used without qualification, is intended to be synonymous with sensation, sensory awareness, and the like" (op. cit., p. 56). It is an instructive task to follow through Margenau's discussion with this weakness in mind, and to observe how it distorts what is in other respects a most illuminating work.

[1] I think this point is overlooked by Dalbiez when he asserts that Janet's interpretation of neuroses in terms of *privation* and Freud's in terms of *opposition* are irreconcilable: "No feat of dialectic can reduce opposition to privation" (*Psychoanalytical Method and the Doctrine of Freud*, I, p. 190 f.). I think he is right if the interpretations are taken as literal descriptions; if, however, they are merely models there need be no more contradiction than there is between the wave and particle concepts of the electron. Each may have its use for particular purposes.

explicit reference to Braithwaite. After briefly sketching the views of Boole, Mach and Frege, she shows how the "constructionalism" of Russell and Whitehead (i.e. the view that scientific objects are simply logical constructs out of sense-data) was shown to be inadequate by F. P. Ramsey, and was abandoned by both its authors in their different ways, so that the projected fourth volume of *Principia Mathematica* never appeared. She then passes on to the somewhat less drastic "operationalism" of Bridgman (i.e. the view that a scientific concept is simply synonymous with the operations by which its measurement is defined), and she describes modern quantum theory as a half-hearted attempt to carry out this programme. Finally she comes to the view that scientific theories are "models" or "analogues" of the physical facts; she uses the word "analogue" in preference to the word "model" to allow for the fact, upon which I have previously commented, that, in defiance of the ideals of the great nineteenth-century British physicists, a scientific theory may operate with concepts that are purely mathematical in their nature and are not endowed with any physical characteristics. She makes the important point that a good model or analogue must satisfy two main conditions: it must have an intelligible character that is not derived simply from the physical observations, and it must be extensible to phenomena other than those for which it was originally devised. Taking up a suggestion of Whitehead, but detaching it from Whitehead's questionable metaphysics, she maintains that, while the Aristotelian theory of substance is to be abandoned, nevertheless, "in so far as scientific language is understood in its proper context, the structures about which it speaks do exist in external nature, and exist just as surely as chairs and tables and scientists and philosophers exist".[1] To the question "Are electrons real?" she answers as follows:

Yes, electrons are real patterns of events in the physical world, but their existence cannot be described in exactly the same way as that of tables and chairs and trees and men. To say that a stone exists is in any case not the same as to say that a tree exists, and both are different from the statement that a man exists. The things we have discovered about electrons, electro-magnetic waves and the like, simply mean that these are different sorts of things from those with

[1] Op. cit., p. 150.

which we are familiar. Problems about their "reality" or "existence" would not worry us if we had not for so long been used to thinking of reality and existence in terms of hard material particles.[1]

As it stands in her book, I find this passage a little indeterminate, but it seems to me to be perfectly capable of development along the lines which I have suggested in the present lecture. If we assert that perception is more than sensation, and that the sense-datum is an *objectum quo*, through which the mind can grasp the intelligible trans-sensible real being, which is the *objectum quod* and is not necessarily isomorphic relationally with the sense-datum, we are, I think, in a position to fill in the gap that Dr Hesse leaves vacant and to specify the peculiar sense in which electrons or other scientific entities are said to "exist". Next, we may notice that Dr Hesse rejects the positivist view of the nature of scientific induction and historical statement, replacing it by a view, which she finds in Whitehead but which might just as easily be extracted from Aquinas, that we have a direct perception of the causal character of the world which we experience. Finally we may note, though this point does not bear upon the present lecture, that Dr Hesse refuses to admit that all the apparent conflicts between religion and science can be dismissed as verbal confusions arising from misunderstandings about two similar but actually distinct types of language, and insists that each conflict must be dealt with on its own merits.[2]

5. THE LANGUAGES OF SCIENCE AND THEISM

The whole question with which we are here concerned has been approached from the linguistic standpoint by Professor I. T. Ramsey in his inaugural lecture in the Nolloth chair of this University. He points out that, by their very nature, scientific sentences and scientific hypotheses are developed with one aim: "towards a comprehensive language dealing with uniformities and repeated patterns". It is true that new facts are from time to time discovered which refuse to fit into the existing hypotheses; but this causes no more than a temporary embarrassment, for hypotheses are flexible and *convertible*.

[1] *Science and the Human Imagination*, p. 156. [2] Ibid., ch. ix.

While scientific language tries for a time to exclude facts which are apparently unwilling to conform, yet it must always work towards a greater and greater inclusiveness. The result is that when at last it includes some unwilling fact into its scheme it finds, at the first move, that its success has turned to defeat in its mouth, for the unwilling fact has now modified the hypothesis which has embraced it. But on reflection it can be content: the old uniformity, and more, is in the new uniformity to which the modified hypothesis relates. An obtuse fact which for a time resists the generalisations of scientific method is rather like a cheeky little mouse which finds itself ultimately enclosed in the crafty cat's jaws. Admittedly, it has the satisfaction of reflecting that, when the cat's digestion has reckoned with its bones and body, the cat will never be the same cat again. But the cat too is content enough: it is still a cat—and the mouse (as the philosophers would say) is transcended in a larger uniformity.[1]

This greater gain in scientific coverage, which comes from expansibility and convertibility, is, Ramsey points out, attained at the cost of increased abstraction: "scientific language may detail uniformities more and more comprehensively; but its very success in so doing means that its pictures are more and more outline sketches of concrete, given fact".[2] Within the language of science there is thus no room for such a word as "miracle"; there is no place in scientific speech for the statement that the laws of nature have been broken, for it is the business of science so to expand its language and convert its hypotheses that the new statement of the scientific law will include the allegedly miraculous phenomenon. This, however, does not mean that statements about miracles, or about any other activity of God, are false or meaningless; it only means that they are not part of the language of science.[3] "Of course", says Ramsey, "if scientific language were the only language and itself all-sufficient, we might at this point find ourselves with the great embarrassment of a Newton who on the one hand wanted to believe in God and pretty certainly in miracles, and yet also had to work towards a uniform overall expansion of scientific language."[4] He remarks on the scandal that has been

---

[1] *Miracles: an Exercise in Logical Mapwork*, p. 6.   [2] Ibid., p. 7.
[3] Cf. C .F. von Weizsäcker: "Even if the hypotheses of Laplace had been false in some particulars, still every scientist must certainly set himself the goal of making the hypothesis 'God' superfluous in his field" (*World View of Physics*, p. 157).   [4] Op. cit., p. 8.

caused to some present-day minds by the fact that theists maintain that no conceivable experience could falsify the statements they make about God. "If events follow a regular pattern (it is said) we speak of God's constant control. It might be expected then that should any irregularity occur, the assertion would be falsified. But not so. When events show irregularity, we speak of God's miraculous 'intervention' as well."[1] (We are reminded here, of course, of Professor John Wisdom's celebrated article on "Gods".)[2] But, says Ramsey, what this really shows is that "God" is not a scientific word, not even a high-grade one. "The word 'God' may well have empirical relevance, but this distinctive relevance will never be displayed by working it in a scientific sentence. For the word has another logical status altogether."[3] We need not follow here the details of Ramsey's discussion of historical language, or of the distinction between God's "first-order" and "second-order" activity (that is, in traditional language, between God's *concursus generalis* in nature and his supernatural activity in miracles). What is important for our present purposes is Ramsey's insistence that the various languages of science need a metaphysical supplement and this for three purposes: (i) to answer their own "limiting questions", (ii) to unite them with one another, and (iii) to counteract their abstractness by raising their abstractive patterns to the level of concreteness which belongs to the "given fact" which they intend to picture. Such a supplement, composed of "metaphysical words", whose function is to act as co-ordinating, boundary, and index words, forms what Ramsey calls a *Kata-language*; its words have the peculiar property that they can be used in all the subordinate languages, though they belong to the logic of none. As examples of such words he mentions "activity", "person", "I" and "God". "The ultimate justification of metaphysical words", he asserts, "lies in the fact that there is a non-inferential awareness more concrete than the observable facts which characterise it abstractly and objectively."[4] Such a contention, if I understand him correctly, was at the heart of Dr A. M. Farrer's argument for

---

[1] *Miracles*, p. 9.

[2] *Proc. Aristotelian Soc.*, 1944–5; reprinted in *Logic and Language* (ed. by A. G. N. Flew), I, p. 187 f.

[3] Op. cit., p. 9.   [4] Ibid., p. 18.

theism in his impressive work *Finite and Infinite*. I have urged the same point myself in my books *He Who Is* and *Existence and Analogy*, and it is common in the writings of a vigorous school of present-day interpreters of St Thomas Aquinas. Ramsey sums up his conclusions in the following words:

> Not only have we tried to show how the conflict with science is a pseudo-conflict, or more positively, to justify a use for the word "miracle" which gives it a distinctive place in historical language. We have also tried to set the word "miracle" on a total language map which includes a metaphysical index; a map by which all discursive knowledge (and as examples we have taken science and history) is integrated, and whose unity, on the view I have barely outlined, relates to the activity of God himself.[1]

6. CONCLUSION

We may briefly summarise this lecture as follows. The assertion which has frequently been made that the theories of natural science are incompatible with the dogmas of the Christian faith clearly depends for its force upon the assumption that the theories of natural science are straightforward literal descriptions of the real constitution of the world. That assumption was commonly made throughout the last three centuries. A detailed examination of two typical modern discussions of the nature of scientific discourse, and a briefer reference to two others, have, however, shown us that the relation between scientific theories and the physical world is very much looser than that. The maps or models which science uses, whether constructed out of physical images or purely mathematical concepts, are no more than deductive systems whose function is to co-ordinate and to predict empirical observations. There is a large margin of arbitrariness as to which theory we adopt in any particular case, and there is no reason to suppose that logical necessity in the structure of a model implies any kind of necessity in the structure of the facts which it depicts. The positivistic setting in which the discussions of Braithwaite and, to a lesser degree, of Toulmin were put was, we argued, not essential to them; and in Ramsey's exposition we saw a vigorous assertion that metaphysical and theological language,

[1] *Miracles*, p. 23.

while never forming part of scientific language, might nevertheless be necessary to complete it, to unify it, and to restore its concrete reference. We saw that the very complexity and obscurity of much modern scientific discussion has forced philosophers of science to discard that superficial literalist view of scientific theories which held the field from the time of Newton almost to the present day. And the lesson of all this for the theologian is that, however conscious he may be of his incapacity to penetrate into the deeper mysteries of contemporary scientific thought, at least he has no need to feel intimidated by the scientists when he considers their parable and the interpretation thereof, the words of the wise and their dark sayings.

Chapter Three

COSMOLOGY AND CONTINGENCY

Omnia in mensura et numero et pondere disposuisti.—
Sap. xi. 21.

I. THE WORLD OF CHRISTIAN THEISM

CHRISTIAN theism (and by this term in the present
context I shall mean the belief about God and his relation to the world which, in spite of certain notable
divergences, has, as a matter of historical fact, been held by
the great body of Christian philosophers) maintains that the
universe owes its existence to a creative act exercised by a self-
existent God, who is both omnipotent and therefore able to
create, and also absolutely free and therefore under no necessity
to do so. It thus stands in sharp contrast to three rival types of
thought, all of which, since they assert the existence of God, might
claim the title "theism", but all of which assert, from different
points of view, that the existence of the universe is necessary.

The first type is represented in its purest form by absolutist
idealism; it holds that the existence of the world follows with
logical necessity from the existence of God, whether the logical
sequence involved is conceived in *static* terms, as by Spinoza, or
in *dynamic* terms, as by Hegel. Not a little of the difficulty of
Christian apologists to-day arises from the fact that many
people, and in particular many philosophers, are under the impression that this is in fact the view of Christian theism. Thus, to
give but one example, in an article which was published in 1939,
Dr C. D. Broad took the cosmological argument for the existence
of God as asserting that the proposition "A world having the
characteristics of the world of our experience exists" is a logical
consequence of the proposition "God exists", this latter proposition being held to be true by logical necessity.[1]

---

[1] *Journal of Theological Studies*, XL, p. 25 f. (1939). A criticism of Dr Broad's
article will be found in my book *He Who Is*, p. 57 f.

The second type of rival view is that of emanationism, according to which the existence of the universe follows with *physical* necessity from the existence of God. It is not always easy to distinguish this from the first type, especially in a metaphysical system in which the distinction between the physical and the logical is not very clearly drawn, but an instance would seem to be provided by the system of Plotinus, if we can give the name "God" to the Plotinian "One". And the third type is that which is associated with the name of Leibnitz, according to which God, being able to create a world, is *morally* bound to do so, and indeed to create the best of all possible worlds; it has been given considerable currency in recent years by Dr W. R. Matthews, who has claimed that it is really the authentically Christian view and that the doctrine which I have described as "Christian theism" (the doctrine that has in fact been continually held by the main tradition of Christian philosophers) is the result of an unsuccessful attempt to fuse Aristotelian metaphysics with the Christian Gospel.[1] According to this view, the existence of the universe follows with *moral* necessity from the existence of God.

I shall not attempt in this lecture to vindicate the traditional Christian theism against rival systems; such an attempt may be found in my book *He Who Is: a Study in Traditional Theism*. I am concerned here only to make plain what traditional Christian theism is. All the three rival types of doctrine to which I have just referred envisage the existence of the universe as following *necessarily* from the existence of God, whether that necessity be conceived in logical, physical or moral terms. In contrast, Christian theism maintains that the existence of the world is altogether *contingent*, in the sense that, while God can create a world if he wills to do so, he is entirely free as regards this exercise of will. (It admits, of course, that the existence of the world is, to use the technical term, necessary *ex suppositione*; that is to say that, if God does will to create a world, the existence of the world will necessarily follow upon this act of will. The existence of the world follows necessarily upon God's decision to create it, but God is entirely free to make this decision or not.) It may help to remove a fairly obvious objection if we add that, while the fact that God has created a world demands the utmost gratitude from the

[1] *God in Christian Thought and Experience*, p. 104.

rational creatures in it, since they owe to God's generosity all that they are and all that they have, nevertheless if God had not created a world nobody would have a grievance against him, for there would in that case be nobody to have it.[1]

For Christian theism, then, the world has a double contingency; first of all a contingency of *existence*, in the sense that God need not have made a world at all, and then a contingency of *nature*, in the sense that, even if God was going to make a world, he need not have made the particular world which he has made. Christian theism rejects altogether the Leibnitian doctrine that the world to which existence is actually given must be the best possible world, for it denies that the attribute "best possible" can apply to any finite being. It is an essential characteristic of finite beings to be finite, that is to say *limited*, and anything which is limited can be exceeded by something in its own order which is greater but is limited in its turn. Only to God can the attribute "best possible" apply; a "best possible *world*" is impossible, for it is a contradiction in terms. God can create or not as he pleases; and if he does create he has an infinity of possible worlds between which he can choose.[2]

This does not mean, however, that there are no conditions upon God's creative activity. He is not bound by anything outside himself, but he is bound by his own nature. And the Christian God is not only a God of omnipotence and freedom, he is also a God of rationality and order. He need not create a cosmos and if

---

[1] I may perhaps refer to my discussion of "God and the Creature" in *Existence and Analogy*, ch. vi.

[2] It is perhaps well at this point to emphasise that the Christian doctrine of creation is not primarily concerned with the question as to whether the universe had a temporal beginning or is of infinite past duration. After a good deal of hesitation on the part of Christian philosophers themselves, the point was made quite clear by St Thomas Aquinas in his *De aeternitate mundi*. For him, the fundamental characteristic of the finite world, upon which the theistic conclusion depends, is not its finite duration but its lack of self-sufficiency. I discuss in a later lecture (ch. iv infra) the very interesting fact, upon which Pope Pius XII commented in his address to the Pontifical Academy of Sciences on November 20th, 1951 (published in the *Tablet* of December 1st, 1951), that four independent lines of reasoning suggest that the universe had a "beginning" between 10^9 and 10^{10} years ago. Even if the universe has always existed, it has, the theist will assert, always been dependent upon the creative act of God; arguments for theism based upon the Second Law of Thermodynamics or the recession of the spiral nebulae can at most be secondary to strictly metaphysical considerations.

he does create one it need not be any particular one, but if he does create one, it will be a *cosmos* and not a *chaos*. It will manifest on its lower contingent level the perfection and coherence of its Creator.

The above account has been given perforce in brief and summary form, with the minimum of argument. I have discussed elsewhere the grounds for belief in Christian theism,[1] and I shall not attempt to repeat that discussion here. All that we are concerned with here is the question what sort of a world will the God of Christian theism create if in fact he creates one; and the point which I have tried to make is that it will be both contingent and orderly, since it is the work of a God who is both free and rational. It will embody regularities and patterns, since its Creator is rational, but the particular regularities and patterns which it embodies cannot be predicted *a priori*, since he is free; they can only be discovered by examination. The world of Christian theism will thus be one whose investigation requires the empirical method, that is to say the method of modern natural science, with its twin techniques of observation and experiment.

Mr M. B. Foster, in an important article which was published in 1934[2] and to which Dr John Baillie has more recently drawn attention,[3] put the question, "What is the source of those un-Greek elements in the modern science of nature by which the peculiar characteristics of the modern science of nature were to be determined?" and gave the answer, "The Christian doctrine of creation". "The method of Galilean science", he wrote in a subsequent article,[4] "presupposes (*a*) that it is impossible that nature should not embody a mathematically intelligible scheme and exhibit laws mathematically definable; but (*b*) that, which of possible alternative schemes it embodies, and which of several laws equally definable mathematically it exhibits, can be decided only by appeal to observation and experiment." In other words, the scientific method makes a double assumption: first, that there

[1] In the two books to which reference has already been made, *He Who Is* and *Existence and Analogy*.

[2] "The Christian Doctrine of Creation and the Rise of Modern Natural Science", *Mind*, XLIII, N.S., p. 446 f.

[3] *Natural Science and the Spiritual Life*, p. 20 f.

[4] "Christian Theology and Modern Science of Nature", *Mind*, XLIV, N.S., p. 439 f. and XLV, p. 1 f.

are *regularities* in the world, otherwise there would be nothing for science to discover; secondly, that these regularities are *contingent* and so need to be looked for; they cannot be predicted *a priori*. This is in marked contrast with the common assumption of Greek thought, namely that in so far as the world is intelligible it is because it embodies the pure forms which are knowable by, and only by, philosophical contemplation (*theoria*), and that inasmuch as it does *not* embody the pure forms it cannot be understood at all. But the scientific assumption is entirely coherent with the Christian doctrine of creation. As far back as 1926 this point was recognised by the late Dr A. N. Whitehead. He described "the inexpugnable belief that every detailed occurrence can be correlated with its antecedents in a perfectly definite manner, exemplifying general principles" as "the greatest contribution of medievalism to the formation of the scientific movement". "It must come", he wrote, "from the medieval insistence on the rationality of God, conceived as with the personal energy of Jehovah and with the rationality of a Greek philosopher." And again: "I am not arguing that the European trust in the scrutability of nature was logically justified even by its own theology. My only point is to understand how it arose. My explanation is that the faith in the possibility of science, generated antecedently to the development of modern scientific theory, is an unconscious derivative from medieval theology."[1]

It is interesting to note that, while Mr Foster and Dr Whitehead both derive the rise of modern natural science from the Christian conception of a God who is both free and rational, with the natural consequence of a world which is both contingent and regular, they tend to place their emphasis in different places. For Mr Foster it is the *freedom* of God and the consequent *contingency* of the world in Christian thought that is the main stimulus provided by Christianity for modern science, in contrast with the logicism and necessaritarianism of the Greeks; for Whitehead it is the *rationality* of God and the *regularity* of the world that is the main stimulus, in contrast with the views of God as either impersonal or altogether arbitrary in Asiatic thought. Foster explains why modern science did not arise in ancient Greece, Whitehead why it did not arise in India; but this

[1] *Science and the Modern World*, chapter I: "The Origins of Modern Science"

difference only serves to bring out more clearly the point at issue, which is that it is precisely the *combination* of the two notions, and not either of them in isolation, which is presupposed by the application of the modern scientific method. For empirical science to arise at all, there must be the belief—or at least the presumption—that the world is both contingent and regular. There must be regularities in the world, otherwise there will be nothing for science to discover; but they must be contingent regularities, otherwise they would not need to be looked for, they could, at any rate if we were clever enough, be thought out *a priori*. It might furthermore be suggested that the spectacular success which has attended the application of the scientific method supplies strong grounds for asserting that the presumption upon which modern science has proceeded is in fact true. There are, I know, people who say that, since all that the scientific method is made for is to discover regularities, there is no particular significance in the fact that it discovers them, just as, to adapt an example of Sir Arthur Eddington's,[1] there is no particular significance in the fact that, if a fishing net has a two-inch mesh, it only catches fish that are more than two inches long. If it did not discover regularities, what could the scientific method do? It is perhaps sufficient to answer "Nothing"; the impressive fact is that, whereas the pre-empirical attempts to investigate the universe did discover nothing, or almost nothing, about it, the empirical method of modern science has discovered so much.[2] To return to Eddington's illustration, there must at least be considerable significance in the fact that the ocean contained the fish which were caught, whatever smaller specimens may have eluded capture; and I should maintain that there is considerable significance in the fact that modern science has managed to find out so much about the universe and how to control its forces, which ancient Greece and Asia failed to discover. An advertisement of Imperial Chemical Industries some years ago characterised the difference between the old-fashioned alchemist and the modern organic chemist by saying that the latter practitioner, in

[1] *The Philosophy of Physical Science*, p. 16.
[2] Cf. C. F. von Weizsäcker: "The often cited principle of economy of thought explains, at the most, why we look for simple laws, but not why we find them" (*World View of Physics*, p. 179).

contrast with his predecessor, is everywhere welcome because the changes which he renders possible are always for the better. It would, I think, be more realistic and less naïve to say that the main difference is that the modern scientist usually succeeds in doing what he set out to do, whereas his predecessors usually failed. It is the *success* of the modern scientific method that is the really impressive thing about it. The scientific method may have originated in an act of blind faith, but, like some other acts of faith, it may claim to have been verified by its results.

It is this peculiar combination of regularity and contingency in the physical world which, I would suggest, accounts for the peculiar interlocking of theory and experiment in physics, and for the alternation of periods of experimental expansion and theoretical development, to which Dr Max Born called attention in a lecture delivered in 1943.[1]

It also, I suggest, explains the way in which science makes use of mathematics without being itself a branch of mathematics. For mathematics can analyse, systematise, correlate, and sometimes even suggest, the regularities which experimental science discovers, but it can never discover them itself. The experimenter always has the last word. At this point, however, a further point arises, on which Dr John Baillie has laid stress.

Commenting on Mr Foster's assertion that the source of those un-Greek elements in the modern science of nature by which the peculiar characteristics of the modern science of nature were to be determined is to be located in the Christian doctrine of creation, Dr Baillie says: "No doubt it will at once be asked why then the new movement in science had to wait for its beginning until the period of the Reformation." His answer is "that the Early Christian ages had no interest in science, old or new, and that the Middle Christian ages were too much under the dominance of the authority of Aristotle".[2] I must confess that the first part of this answer seems to me to do little more than repeat the question in another form, for what we presumably want to know is precisely why the early Christian ages, with their belief in a free and rational Creator, should not have acted upon the consequences of that belief and developed the experimental method. It is, of course, true that until the establishment of Christianity by

---

[1] *Experiment and Theory in Physics.*   [2] Op. cit., p. 20.

Constantine the emphasis of Christian thought was other-worldly and eschatological, but from the fourth century on-wards it became highly concerned with the historical created order. I am inclined to think that the real reason is one that repeatedly appears among modern natural scientists themselves, and that there is a very natural tendency in the human mind to exaggerate the element of rationality in the universe in comparison with the element of contingency, and so to minimise the place of experiment in comparison with that of theory.[1]

2. RATIONALITY AND CONTINGENCY IN CLASSICAL PHYSICS

I have said that this tendency is a very natural one, and the reason for this is as follows. However much it must recognise in principle the contingency of the universe, what science is looking for is its rationality. The rationality, in so far as it can be dis-

[1] I feel bound in honesty to say that it seems to me to be likely that in one respect (though a subsidiary one) the acceptance of the Christian doctrine of creation may itself have done something to retard the development of the experimental method. Some Christian believers may conceivably have felt that there was something impious in manipulating, from motives of mere intellectual curiosity, a world which was believed to be the creation of God. This feeling would not, of course, retard the progress of observational, as distinct from experimental, science, and it may be significant that astronomy is the observational science *par excellence*. To settle this would need detailed historical investigation. Such an array of evidence as that collected by Dr A. C. Crombie in his recent book *Augustine to Galileo* in fact suggests that the neglect of science in the medieval period was by no means as complete as has been generally assumed, and that there was a steady development of scientific interest and enquiry which by the sixteenth century was ready to burst into full blossom. Dr Crombie admits, however, that the causes are obscure (op. cit., p. 274).

A very different type of explanation, based upon economic and technical considerations, will be found in the chapter by Professor M. Postan on "Why was Science backward in the Middle Ages?" in the broadcast symposium *The History of Science: Origins and Results of the Scientific Revolution*, edited by Jean Lindsay.

I would add that I do not believe the feeling to which I have referred to be justified on theological grounds if man is, as the Christian religion asserts, God's vice-gerent over creation. I think, however, it would be generally agreed that there must be *some* limits to what is morally justifiable in the realm of experimentation and that, for example, certain experiments in human genetics, such as those described in Mr von Kühnelt-Leddihn's novel *Moscow 1979*, or an attempt to set up a nuclear chain-reaction in the hydrogen of the ocean, could hardly be justified on grounds of scientific curiosity.

cerned at all, is manifested in uniformities of behaviour which can be expressed in mathematical formulae, and these can then be used to predict the results of future observations and experiments; the contingency can only be recognised and accepted, there is no way of putting it into a formula. If the pun may be allowed, we might say that it is only the rationality that can be rationalised; the contingency cannot be. For when I said earlier in this lecture that the only way in which we can discover what a universe which is the creation of a free and omnipotent God is like, is by looking at it in order to see, I was not speaking altogether accurately. There is another method; it consists in being let into the secrets of God. If only we could know what particular uniformities God had decided that the world was to manifest, then we could do our science *a priori* just as successfully as if the universe was not contingent at all. The most satisfactory way of knowing this would be, of course, by a direct revelation from God; and there have been some Christians who have claimed to find such a revelation in the Scriptures. The opponents of Galileo did not claim that it was impossible that the solar system should have been constructed on the Copernican model, but they did say that it was revealed in Scripture that the heavens were spread out like a tent and that it therefore had not in fact been so constructed. Such a direct appeal to the Biblical texts for scientific information has not, however, been characteristic of Christian thought in general; the Ptolemaic system, which was widely assumed in the Middle Ages, was just as difficult to reconcile with a literal interpretation of the Biblical texts as was the Copernican. What does, however, seem to have characterised pre-Renaissance cosmology was the assumption that the regularities in the universe are much more easy to discover than in fact they are. Experiment was hardly considered to be necessary at all; a few simple observations would suffice to indicate the regularities, and when they had been found we should not need experiment or observation any more, except to strengthen our confidence in our success by providing verifications of the results of our calculations. The tendency was therefore strong to minimise or by-pass experiment in favour of theory, and, as we shall see later on, the ideal of substituting theory for experiment has managed to survive even the experimental triumphs of the last three centuries, and to do so in the citadel of science itself. This, I suggest, is the ultimate explanation of the length of time which lay between the acceptance of the Christian doctrine of creation and the development of empirical science, rather than any lack of interest in science as such; and so far as the Middle Ages were too much under the domination of the authority of Aristotle, this would seem to be the reason for it. For if only a few simple observations were needed and Aristotle had made them, why should we repeat them? Even when the scientific method was getting well under way, there was a notable reluctance to go in for experiment more than was necessary. As Professor Herbert Butterfield has pointed out, the Copernican theory supplanted the Ptolemaic theory chiefly on theoretical grounds and largely in the teeth of astronomical observation as it was at the time,[1] and even the experiments of such an alleged founder of the experimental method as Galileo were very largely "thought-experiments", arguments as to what would happen if you were to do a certain experiment rather than observations of what happened if you actually did it.[2] And at a still later date, Descartes did his best to follow out a programme of reducing the whole of physical science to a mathematical scheme deduced from a few simple first principles, in spite of the errors to which this led him; as M. Gilson has remarked, "the learned world was then called upon to witness that surprising spectacle: Descartes, who had not discovered the circulation of the blood, explaining it to Harvey, who had made the discovery, and adding to it as many mistakes as he was adding explanations".[3] And even later, Leibnitz's famous correction of the Cartesian discussion of the dynamics of impact was every bit as theoretical as Descartes' own argument had been and just as little based upon experiment,[4] though Leibnitz was fortunate enough to be right where Descartes was unfortunate enough to be wrong. What in fact seems to have been necessary before the empirical method of

[1] *Origins of Modern Science*, p. 23 f.
[2] Ibid., p. 71 f. Cf. A. R. Hall, *The Scientific Revolution*, p. 174.
[3] *The Unity of Philosophical Experience*, p. 150.
[4] Letter to Boyle, *Philosophical Writings of Leibnitz* (Everyman ed., p. 91 f.). Descartes started from the *a priori* assertion that, if the whole impetus of a body of mass 4 pounds moving with a velocity of 1 unit is transferred to a body of mass 1 pound, the latter will acquire a velocity of 4 units; Leibnitz started from the *a priori* assertion that the same force which will raise a body of 4 pounds through 1 foot will raise a body of 1 pound through 4 feet.

modern science could get really under way was the recognition that not only is the universe a universe of contingent regularities, but also that it is a much more mysterious place than had been previously suspected, that God's secrets require much more seeking out than had been thought, and in particular that it is extremely hazardous to try to forecast what sort of regularities God will embody in his world. This was a lesson which could be learned only by bitter experience. Even so, right down to the present day the obstinately aprioristic tendency of the human mind has persisted; and it reappears in the most unexpected quarters. Time after time we meet with a situation in which, when some highly general regularity has been extracted from a mass of observational and experimental data and has been expressed in a mathematical formula, the attempt is then made to show that the formula is one which we should have been able to predict antecedently to observation and experiment if only we had been clever enough.[1] When, however, this takes place in a setting which is no longer dominated by the traditional Christian theism, with its fundamental conviction of the contingency of the world, the assertion tends no longer to be that God has revealed to us, in Scripture or through some other organ, the particular regularities that he has decided to embody, but rather that, in spite of all appearances, they are not really contingent at all. So we get a whole series of cases in which a more or less simple scientific law is derived by immense analytic labour from a mass of physical data which was obtained by protracted and laborious observation and experiment, and then subsequently the same scientific law is either alleged to be self-evident, or else is derived, possibly by equally laborious calculation, from principles which are themselves alleged to be self-evident. The suspicious feature of this procedure is that the process of theoretical deduction almost always takes place subsequently to the process of derivation from experiment, so that in fact the apriorist almost always knows what the result is that he is required to obtain; indeed in many cases it looks as if a number of different "self-evident" principles have been tried in order to see which one will give the required result, and only when a particular one has been found to give that result have some more or less convincing grounds for its self-evidence been manufactured.[1]

[1] Cf. the remarks of Dr H. Jeffreys, *Scientific Inference*, 2nd ed., p. 245.

I shall illustrate this by giving a number of examples, but before doing so I wish to make plain how this bears upon the question with which we are concerned in this lecture. The point is simply this. We have asserted that Christian theism and the modern scientific method agree in making the assumption that the universe is not necessary but contingent, in the sense that it might quite well have been other than it is, so that its nature cannot be discovered by mere theory but only by examination. It has, however, been frequently asserted that scientific laws which have been discovered by examination can be shown to be logically necessary and that in consequence, in spite of appearances, the nature of the universe is not contingent at all. If this conclusion holds, then the experimental method is only an alternative, though perhaps a more expeditious and convenient, way of discovering truths about the world which might in principle be discovered by pure thought. Since some of the truths in question are alleged to be quite fundamental ones of universal application, it is a matter of some importance to see whether this assertion can be justified. And the only way to do this would seem to be to take some typical and important examples.

The first example which I shall take is provided by Newtonian dynamical and gravitational theory. It is well known that the formulation by Newton of the famous three laws of motion and the inverse-square law of gravitation, as the fundamental laws governing the behaviour of the physical universe, was the result of a long attempt, in which others as well as Newton had taken part, to bring into one coherent scheme Kepler's three laws of planetary motion and the numerical values which had been determined for the acceleration of the moon in its orbit and the acceleration due to gravity at the earth's surface. Nothing could be more obviously empirical than the basis of the Newtonian system. Nevertheless, once Newton's laws had been formulated it was impossible not to be struck by their elegance and simplicity, and attempts were very soon made to prove that they were only what ought to have been expected on *a priori* grounds. If gravitation is thought of as an influence radiating out from the attracting body into a Euclidean space, what could be more reasonable than that it should fall off according to an inverse-square law, in the same way as that in which the intensity of light falls off as one moves away from a luminous source? Nevertheless, it is important to notice that the force of attraction is not only inversely proportional to the square of the distance of the attracted from the attracting body. It is also proportional to the mass of the attracted body; and you can have as big an attractive force at any point as you like if only you place there a body of sufficient mass. In fact, if we are to think in terms of radiation, what must be conceived of as radiating is not gravitational force but a much less easily pictured entity, gravitational field-strength (i.e. force per unit of attracted mass). Or, to state the point in another way, gravitational attraction is not merely a force exerted by an attracting body upon an attracted body; it is a mutual attraction proportional to the mass of each. Once this is realised it is seen that the picturing of gravitation as a kind of radiation is of limited validity, though it is interesting to note that the analogy has reappeared in some recent attempts in relativity theory to show that gravitation is propagated with the speed of light. Again, as Dr Whitrow has recently reminded us,[1] the great mathematical physicist James Clerk Maxwell attempted in 1877 to give an *a priori* proof of the First Law of Motion, the law which states that if a body is isolated from the action of forces its velocity will continue unchanged. Maxwell's argument is, in effect, an appeal to Leibnitz's principle of sufficient reason; if there is nothing to change the velocity, why should the velocity change? It is perhaps sufficient to remark that the same argument might be used to show the constancy of the acceleration or of any of the higher time-derivatives of the co-ordinates of an isolated body. It might even be used to show the constancy of the co-ordinates themselves; and this is, in principle, what was done in the pre-Newtonian physics, which held that, unless a force acted upon a body, there was no reason why the body's position should change at all. Of course if we take the Second Law (according to which the rate of change of momentum is proportional to impressed force) as not strictly a law but as merely a definition of force, the First Law becomes simply a logical tautology. It seems, however, quite impossible to suppose that Newton intended the Second Law as a definition, whatever it may have become as a result of the determination of later scientists to make it cover non-gravita-

[1] "On the Foundations of Dynamics", *B.J.P.S.*, I, p. 98 f. (1950).

tional phenomena, such as those of electrostatics and electro-magnetics. And in any case, what Maxwell was trying to do was not to prove that the First Law was a tautology but that it was an *a priori* synthetic truth about the universe; and it seems quite clear that his argument is fallacious. In spite of their extremely simple form and their highly abstract character, the Newtonian laws are empirical statements about the physical universe, based upon experiment and observation.[1] And that is, of course, why it has been possible for relativity-physicists to assert that they are only approximately true under ordinary conditions, and not even approximately true in certain cases.

3. RELATIVITY AND THE A PRIORI

However, the relativity-physicists in their turn have shown themselves only too ready to succumb to the tendency to apriorism. The experimental origin of the Theory of Relativity is to be found in the famous experiment performed by Michelson and Morley in 1887, which attempted to determine the velocity of the earth through the ether or, what many physicists of the day would have considered to be the same thing, the absolute velocity of the earth through space. The result of the experiment was altogether negative, not merely in the sense that the absolute velocity of the earth was found to be zero at one particular moment, but in the much more drastic sense that, having been measured when the earth was at one point of its orbit and being measured again when the earth was at another point at which it

---

[1] I do not mean by this that the Newtonian laws are empirical statements in the sense in which "Arsenic is poisonous" is an empirical statement, that they contain no theoretical elements. It is perfectly possible for one and the same truth about the physical world to be expressed by two mathematical formulations of very different form, as for example a set of differential equations and the station-ary-property of an integral. And the different formulations may each be of use for particular purposes. Nevertheless, the fact that the formulations do express a truth about the physical world is known in the last resort from observation or experiment. In this sense the laws may be described as intellectual tools, devised for particular purposes, rather than as straightforward empirical statements. Nevertheless, the fact that a tool can be successfully used on a large scale is a fact not only about the tool but also about the material upon which it is used, in this case the physical universe.

See G. Buchdahl on "Science and Logic: Some Thoughts on Newton's Second Law of Motion in Classical Mechanics", in *B.J.P.S.*, II, p. 217 f. (1951).

was moving with a considerable velocity relative to its former position, the absolute velocity was found to be zero in both cases. A pre-Copernican astronomer would no doubt have claimed this result as providing a striking confirmation of the truth of the cosmological theory of Ptolemy, or perhaps of that of Tycho Brahe; the earth, he would have declared in triumph, is immovable after all. Such a conclusion was, however, more than nineteenth-century scientists were prepared to accept; it would, moreover, have introduced complications into other parts of physics; and, after unsuccessfully trying out such explanations as that the ether was dragged round with the earth in its orbit, they came to realise that what the Michelson-Morley and other experiments showed was that, so long as we confine ourselves to so-called inertial or Galilean frames of reference[1] (and this is a large restriction to make), the notion of absolute motion becomes inapplicable to physics. In spite of its novelty, such a view was not altogether unacceptable, for, although Newton in two famous scholia had asserted dogmatically the existence of absolute time and absolute space, it was a consequence of the Newtonian laws themselves that no dynamical experiment could ever discover whether a body was at rest in absolute space or not (the Michelson-Morley experiment, we must remember, was not a dynamical experiment

---

[1] An inertial frame of reference may be roughly defined as (a) the frame of reference of a body which is not subject to the action of forces of any kind or (b) any frame of reference moving with uniform rectilinear velocity relative to such a frame. (We are not concerned here with the logical complexities of this definition.) A more rigid definition of an inertial system will be found in Whittaker, *From Euclid to Eddington*, p. 54.

It is interesting to note that a series of repetitions of the Michelson-Morley experiment by the American physicist D. C. Miller have given a small but definite value for the velocity of the earth through the ether. R. S. Shankland and others appear, however, to have shown that Miller misinterpreted his results (*Rev. of Modern Physics*, XXVII, p. 167 f. (1955)). Furthermore, although one of the classical tests of the Theory has survived with increased force, the other two have been called in question. The confirmation given by the motion of the perihelion of Mercury has been reinforced by the detection of a smaller motion in the case of the earth, in agreement with the predictions of the Theory. On the other hand, recent measurements of the bending of light by the gravitational fields of stars and of the shift of spectral lines in light emitted in a strong gravitational field have given very indeterminate results. But in any case the Theory of Relativity is now far too firmly established to be dislodged on experimental grounds! (Cf. W. B. Bonnor on "Fifty Years of Relativity" in *Science News* 37 (1955).)

but an optical one). What is, however, significant for our purposes is the fact that, once they had been brought to recognise this consequence, many physicists were not content to say simply that the notion of absolute motion was inapplicable, but went on to say that it was nonsensical. One frequently finds it stated, especially in popular or semi-popular expositions of relativity theory, that what the Michelson-Morley experiment proved was the meaninglessness of the idea of absolute motion. It needs, however, only a moment's thought to make it clear that no experiment is ever needed to prove that something is meaningless, and indeed that no experiment can do so. Even the statement that twice two is five cannot be shown to be nonsensical by experiment; it can only be shown to be false. If the notion of absolute velocity was meaningless, it would hardly need something as expensive and complicated as the Michelson-Morley experiment to prove it; all that would be needed would be a clear mind and leisure for thought. It is, of course, possible that, if we had never given much previous thought to a certain notion, an experiment which showed that the notion was inapplicable might lead us to wonder whether perhaps it was not merely inapplicable but also nonsensical. It is possible that, if we had never given much previous thought to a certain statement, an experiment which showed that the statement was false might lead us to wonder whether perhaps it was not merely false but also self-contradictory. In the present case, however, this does not seem to be what happened. The idea of absolute motion, and statements such as "The absolute velocity of body A is v feet per second", had certainly been given a great deal of thought ever since the time of Newton, and their utility and applicability had indeed at times been called in question. Nobody, however, had shown them to be self-contradictory, and there was at least one very good reason for supposing that nobody ever would. If it was the *absoluteness* of absolute uniform rectilinear motion that was alleged to make it nonsensical, it was very difficult to see why, on the same grounds, the notions of absolute *accelerated* rectilinear motion and of absolute *rotary* motion were not equally nonsensical. But so far from these last two notions being nonsensical, their numerical magnitudes could actually be measured. That is to say, if we take any inertial frame A, another frame B moving with uniform rectilinear velocity relative to A (so that B is a second inertial frame), a third frame C moving with *accelerated* rectilinear velocity relative to A, and a fourth frame D moving with uniform *rotary* velocity relative to A, then the laws of a universe governed by Newtonian dynamics will take precisely the same form relative to B as they take relative to A, but they will take quite a different form relative to C, and a still different one relative to D. Furthermore, by comparing the four sets of laws, we can determine the absolute linear acceleration of C and the absolute angular velocity of D. But we can never find out the absolute rectilinear velocities of either A or B; one of them may be at absolute rest or both may be in absolute motion, but Newtonian dynamics can give us no help in the matter.[1] This is why a simple dynamical experiment like that of Foucault's pendulum was sufficient to demonstrate and to measure the absolute rotation of the earth, while it took an elaborate optical experiment like that of Michelson and Morley to investigate the question of the earth's absolute translatory velocity. If one is going to be thoroughly aprioristic one can hardly stop at the level of the Special Theory of Relativity; one must pass on to the standpoint of the General Theory, which attempted to build up a scheme of the physical universe in which *all* frames of reference, inertial and non-inertial alike, had the same status as one another.

There was, however, nothing particularly aprioristic about General Relativity in its inception. It arose from a realisation of the inadequacy, from both the theoretical and the practical point of view, of Special Relativity and from the desire, which was of long standing, to achieve a unitary theory of the physical world which would include in one scheme gravitational, electro-magnetic and optical phenomena. Its starting point was Einstein's recognition, in his famous Principle of Equivalence, of the fact that the adoption of a frame of reference which is in uniformly accelerated motion relative to an inertial frame is physically indistinguishable from the imposition of a uniform gravitational field. The significance of this is that it brings about a unification of the dynamical and the gravitational properties of the universe; it substitutes for

---

[1] This argument assumes that either the bodies on which observations are made are not subject to forces or that, if they are, we know the forces. It was the recognition of this fact that ultimately led to Einstein's Principle of Equivalence.

the notion of a Euclidean universe permeated by mysterious gravitational forces the notion of a non-Euclidean universe in which gravitational phenomena simply express the way in which the universe is non-Euclidean. The further introduction of the notion of parallel transport made it possible to include electromagnetic phenomena as well as gravitational ones. The fact that Einstein's theory is sometimes described in terms of the notion of curvature of space-time merely means that it is sometimes easier for the mind to think of a Euclidean continuum of ten dimensions than of a non-Euclidean continuum of three or four.[1] The ultimate foundation of Einstein's theory was thoroughly empirical; he was simply trying to find a set of concepts and of highly general laws which would unify a very large range of observational and experimental data. When, for example, he stated his law of gravitation in the form that the ten principal coefficients of curvature of the four-dimensional space-time continuum are zero in empty space (or, alternatively, that the radius of spherical curvature of every three-dimensional section of the world, cut in any direction at any point of empty space, is always the same constant length), he was doing the same kind of thing that Newton was doing when he stated his law of gravitation in the form that the gravitational field produced by a massive body at any point is directly proportional to the mass of the body and inversely proportional to the square of its distance from the point. (This does not, of course, in any way contradict the fact that Einstein succeeded in doing something that Newton had not succeeded in doing, namely unifying the gravitational and dynamical properties of matter under a more inclusive generalisation.) But, just as Newton's laws of gravitation and of dynamics, once they had been formulated, were so simple that they seemed to many people to be only what one ought to have expected all along, so it was with Einstein's. When Eddington, having re-stated Einstein's law in the form that when the standard metre takes up a new position or direction it takes up an extension which is a definite fraction of the directed radius, goes on to explain this by saying that it wants to do just what it did before and there is nothing else that it can do, he is in effect adopting the same kind of argument that Maxwell adopted in his attempt to prove from

[1] Cf. Eddington, *Nature of the Physical World*, p. 159.

a priori considerations Newton's First Law of Motion. Where, however, Eddington out-Maxwelled Maxwell and made his apriorisms so much more impressive was in the further attempt which he made in 1946, in his book *Fundamental Theory*, to derive by purely theoretical considerations not merely the general form of the fundamental laws of physics, but also the numerical values of the constants of nature.[1] Nor did he restrict his claim to general relativity theory; he widened it to include quantum theory as well. If the claim can be substantiated which he is generally supposed to have made (though we shall see that even Eddington was not perhaps quite so sweeping as he has generally been supposed to be), the conclusion would follow that, even if the existence of the universe was contingent, its nature was altogether determined; that is to say, that, although there might not have been a world at all, if there was to be a world it would have to manifest in every respect, down to its most trivial detail, the characteristics that empirical observation of the world of our experience shows it to have. In other words, there is only one possible world. According to Eddington, it is a necessity of thought that the so-called cosmical number (which is roughly identified with the number of particles in the universe) should have the value $1 \cdot 4 \times 10^{79}$, that the mass-ratio of the proton to the electron should have the value $1834 \cdot 34$, that the ratio of the electric to the gravitational force between a proton and an electron should have the value $22 \cdot 7 \times 10^{39}$, that the fine-structure constant of spectroscopy should have the value 137, and so on.[2] This is a truly remarkable claim, and it is not surprising that it has been received with a certain amount of scepticism.

As Professor S. Chapman has remarked, "whereas Eddington was regarded among astronomers throughout the world with immense admiration and respect, his work on 'fundamental theory' brought him obloquy, scoffing and suspicion from the theoretical physicists. At best he was pronounced incomprehensible, at worst he was accused of fudging his formulae (if not intentionally, yet nevertheless actually)."[3]

[1] Op. cit., p. 143.

[2] Eddington also deduced the values of a number of physical quantities which are not pure numbers, such as the respective masses of the proton and the electron, the magnetic moment of the neutron, and so on.

[3] Quoted by G. J. Whitrow, *Structure of the Universe*, p. 96.

4. THE SELECTIVE SUBJECTIVISM OF EDDINGTON

The type of necessity which Eddington claims for the universe of our experience is not so much logical as epistemological. The possibility of demonstrating his thesis depends upon his view that all the characteristics which we generally suppose ourselves to discover in the universe (even such apparently non-subjective characteristics as the number of stars in the heavens or the number of electrons that the universe contains) are in fact manufactured by ourselves in the acts by which we observe it. This is, of course, broadly speaking, a Kantian position, but there are important differences between Kant's doctrine and the "selective subjectivism" of Eddington. For Eddington the imposition of the universe's nature upon it by the observer arises not so much from the fact that he *perceives* it as from the fact that, in so far as he is acting as a physical scientist, he *measures* it. It would perhaps be more accurate, therefore, to describe the necessity which Eddington attributes to the physical universe as *metrological* rather than as merely *epistemological*. The broad outlines of his argument can be found in several of his semi-popular works,[1] but its detailed exposition is extremely technical and even the experts appear to have found it very difficult to follow and to assess.[2] "The nature of the mathematics involved", writes Dr H. Dingle, "is such that very few persons are competent to criticise it, and for them the labour would be very great."[3] It is interesting to notice that in 1950 the Institut International des Sciences Théoriques offered a prize of 50,000 Belgian francs for the best essay which would show what Eddington's epistemological principles were and would justify or refute the conception which Eddington gave to the "philosophy of the science of physics". The matter cannot be considered to be finally settled, but it will be relevant to refer to a few typical reactions to Eddington's claim.

Dr E. F. Caldin, in an article in *Blackfriars* for March 1930 and later in his book *The Power and Limits of Science*, published in 1949, has affirmed emphatically that Eddington incorporated into

---

[1] *Nature of the Physical World*, ch. xi; *New Pathways in Science*, ch. xi; *Philosophy of Physical Science*, passim.

[2] Compare the amusing remarks of H. Bondi, *Cosmology*, p. 158.

[3] *The Sources of Eddington's Philosophy*, p. 58.

his argument a considerable body of empirically derived information without apparently realising that he was doing this.[1] Eddington's results, he says, are not deduced solely from propositions whose truth or falsehood is independent of particular experiments, but require also propositions which are dependent upon the results of particular observations. "On this view", Caldin writes,

> the significance of Eddington's results is that the particular forms of the fundamental laws of physics, and the particular values of the constants that occur in them, can be deduced, using symbolic logic, from a consideration of the general metrical method of physics, *plus* certain methods which by reason of their success are always used in interpreting experimental results, *plus* the inductively based propositions of relativity and quantum theory. That this is a very remarkable contribution to science is obvious. But the point here is that it seems incorrect to claim for these results a certainty greater than inductive. Eddington's work, on the present view, has the status of a unifying theory, whose likelihood is improved by every deduction from it which accords with experiment.[2]

Caldin goes on to accuse Eddington of confusing three different senses of the term *a priori*. He draws the final conclusion that "it does not appear that the claim that the fundamentals of physical theory are independent of experiment has been substantiated".[3]

A very similar judgment has been passed by Dr Max Born. "Eddington's treatment", he writes,

> gives the impression that the results could have been obtained—or even have been obtained—by pure reason, using epistemological principles. I need not say that this is wrong and misleading. There was, of course, a philosophical urge behind Einstein's relentless effort; in particular the violation of contiguity in Newton's theory seemed to him unacceptable. Yet the greatness of his achievement was just that he based his own theory not on preconceived notions but on hard facts, facts which were obvious to everybody, but noticed by nobody. The main fact was the identity of inertial and gravitational mass, which he expressed as the principle of equivalence between acceleration and gravitation.[4]

[1] Cf. A. D. Ritchie, *Reflections on the Philosophy of Sir Arthur Eddington*, p. 28.
[2] Op. cit., p. 95.   [3] Ibid., p. 104.
[4] *Natural Philosophy of Cause and Chance*, p. 141. Cf. *Experiment and Theory in Physics*, p. 38.

Sir Edmund Whittaker, in his book *From Euclid to Eddington*, writes as follows:

> It must be admitted that in some places [Eddington] did assert that what he called *epistemological principles*—principles relating to the method or ground of knowledge—were adequate to supersede observation and experiment as the basis of physical science. But an examination of his published work shows that in effect the epistemological principles were by no means independent of knowledge derived from sense-perception.

He compares Eddington's work with Archimedes' calculation of the value of π from the axioms and propositions of Euclid's geometry. "What Archimedes did was to assume the *qualitative* part of geometry and to deduce a *quantitative* aspect of it. . . . Now Eddington", Sir Edmund continues,

> is simply the modern Archimedes. He regarded himself as at liberty to borrow anything in *qualitative* physics—he did in fact assume the identity of mass and energy, the theory of the energy tensor and the interpretation of its elements, the exclusion principle, and other propositions of the most advanced physical theory—but he did *not* assume any number determined experimentally; and he deduced the *quantitative* propositions of physics, i.e. the exact values of the pure numbers that are constants of science—the numbers that are analogous to the number π in geometry.[1]

Dr G. J. Whitrow has pointed out that even Eddington himself

> did not claim that it was possible to deduce *a priori* the complete structure of the physical universe, the sun, the moon, and all the stars, from the rules of measurement. Instead, he maintained that the fundamental numerical constants occurring in the general laws by which we select and order natural phenomena . . . can be calculated without reference to particular measurements made in the laboratory. In other words, these universal numbers need not be obtained as inductive generalisations from a limited number of measurements of particular phenomena; instead, they arise as deductive consequences of the general principles of metrology and the theory of knowledge.
>
> The vital stage [Whitrow continues] in any *a priori* theory of physical phenomena, such as Eddington's, is the identification of the

[1] Op. cit., pp. 185, 186. Cf. Whittaker's Eddington Lecture, *Eddington's Principle in the Philosophy of Science*, passim.

various symbols of the abstract structural pattern with the concepts employed in observation and experiment. Eddington compared scientific method to a fishing net, pointing out that many of the characteristics of the fish which can be caught by the net could be predicted by studying its mesh. Those characteristics which could not be predicted in this way he regarded as "irrelevant", at least for physics. Hence, the properties which are considered significant for physics ought to be completely specified by his method.[1]

Whitrow goes on to suggest that it appears probable that Eddington's attempt is incomplete, since, reasoning from a different set of equally *a priori* principles, Professor E. A. Milne constructed a world-model which is notably different from that of Eddington. However, "despite mutual inconsistencies", he writes,

the two are not necessarily mutually exclusive, for they may provide complementary perspectives of the physical universe. . . . In Eddington's theory the spatial aspect is more thoroughly analysed than the temporal, whereas in Milne's, primary emphasis is laid on the flux of time. Eddington's concept of physical measurement is associated with the idea of the ruler, Milne's with the idea of the clock.[2]

It is perhaps important to emphasise that Eddington himself, while he claimed for his theory a more inclusive application than even his most sympathetic commentators seem to have been able to accord him, admitted that there are some characteristics of the universe that cannot be determined *a priori*. It was, of course, fundamental to his thesis to maintain that many or most of the features which have commonly been regarded as "special facts" in contrast to "laws of nature" (e.g. the number which has usually been interpreted as "the number of fundamental particles in the universe") can be calculated on purely epistemological and metrological principles, but he explicitly asserted that two special facts remained outside his deductive scheme. One of these is the comparatively small proportion of the total volume of the universe that is occupied by matter. "It is a special fact that most of space is empty, the matter being aggregated in comparatively small islands. No one", he says, "has suggested that this should be ranked as a fundamental law of physics; we are indeed dis-

[1] *Structure of the Universe*, p. 151.   [2] Ibid., p. 152.

posed to think that it is a lately developed feature, the primordial distribution of the matter having been a continuous nebula."[1] The second of these special facts is the comparatively small proportion of the total matter in the universe which is subject to what, in his discussion of quantum phenomena, Eddington describes as "correlation" and identifies with the effect of conscious volition. "It is a special fact", he writes,

> that matter is normally unassociated with consciousness, just as it is a special fact that space is normally empty or nearly empty. Physics would not have taken the form it has taken if it were the rule, rather than the exception, for matter to be under the influence of conscious volition; but equally physics would not have taken the form it has taken if the matter encountered in normal experience had been distributed continuously as it is in the interior of a star.[2]

This point has been made with some emphasis by Dr Herbert Dingle in his Eddington Memorial Lecture for 1954 on *The Sources of Eddington's Philosophy*.[3] He quotes the following highly relevant passage from Eddington's *Relativity Theory of Protons and Electrons*:

> An intelligence, unacquainted with our universe, but acquainted with the system of thought by which the human mind interprets to itself the content of its sensory experience, should be able to attain all the knowledge of physics that we have attained by experiment. He would not deduce the particular events and objects of our experience, but he would deduce the generalisations we have based on them. For example, he would infer the existence and properties of radium, but not the dimensions of the earth.[4]

Dingle's comment on this passage is as follows:

> Let us note at the beginning that he distinguishes sharply between the *laws* of physics and the *actual entities* among which we find our-

---

[1] *Philosophy of Physical Science*, p. 218. Somebody might, I suppose, assert as a logically necessary fundamental law of physics that the distribution of matter must start by being continuous and then become more and more discrete as time goes on, but I do not think Eddington made this assertion. The Second Law of Thermodynamics, which some people *have* tried to affirm as logically necessary, would lead to precisely the opposite conclusion.

[2] Ibid.

[3] Cf. also the discussion in Dingle's *Scientific Adventure*, ch. xii.

[4] Op. cit., p. 327, quoted by Dingle, p. 42.

selves and which obey those laws. This is important, because he has sometimes been unjustly charged with supposing that the whole of our experience could have been predicted by a perfect reasoner, whereas in fact he supposed that none of it could. The laws of physics characterise the behaviour of *any conceivable* physical world, and therefore tell you nothing at all about which of the conceivable ones is the actual one; for knowledge of that we must depend on experience. This he maintained from his earliest to his latest writings on this subject, and it is certainly not his fault that it is not fully understood. But his actual claim, that the laws of physics—which he freely admitted had in fact been derived by generalisation from the facts of experience—could have been foreseen and are inherent in the procedure by which we generalise, is sufficiently startling, and demands the closest examination before judgment is passed on it. This it has not always received.[1]

Dingle's comment seems to me to be perfectly accurate, and I shall not at this point discuss this particular question any further. It is, however, well to recall that for Eddington the laws of nature, in the sense in which the term is used in the passage above, include such numerical quantities as the cosmical number and the mass-ratio of the proton to the electron, which in most cosmological theories have been looked upon as purely contingent.

Dingle's main discussion, in which he tries to disentangle the notorious confusion of Eddington's general philosophical position, is, I think, much more open to objection. He sees Eddington as having forced into the conceptual structure of relativity physics a belief in the existence of a real external world which is incompatible with it and is derived from Victorian religious prejudices. "He knew", writes Dingle,

> that physical quantities were simply the results of measurements and were not properties of particles. He knew that an electron was a part of a conceptual physical world, something whose definition was wholly contained in the definitions of the measurements of other, observable, things that had made it possible consistently to conceive it. But he could not rid his mind of another world behind the physical one and symbolised by it—the external world as I have called it—in which the electron "in itself" existed.[2]

The consequence of this, we are told, was that, where other

---

[1] Op. cit., p. 43.   [2] Ibid., p. 23.

apologists for religion have frequently divided reality into the realms of the material and the spiritual, Eddington divided it into the realms of the metrical and the non-metrical. Physics was metrical and found no place for religious categories; religion was to be found in the non-metrical realm, the realm of the theologian, the artist and the biologist.

Now all this is no doubt highly deplorable, but I do not think that the trouble lies in Eddington's assumption of the existence of an "external world". I think it lies in his theory of the relation between the external world and the conceptual world of physics. There were, says Dingle,

> three distinct entities out of which his philosophy was built: first, physical quantities which are simply the results of actual measurements, i.e. such things as ordinary measurements of lengths, volumes, masses, etc.; secondly, the physical world, which is an imaginary structure of which the physical quantities can be regarded as affording indirect measures and which comprises the ordinary entities of present-day physics—fundamental particles, fields of force, etc.; and finally, the external world, consisting of entities unknowable in themselves but of which the physical quantities are symbols and of the structure of which the physical world is a representation.[1]

Dingle is right in adding that "it needs but a brief reflexion on this state of affairs to make it clear that the external world plays no part at all in the business, and could be left out without the loss of anything", if he means that the external world does not enter into the equations of physics. I think, however, that he is wrong if he means that physics as a concrete discipline is un-interested in the existence of an external world and is concerned solely with the systematisation of the measurable characteristics of our sense-data. The position which I myself would maintain is that which I outlined in the last lecture, that, although physical science is concerned only with sense-data directly, those sense-data are media through which we cognise an intelligible world which exists independently of our experience of it. I think that Eddington was right in his concern to maintain that our senses provide us with knowledge about a real world external to our-selves. But I think he was wrong in assuming that the external

[1] *Scientific Adventure*, p. 24.

world was related to the sensory continuum in the way laid down by his quasi-Kantian doctrine of "selective subjectivism". And I think that Dingle too is wrong in assuming, as he apparently does, that if you reject this doctrine you banish the external world as well.

5. THE KINEMATIC RELATIVITY OF MILNE

Something ought to be said at this point about the alternative cosmological theory of Milne, which is known as Kinematic Relativity, and which, as we have just observed, while as *a priori* as Eddington's, is based upon a different set of *a priori* principles. Milne's system has received nothing like such attention as Eddington's, though Dr Martin Johnson devoted to it his book *Time, Knowledge and the Nebulae*, and it received considerable discussion in Whitrow's book *The Structure of the Universe*. Its theological implications have been given explicit statement in Milne's posthumously published book *Modern Cosmology and the Christian Idea of God*, and I shall make some observations on that work after briefly describing the comments of Johnson and Whitrow on his earlier writings. The basis of Milne's argument is the principle that the existence of physics necessitates that different "fundamental" observers should be able to communicate with one another and that all such observers are equivalent to one another as regards the formulation of physical laws. No location is privileged as regards observational status; "you can never tell where you are in the universe". "Milne's 'gravitating world'", wrote Johnson, "means the intelligible world, and naturally consists of those motions out of which observers could construct a coherent science instead of a chaos of individual opinions". "Perhaps the most suggestive clue to the relation between kinematics and dynamics in gravitation", he tells us,

> is that Milne can assign a mass to a cosmic condensation *depending upon* the existent accelerations: an older science would say that the mass *gives rise to* these accelerations. Since the motions ultimately are those necessary to the mutual consistency of all observers' recording, laws of intertia and of gravitation appear as laws of logic itself and of an entirely different status from the empirical generalisations of Newtonian science.[1]

[1] Op. cit., p. 105.

Milne's system thus claims to be every bit as aprioristic as Eddington's; and its supporters would claim that it is even more successful in its power to predict the characteristics of the physical universe, such as, for example, the distribution of the extra-galactic nebulae. Nevertheless Johnson doubted whether Milne's discussion had altogether made good its claim. "The most remarkable fact", he wrote,

is that so many conclusions closely resembling previous discoveries in empirical physics, and yet often differing in important details or extending therefrom, emerge as deductions from the logical structure of Milne's definitions. These definitions involve only the equivalence of observers, or the need to interconnect individual temporal experiences if science is to become more than a chaos of unrelatable opinions. Obviously the question of greatest importance for any theory of knowledge is the reason for these resemblances and subtle differences between logical implications in "communicability", on the one hand, and empirical exploration of Nature on the other hand. This question will not be solved until every theorem which mentions as deductive inference a quantity described also in language of the experimental physicist is made explicit and obvious, and forced to show clearly where one meaning overlaps the other. Milne's successive papers suggest that he has not yet stabilised such a transition from the deductive to the empirical.[1]

Dr Johnson went on to list a number of points as regards which further clarification seemed to be needed.

Traditional relativity is characterised by measured constancy of light velocity, in many accounts elevated to a "Principle", but Milne has claimed his essentially constant "c" for idealised signalling as a novelty in being an *a priori* convention, an "agreed number" independent of the empirical. But if I am correct in concentrating the epistemology of physics upon the isolating of those conditions which allow experience to be formulated in communicable laws, then both Einstein and Milne are here of identical logical status: they must have this one feature in common, some "communication" process invariant for all transformations. If the universality of "c" adequately expresses this feature, then to accept this necessity as result of observation and to construct transformations for preserving it, or to postulate observers intelligent enough to anticipate

[1] Op. cit., p. 117.

it and to "adopt" the same "number", seem merely alternative expressions of a purely logical necessity, binding all research.[1]

Again:

> If inertia is a property imposed by motions whose nature is determined by needing to be capable of correlation between observers, what is its quantitative measure? Have we attained the dream of the earlier physicists, in which the "total amount of matter in the universe" decides the empirical mass of any particle and not only its gravitational habits?[2]

Further, referring to the famous equation

$$\tau = t_0 \log \frac{t}{t_0} + t_0$$

connecting Milne's two time-scales, the scale of kinematic or microscopic time t and the scale of dynamical or macroscopic time τ, Johnson put the two questions: (1) Is there any reason for t_0 (the "age of the universe" or "epoch of creation" on the t-scale) to have the approximate magnitude 2×10^9 years, except that empirical astrophysics and geophysics suggest it?[3] (2) Is the selection of one or other of these time-scales an empirical or a rational necessity? "The limits of the formal structure of physics,

---

[1] *Time, Knowledge and the Nebulae*, p. 118.   [2] Ibid.

[3] Milne himself has more recently touched on this point. "Since this zero measures the position of the epoch of creation, we see that every dynamical equation on the absolute [i.e. the t-] scale refers explicitly to the fact that the universe was created so many years ago. Or rather, it insists on mentioning explicitly the time *after* creation at which the particular phenomenon being described by the particular equation actually occurs. In using an equation on the absolute scale, we are bound to pay homage to the occurrence of that great antecedent event, creation itself, without which the later phenomenon would not be possible" (*Modern Cosmology and the Christian Idea of God*, p. 95). (In consequence, as we describe the successive events in the universe, we have constantly to change the value of t_0 in our equations.) Again he writes: "There is necessarily an empirically determined quantity, t [i.e. what is above called t_0], occurring in these expressions, for this simply measures the position of the instant at which we happen to be viewing the universe. This, of course, is incapable of prediction. The same quantity occurs in the ratio of distance to velocity for the external galaxies, at the present moment. The circumstance that Eddington's theory of the constants of nature appears to predict this ratio on *a priori* grounds seems to me an argument against the validity of Eddington's theory in this respect, for it appears to be equivalent to the feat of predicting the age of the universe at the moment we happen to be viewing it; which would be absurd" (ibid., p. 158).

as imposed by the need for communicability of its laws", wrote Johnson, "have never yet been clearly seen; when they are, we may be able to understand whether 'formal pattern' and 'insertion of magnitudes into the form' are two kinds of information sought by physicists or only one kind. If they are two, the distinction may possibly turn out to be that between rational and empirical. This stage", he concluded, "has not yet been reached."[1]

In his book *The Structure of the Universe*, Dr G. J. Whitrow devoted some considerable space to the work which Milne and he had performed together in developing Milne's theory. He also drew an important contrast, to which I have already referred, between the spatial approach of Eddington, with its emphasis upon measurability, and the temporal approach of Milne, with its emphasis upon communicability. For Eddington the essential feature of the physical universe is that one observer shall be able to measure it; for Milne the essential feature of it is that different co-equal inhabitants shall be able to communicate with each other. Or, to put the point from a slightly different angle, Eddington's world receives its physical nature from the physicist's determination to measure it, Milne's from his determination to communicate with other physicists. But, as Whitrow remarked, they both agree in one very important respect.

There is an interesting parallelism between the ways in which Eddington and Milne developed their respective theories of the universe and its laws. First, each began with a definite world-model and analysed its properties in detail. In Eddington's case this was the Einstein universe, in Milne's the uniformly expanding universe suggested by the Special Theory of Relativity. Despite many novel features, this phase of their respective investigations was in general agreement with the methods adopted by other theoretical cosmologists.

"But", he continued significantly, "in the later phase of their work, the break with traditional methods was radical. *Each attempted to deduce the model he had originally accepted as given*."[2] In fact what both Eddington and Milne were trying to do was to prove that, in spite of its apparent contingency, the physical universe is necessary, both in its general laws and in its detailed

---

[1] Op. cit., p. 119.   [2] Op. cit., p. 152 (italics mine).

characteristics. They were trying to do, and to do more radically, for relativity and quantum theory what Maxwell and others had tried to do for the dynamics of Newton.

How far Milne came in the end to believe that he had achieved this ideal, and how far his belief was justified, can to some extent be judged if we now turn to the posthumous work to which reference has already been made, *Modern Cosmology and the Christian Idea of God*. Briefly stated, Milne's thesis in this book is that the universe is rational and that a rational universe implies a rational Creator.[1] The *fact* of creation—the fact that a universe exists at all—is admittedly irrational, and no reason can be assigned for it; but given Milne's initial assumptions, there are reasons, and compelling ones why this should be so; the epoch of creation is a transcendental singularity.

> We can make no propositions about the state of affairs *at* $t = 0$; in the divine act of creation, God is unobserved and unwitnessed, even in principle. . . . We can form no idea of an actual event occurring at $t = 0$; we can make propositions in principle only *after* the event $t = 0$. As for why the event happened, we can only say that had no such event happened, we should not be here to discuss it. The event cannot be said to have happened *in time*; for there was no method of keeping time before $t = 0$. We can only say, from evidence which we may mention later, that we are living so many years after the event happened.[2]

Creation is a "stupendous irrationality".[3] But everything else about the universe is rational, and "to say that the universe is rational is to say that its Creator is rational".[4] Clearly, before one can discuss the cogency of this argument one must know precisely what, in this context, the word "rational" means; and this is unfortunately not at all easy to determine.

At the beginning of his discussion Milne seems to mean, by the statement that the universe is rational, that all its characteristics are logically necessary. "It will be a test of the correctness of our path that we should find at no point any *bifurcation of possibility*. Our path should nowhere provide any alternatives. The account of the universe I am about to put forward has this

---

[1] Op. cit., p. 23 *et al.*   [2] Ibid., p. 58.   [3] Ibid., p. 23.   [4] Ibid.

property—that at no point does it give alternatives."[1] And, says Milne, "I think that the argument that the uniqueness of the universe implies an absence of rational alternatives in creation is a genuine argument for both the rationality and the oneness of God".[2] This is very queer, for if the universe is rational in the sense that it is in every detail logically necessary, it is difficult to see how any theistic implication could follow; even if there were no God, the laws of logic would presumably still be obeyed. Traditional cosmological theism has, of course, based itself upon the assertion that the universe is neither logically necessary nor logically contradictory; but that it is logically possible and in fact exists. Strangely enough, there are places in which, in spite of assertions such as those just quoted, Milne seems to be in fact trying to say this.

> If we found objects in nature disobeying the laws deduced by inference as holding good in a rational universe—*as I agree it is possible to conceive such a disobedience*—then we should admit that the universe was irrational. The fact that we find so many empirical physical laws actually identical with those deduced logically from the statement of a model of the material content of the universe— this empirical fact is the proof that the universe is rational. But if rational, then its Creator must be rational; that is to say God is a rational being.[3]

And again,

> An almighty demon could direct the matter of the universe in paths that contradicted the rationally deduced "laws of nature", or theorems. But such a demon would not be entitled to our respect, much less devotion. Actually, the fact of the rationality of nature, in accordance with man's idea of rationality, shows that God is not less than man in that feature which distinguishes man from the animals—intellect.[4]

The meaning of "rational" here must surely be "systematic, coherent, patterned", but hardly "logically necessary". And if it were suggested that, although he uses the word "rational" in two senses, Milne avoids confusing them, it should be replied that, in the passage just quoted, even the laws of nature are described as

---

[1] *Modern Cosmology and the Christian Idea of God*, p. 49 (italics in original).
[2] Ibid., p. 50.   [3] Ibid., p. 155 (italics not in original).   [4] Ibid., p. 156.

"rationally deduced" only in a sense which would allow of their violation by an evilly-intentioned almighty demon; this is a far cry from the assertion that there is "at no point any *bifurcation of possibility*". And indeed Milne explicitly deserts his apriorism when he leaves the realm of physics for that of biology. "I will remark", he says, "that I have not suggested that this determining of natural law applies in the field of biology, nor have I excluded the possibility of divine interference in the details of biological evolution."[1]

There would, in fact, seem to be four conceivable alternative positions that might be held, and for which arguments might be urged. The first would be that both the existence and the nature of the universe are logically necessary. If this could be shown, obviously no theistic—and equally no atheistic—conclusion could be drawn; whether God exists or not, the laws of logic must hold. The second position would be that neither the existence of the universe nor the nature which it in fact has is logically necessary; this has been in general the position of traditional theism, though when it has been at its metaphysical best it has put the primary emphasis upon existence rather than upon nature. The third position would be that the existence of the world is logically necessary, but its nature logically contingent; I do not know whether anyone has held this, but with the substitution of "morally necessary" for "logically necessary" it would seem to be the position of Dr W. R. Matthews. The fourth position would be that the existence of the universe is not logically necessary, but that the nature which it will have if it does exist *is*; this seems to me, on reflection, to be the position which Milne believed himself to hold, though with two important qualifications. The first qualification is that he allowed himself to indulge at times in *per impossible* speculations about a logically contradictory universe that might have been created by an irrational deity. I have suggested that this is due to an ambiguity in his use of the word "rational". The second qualification is that in the biological realm he seems to be quite ready to admit a radical contingency in the world and to allow for direct interpositions of the deity, in which the existence of God is shown precisely by the fact that he sometimes does things which are *not*

[1] *Modern Cosmology and the Christian Idea of God*, p. 133.

logically necessary. This is surprising because, in the realm of physics, Milne clearly finds the notion of a God who intervenes in a logically unnecessary way repugnant not only on scientific but also on religious grounds. A deity who continuously creates matter, he says, "is not a Providence that I for one could worship as God".[1] It seems, in fact, as if Milne reconciled his religious desire for a God who acts and his mathematical desire for a tidy cosmology, by banishing God's activity to the epoch of creation, where, on Milne's theory, he is just beyond the reach of the cosmologist, and to the biological realm, where what he does is not the cosmologist's business. And it must, I fear, be admitted that, by this ambiguous use of the word "rational", he contrives to run with the hares of contingency and follow with the hounds of determinism.

The following passage gives Milne's own summary of his view of the relation of God to the universe:

> It is more consonant with our idea of an infinite transcendental God, who has created the universe as a transcendental point-singularity, to regard him as fully employed in the subsequent history of this universe, in causing an infinite number of occasions for the exercise of the occurrence of mutations. God, that is to say, did not wind up the world and leave it to itself; he created the universe, and therewith also endowed it with the only laws of inorganic nature consistent with its content, as we have seen in earlier lectures; and then he tended his creation in guiding its subsequent organic evolution on an infinite number of occasions in an infinite number of spatial regions. That is of the essence of Christianity, that God actually intervenes in history.[2]

The God whose activity is described in this statement is indeed different from the God of Milne's *a priori* cosmology, for whom there are no bifurcations of possibility. We can only surmise to what extent the points which have been left obscure would have been cleared up if Milne had lived to give the final revision to his manuscript. It seems at least to be clear that the ideal which Milne set himself as a cosmologist was to deduce the nature of the universe from first principles; how far he succeeded is open to very great doubt. As we have seen, his fellow-cosmologists were

---

[1] *Modern Cosmology and the Christian Idea of God*, p. 77. Cf. p. 23.
[2] Ibid., p. 153.

far from being convinced; and even Milne himself seems to have had his misgivings. Apart from his concessions in the biological realm, of which he seems to have failed to see the full significance, there are indications of incompleteness elsewhere. We do not know to what time-scale to refer the ages of the terrestrial rocks.[1] In spite of the notice "No bifurcation of possibilities", there is one point at which an alternative is dismissed as being pathological, although logically possible.[2] And Milne admits that his theory, while more broadly based, as he claims, than Eddington's, does not go so deep in the quantum theory direction.[3] Furthermore, as is well known, some scientists have seen an element of legerde-main in Milne's adroit handling of his two time-scales.

6. CONCLUSIONS

Is it possible, in spite of the complexity and obscurity in which the matter is involved, to draw any general conclusions about the results of the attempts of Eddington and Milne? I think that it is.

In the first place, it is important to distinguish between two distinct senses in which a scheme such as that of Eddington or of Milne might be described as aprioristic. (This point has been referred to already in connection with Dr Caldin.) In saying that the scheme was aprioristic we might mean simply that it claimed to show that the detailed characteristics of the universe could be derived by a purely deductive process from certain highly general fundamental postulates. We might, on the other hand, mean that it claimed not only this but also that the fundamental postulates could be seen to be logically necessary. Only if this latter claim were substantiated would the actual universe be shown to be logically necessary and its apparent contingency be shown to be an illusion. In other words, to prove the necessity of the actual universe two things must be done. First, certain funda-mental cosmological principles must be shown to be necessary. Secondly, it must be shown that, given those fundamental cosmo-logical principles, the world that actually exists follows with logical necessity from them. Both these points need examination.

First, then, can it be claimed that the fundamental cosmological principles of either Eddington or Milne can be seen to be logically

---

[1] *Modern Cosmology and the Christian Idea of God*, p. 10. [2] Ibid., p. 52.
[3] Ibid., p. 101.

necessary? We may well feel a certain reserve in the matter, since both Eddington and Milne seem to have made this claim for their respective principles, while it is by no means clear that the two are identical or even compatible. For Eddington it was clear beyond dispute that the fundamental characteristic of a physical world was that it should be *measurable*; for Milne it was equally clear that the fundamental characteristic of a physical world was that it should be one in which *communication* was possible. There is something disquieting in being presented with two different starting-points, each of which alleges that it can be clearly seen to be the only right one. This might not, however, matter very much if the consequences of the two assumptions were the same. It might then be argued that the fact that the universe must be one in which measurement was possible and the fact that it must be one in which communication was possible were only two aspects of the same fundamental necessity, and that whether you took the one or the other as obvious would depend simply on whether you were more interested in measuring or in conversing. But if this were so, it should be possible to prove that each of the assumptions implied the other; and until this had been proved their equivalence would be highly doubtful. In fact, not only has this equivalence not been proved, but it seems pretty clearly to have been disproved. For, unless mistakes have been made in the working, Eddington's assumption and Milne's assumption lead to incompatible consequences in the empirical realm; and no two propositions can be equivalent if their respective consequences are mutually inconsistent. It would seem to follow that, in spite of their plausibility as candidates for the position of self-evident cosmological principle, either Eddington's measurability-principle or Milne's communicability-principle is an impostor, or else each of them is. It certainly is difficult to conceive of a physical world in which measurement and communication were not both possible. But the incompatibility to which attention has been drawn seems to suggest that the question needs further investigation.

The second pre-requisite for a necessary universe is that, given the fundamental cosmological principles, the actual world should be shown to follow with logical necessity from them. It seems quite clear that neither in Eddington's system nor in Milne's is this the case. We have already noticed that Eddington himself admitted that the universe has characteristics which cannot be deduced from his cosmological scheme but have to be accepted as brute fact; and, as we have seen, most of Eddington's commentators hold that he incorporated into his scheme a number of purely empirical facts without realising that he was doing so. Nor does Milne appear to have claimed to deduce from his cosmological principles the detailed structure of the world; the fact that he had to compare his model with nature before he could identify his "constituent particles" with the nebulae[1] seems to indicate this. And, as Dr Martin Johnson pointed out in the remarks to which I have already referred, Milne's re-graduation of the time-scale raises questions which suggest that his procedure was not directed by purely theoretical considerations but relied a good deal upon empirical knowledge.

The conclusions would seem to be that neither Eddington's nor Milne's cosmology has provided the world with the kind of logical necessity which some of their admirers have alleged. Neither Eddington nor Milne seems to have thought that every detail of the physical universe could be shown to follow from the fundamental cosmological postulate. On the other hand, each of them thought that the general character of the universe could be so derived, each of them thought that his cosmological postulate was self-evident, and each of them claimed to have deduced from it the numerical values of the basic constants of nature. How far these claims are justified is a matter of considerable controversy among those best qualified to judge. We shall not perhaps be rash in guessing that each of them achieved remarkable success, though probably not as much as he thought. Unless we are to reject their claims *in toto*, the conclusion to which we seem to be compelled is that the universe is necessarily permeated by a very much greater element of pattern than even the triumphs of pre-relativity science had led us to suspect. The regularity in the universe is greater than we had imagined. But to say this is not to deny that the universe is contingent. We may remind ourselves of the remark of Sir Edmund Whittaker already quoted, that Eddington is the modern Archimedes. That the universe has certain necessary

---

[1] Whitrow, *Structure of the Universe*, p. 112. Cf. Milne, *Modern Cosmology and the Christian Idea of God*, p. 55.

characteristics which are based on metrological considerations is something that we have known for a long time. That the ratio of the circumference of a circle to its radius in a Euclidean world has a fixed value, or that in a right-angled triangle the length of the hypotenuse is determined by the lengths of the other two sides, might well seem to the geometrical neophyte as a shocking restriction upon the freedom both of the Creator and of his creatures, but we have all got used to it. What Eddington and Milne have shown, if their arguments are valid, is simply that regularities and co-ordinations of this kind are more pervasive than had previously been realised. Nor ought we to be shocked by the unexpected nature of some of the quantities that are determined in this way. There is a well-known story about a man who refused to accept a certain actuarial formula used in calculations of life-insurance, on the ground that it contained the number π. "What can the circumference and diameter of a circle", he protested, "have to do with the length of a man's life?" Similarly we may not unnaturally ask what can be the connection between the fact that the universe is measurable and the number of elementary particles that the universe contains? It is perhaps well to recall the fact on which Dr Bridgman laid stress as long ago as 1927, in his *Logic of Modern Physics*, that the names which we give to physical qualities have frequently a very Pickwickian sense; that, for example, "the distance of a nebula" is defined in purely optical terms and has nothing to do with placing measuring rods end to end. Similarly, when we describe the cosmical number N as "the number of particles in the universe", it would be quite wrong to think of this as a number which can in principle be determined by checking off the particles against the natural integers in the way in which we should count the people in a room; indeed the suppositions on which the number is defined are such as to make any such process impossible. The simplest way in which to characterise the view of the universe which lies behind the theories of modern physics is perhaps to say that it assumes that there is a fundamental connection between the structure of the universe and its contents. This, of course, involves the rejection of the Newtonian view of space and time as "receptacles" in which material objects are located but which are themselves unmodified by the presence of the objects. It removes a certain kind of arbitrariness from the universe, but it does not destroy its contingency. And it rests in the last resort upon empirical observation.

It is perhaps worth while to emphasise a point which I have already made, that the relation between the actual universe and a physical or mathematical model which is successful in co-ordinating a large range of phenomena is generally much less tightly knit than we are sometimes tempted to suppose. Two very different physical systems may have the same formal logical or mathematical structure, and it is therefore very rash to assume that because we have succeeded in constructing out of familiar constituents a model which accurately reproduces the observable characteristics of some obscure phenomenon therefore the phenomenon is "really" composed of the same constituents as the model. Such an assumption underlay many of the mechanical-ether theories of the end of the last century; but the point at issue has been amusingly illustrated by other examples given by Eddington and Whittaker. "Some years ago", Eddington wrote in 1934,

> I worked out the structure of this group of operators [the *E*-operators] in connection with Dirac's theory of the electron. I afterwards learned that a great deal of what I had written was to be found in a treatise on Kummer's quartic surface. There happens to be a model of Kummer's quartic surface in my lecture-room, at which I had sometimes glanced with curiosity, wondering what it was all about. The last thing that entered my head was that I had written (somewhat belatedly) a paper on its structure. Perhaps the author of the treatise would have been equally surprised to learn that he was dealing with the behaviour of an electron. But then, you see, we super-mathematicians never do know what we are doing.[1]

My second example I have quoted before,[2] but I shall venture to repeat it. It occurs in Whittaker's Riddell Memorial Lecture *The Beginning and End of the World*.

> The vibrations of a membrane which has the shape of an ellipse can be calculated by means of a differential equation known as Mathieu's equation: but this same equation is also arrived at when we study the dynamics of a circus performer, who holds an assistant balanced on a pole while he himself stands on a spherical ball rolling

[1] *New Pathways in Science*, p. 271.   [2] Cf. p. 22 supra.

on the ground. If now we imagine an observer who discovers that the future course of a certain phenomenon can be predicted by Mathieu's equation, but who is unable for some reason to perceive the system which generates the phenomenon, then evidently he would be unable to tell whether the system in question is an elliptic membrane or a variety artiste.[1]

In each of these examples the formal similarity in question holds between two physical systems, between an electron and a material object in the lecture-room in the first case, and between a membrane and a circus performer in the second. But the point holds with equal force when one of the systems is in no sense physical but has a purely logical structure. As we saw in the last lecture, Professor R. B. Braithwaite has shown in his book *Scientific Explanation* that it is perfectly possible for a particular scientific theory to be represented by two different deductive systems, and furthermore that logically necessary relations between concepts in one system may correspond to purely contingent relations between the corresponding concepts in the other. It follows that we can never argue simply from the logically necessary elements in a model to a corresponding logical necessity in the physical facts which the model pictures. This point has frequently been overlooked, and indeed Braithwaite suggests that Eddington failed to see its relevance.[2] If this is so, then it may well be that much of the necessity which Eddington claimed to have found in the universe really existed only in his representation of it.

A few final remarks may be added. It is important to stress that the adoption of the cosmological theory of Eddington or of Milne does not seem to involve the adoption of any particular theological or philosophical doctrines. Dr Caldin may perhaps go too far in his assertion that science has no philosophical presuppositions or implications, except the presupposition that there is order in nature,[3] but it seems at least to be clear that many of the philosophical conclusions which scientists have claimed to draw from science depend upon ancillary philosophical presuppositions which have been surreptitiously smuggled in. If, for example, Eddington and Milne had shown (though they have

---

[1] Op. cit., p. 17. [2] Op. cit., p. 109.
[3] "Science and Philosophy; Implications or Presuppositions?", *B.J.P.S.*, I, p. 196 f. (1950).

probably not) that any universe in which observation and communication were possible must have the characteristics that are possessed by the universe which in fact we experience, this would be perfectly consistent with Eddington's view that the universe which we do experience is manufactured by us, by a process of "subjective selection", in the activity by which we observe it. But it would be equally consistent with the view that God has given the universe these characteristics in order that we shall be able to experience it as it really is. The principle that experience involves an *adaequatio intellectus et rei* is fundamental to any theory of knowledge. It is a mere tautology to say that we can only know what is knowable. And if modern cosmologists have been clever enough to discover by general epistemological principles what the detailed nature of a knowable universe must be, we can only be grateful to them. Their success in this endeavour leaves it, however, an entirely open question why such a universe should exist and should be experienced. The reason may be, as the Kantians would hold, that in the act of experience we have moulded the universe into an intelligible form in order to have something to know. It may be, on the other hand, as certain biologists have suggested, that in the course of evolution the human mind has had to adapt itself to an obstinately unsubjective universe in order to survive. Or it may be that God has made us in his own image as intelligent beings and has placed us in a world which is an adequate object of our intelligence, in order that we shall know the rest of his creatures as they are and shall, in knowing them, know him. I do not see how epistemological considerations can decide between these alternatives. All that they can do is to tell us what an intelligible universe is like. But why there is an intelligible universe at all and how it comes to exist is entirely outside their scope, and must be determined in some other way if it is to be determined at all. Whether the world has been manufactured by the mind, or the mind manufactured by the world, or both manufactured by God is a question that lies outside the scope of physical science. The Christian, who believes that the world is God's creation, will rejoice in humility as he contemplates the glory of him who has disposed all things in measure and number and weight.

Chapter Four

CREATION IN THEOLOGY AND SCIENCE

Mundus per ipsum factus est, et mundus eum non cognovit.—Johan. i. 10.

1. THEISTIC AND DEISTIC VIEWS OF CREATION

IT was argued in the last lecture that, whether or not they are connected *de facto*—and this is a matter for investigation by historians—there is at any rate a very close connection *de jure* between the Christian belief in a God who is both rational and free and the empirical method of modern science. A world which is created by the Christian God will be both contingent and orderly. It will embody regularities and patterns, since its Maker is rational, but the particular regularities and patterns which it will embody cannot be predicted *a priori*, since he is free; they can be discovered only by examination. The world, as Christian theism conceives it, is thus an ideal field for the application of the scientific method, with its twin techniques of observation and experiment.

I intend to devote this lecture to the discussion of creation and some cognate questions, for the word "creation" is heard fairly frequently on the lips of theologians and scientists alike. Bergson's "creative evolution", Hoyle's "continuous creation" of matter, strike a familiar note to many ears. It is, however, important to note that, although when scientists use the word "creation" they are borrowing a term from the theologians, they frequently use it in a very different sense from that which it bears in theology. I shall therefore begin by making as clear as I can what the theological sense of "creation" is.

The first point that needs to be emphasised is that for Christian theology the notion of creation is not primarily concerned with a hypothetical act by which God brought the world into existence at some moment in the past, but with the incessant act by which he preserves the world in existence so long as he wills that it shall

exist. It is true that the great majority of Christians have interpreted the opening passages of Genesis as describing, however
metaphorically or pictorially, the first beginning of the finite
world, whether or not they have adopted Archbishop Ussher's
dating of the event as 4004 B.C. It is also true that Old-Testament
scholars commonly use the term "creation-narratives" to denote
the passages in question, and draw comparisons and contrasts
between them and the creation-narratives of other religions.
Again, the name "creation" is often given to the activity by
which, in Plato's *Timaeus*, the Demiurge or divine artificer imposes form upon eternally pre-existent matter and brings cosmos
out of chaos. Christian theology, however, was not slow to
understand that, however the Genesis-narratives are to be understood, the relation between God and the world, to which the
term "creation" applies, is to be identified not with an act in the
past by which the world was originated, but with an incessant
activity by which it is conserved in existence. Historically, this
conviction is clearly derived from two basic beliefs of Judaism,
which the teaching of Christ endorsed and reinforced; namely,
the unqualified transcendence and sovereignty of God, from
which no finite being or operation escapes, and the providence
of God, who makes the sun to shine and the rain to fall upon just
and unjust alike and without whom no sparrow falls to the
ground. The radical monotheism of the Judaeo-Christian revelation could never make the separation, which is so congenial
to less robust theologies, between an august Creator who
fashioned the world at its beginning and a lower order of
spirits or forces who are solely responsible for its subsequent
functioning.

So clear had this conception become in the thought of the
great thirteenth-century theologian St Thomas Aquinas that, to
the scandal of his contemporaries, though with the approbation of
most of his successors, he asserted that, while it could be proved
by human reason that the world was created by God, the fact that
it had not always existed was known to us by revelation alone.
Admittedly, when he is making concessions to the limitations of
the human imagination, he sometimes permits himself to speak
in a way which might seem to imply the contrary; as, for example,
in his exposition of the argument from "motion" which forms

the "First Way" in his demonstration of the existence of God.[1] But as his discussion develops he becomes quite explicit: "By faith alone", he declares, "is it known that the world has not always existed; and it cannot be proved by demonstration."[2] Preservation and creation are really identical, for they are both the communication of being: "As it depends on the will of God that he produces things into being, so it depends on his will that he preserves them in being; for he does not preserve them in any other way than by always giving them being; hence, if he withdrew his action from them, all things would be reduced to nothing."[3] Furthermore, this continuous activity of God is not to be thought of as if it were the insertion of the creatures into a time-flow which existed antecedently to them, a launching of them out of the divine mind into the river of time. Where there are no creatures there is no time: "the instant in which the world began", says St Thomas, accepting the existence of such an instant from revelation, "was not time; it was however connected with time (*aliquid temporis*), but as a limit and not as a part of it".[4] (Milne would agree with him here!) So far is it from being the case that, in order to create, God needs time as an antecedent medium in which to operate, that the Angelic Doctor insists that creation is not a *change* (*mutatio*) at all, in the strict sense of that word, though it may sometimes be convenient to speak as if it were; it is a pure relation, a relation which is "notional" (*secundum rationem tantum*) in God, since it makes no difference in him, but is "real" in the creature, since for the creature it makes all the difference between existence and non-existence.[5] Thus there is no *process* called "creation" which bridges a gulf between God and his creatures. There is in fact no gulf. There are simply two kinds of being: God, who is self-existent; and creatures, which exist solely because God wills them. The very notion of creation is an abstraction, though it is an abstraction that stands for a fundamental truth. The fact—if it is a fact—that creatures begin in time is really altogether irrelevant to creation; creatures are created, whether they begin in time or not, provided only that

---

[1] *S. Theol.*, I, ii, 3c.   [2] Ibid., xlvi, 2c.   [3] Ibid., ix, 2c.
[4] *De Pot.*, iii, 17 *ad* 5. Cf. 2c: *ante mundum tempus non erat.*
[5] *S. Theol.*, I, xiii, 7; xlv, 2 *ad* 2, 3 *ad* 1. Cf. *De Pot.*, iii, 2 *et* 3; *S.c.G.*, II, xvii; *et al.*

they exist. And even when we describe creation as a *continuous* act of God, this does not mean that God is himself in time, exercising continuous activity. Time is the condition of existence of creatures, not of God; God himself is "above" or "outside" time. The act by which God creates the world does not occur *in* time, for time is itself an attribute of that which is created. The difference between the creation of a world which had a beginning and the creation of a world which has always existed is not the difference between an act which began at a certain moment and an act which has always been going on. It is the difference between two acts which are both timeless: the act of creating a world whose temporal measure has a lower boundary and the act of creating a world whose temporal measure has not. Thus St Thomas writes: "God brought into being both the creature and time together."[1] "The preservation of things by God does not take place by some new action, but by a prolongation of that action by which he gives existence; and this action is without change or time."[2] There are thus two basic notions in the Thomist doctrine of creation: the first is that creation is a divine act which operates upon a creature not merely at the moment when it comes into being but at every moment of its existence; the second, that creation does not itself take place in time, since time is one of the attributes of the creature and is created with it.

I have discussed at some length elsewhere some of the consequences of the Christian doctrine of creation;[3] what I have said above will suffice for our present purposes. It is important to emphasise that, whatever differences of detail and nuance there may be between Christian theologians, the Thomist view, as I have outlined it, represents in its broad features the consistent teaching of the classical Christian tradition. This is not always realised by those who are not professional theologians, owing to the dominance in the modern mind of that highly unrepresentative but influential body of eighteenth-century thought which goes by the name of deism. Deism may be briefly characterised as an attempt to reconcile belief in a transcendent God with the acceptance of mechanistic Newtonian physics. It has been lucidly summarised as follows:

[1] *S.c.G.*, II, xxxv.   [2] *S. Theol.*, I, civ, 1 *ad* 4.
[3] *He Who Is*, ch. viii; *Existence and Analogy*, ch. vi.

The fabric of the universe is supposed to stand to God in the relation which the instrument bears to its maker. The heavens are the work of his hands, just as the watch is the work of the watchmaker. As the craftsman determines the characteristic properties of his machine, the correlation of its parts, their positions and their functions, so is God conceived to have dealt with the world. He brought it into being and ordained its laws. He imparted to it once for all the energy which serves as the driving power of the stupendous mechanism. The Deist recognises in God the ultimate source of matter and motion, and, consistently with this conception, admits the possibility of occasional interferences on the part of the Deity. But, though the possibility of such interference is granted, the probability is called in question. It seems more in accordance with the principles of Deism that Nature should be left to work itself out in obedience to laws originally given. Any suggestion of a deviation from the established order is resented, as though to admit it were to be wanting in due respect for the inviolable majesty of God's unchangeableness and the original perfection of his work. A perfect machine, it is supposed, would not require from time to time to be adjusted by its maker; nor would the Unchangeable introduce any later corrections into a creation which from the first reflected his omniscience and omnipotence.[1]

One remarkable result of the dominance of the deistic view was that, whereas for traditional theism one of the most compelling evidences for the existence of God was to be found in the fragility of the finite world, for the religiously minded man of the eighteenth or nineteenth century great spiritual consolation was to be derived from the fact that he believed the universe to be stable and eternal. "All this most lovely fabric of things exceeding good", wrote St Augustine in the fourth century, "when its measures are accomplished, will pass away; they have their morning, and their evening."[2] But Professor O. M. Mitchell, whose book *The Orbs of Heaven* was repeatedly reprinted throughout the latter half of the nineteenth century, reflecting upon the dynamical stability of the solar system, exulted as follows:

> Are we to believe that the Divine Architect constructed this admirably adjusted system to wear out, and to fall in ruins, even

[1] G. C. Joyce, *Encyc. of Religion and Ethics*, IV, p. 541, s.v. "Deism".

[2] *Omnis quippe iste ordo pulcherrimus rerum valde bonarum modis suis peractis transiturus est; et mane quippe in eis factum est et vespera* (*Confessions*, XIII, xxxv).

before one single revolution of its complex scheme of wheels had been performed? No; I see the mighty orbits of the planets slowly rocking to and fro, their figures expanding and contracting, their axes revolving in their vast periods; but stability is there. Every change shall wear away, and after sweeping through the grand cycle of cycles, the whole system shall return to its primitive condition of perfection and beauty.[1]

For the deist, all that we see when we look at the universe around us is the operation of the universe's forces and laws; only indirectly and remotely are the existence and the attributes of God indicated to us, as the agent who, at some time in the distant past, made the whole structure, endowed it with its energies, and launched it on its way. God created the primeval matter, with its positions and its velocities, he decreed that it should move in accordance with Newton's laws of motion and gravitation, and the subsequent course of the universe was settled once and for all.

> Laws which never shall be broken
> For their guidance hath he made.

But why, from the deistic point of view, should it be supposed that the world had a beginning at all? That it had was, from the point of view of physics, a pure assumption, for the operation of Newton's laws could be extended back into the limitless past just as it could be extended forward into the infinite future. Many scientists did, of course, cheerfully eliminate God from the universe, but some of them, such as Professor Mitchell, did not. It is difficult to reconstruct the train of thought of the scientific deist, but presumably it ran something like this. There must be a creator, otherwise there would not be a world. But we do not need a creator to account for the world's present functioning; that is adequately looked after by the laws of physics, which have a simplicity that is virtually self-justifying. What, then, do we need a creator for? What is there left for a creator to do? Only to make the world in the first place. Therefore, the world must have had a beginning, otherwise there would be no need for God.

The unsatisfactory character of this type of argument is obvious, more so than we sometimes recognise to-day. For it is important to recall that, in the heyday of deism, there was no

[1] Op. cit., 4th ed., p. 125.

scientific evidence that the world had not always existed. The stability which so much impressed Professor Mitchell in the boundless future could with equal justification be projected into the boundless past. An objector might well have maintained that the deist's argument was scandalously circular. Let us state his case for him. "You say", we hear him objecting, "that there must be a God, because otherwise the universe could not have begun. But what are your grounds for asserting that the universe had a beginning? Only, so far as I can see, that otherwise there would be no need to postulate the existence of God. Why should we not eliminate God and the beginning of the world together, at one fell swoop? Why should we not endorse the famous reply, too well known to need repetition, which Laplace gave to Napoleon? You did, of course, begin with the general assertion that there must be a creator or else the world would not exist. That is an assertion with a long and distinguished ancestry. But when it was made in the past, it was made by people who believed that God's creative activity was needed in order to keep the world functioning *now*. St Thomas Aquinas, I gather, made himself somewhat unpopular in certain circles by maintaining that the argument from the existence of the world to the existence of God would be perfectly valid even if the world had always existed. *Mais nous avons changé tout cela.* As Mr Pope has reminded us,

> Scotists and Thomists, now, in peace remain,
> Amidst their kindred cobwebs in Duck-lane,[1]

and neither you nor I accept the gross superstition that the planets go round only because God is pushing them. Why, then, do we need a God at all? I am afraid we shall after all have to say it, however hackneyed it is: *nous n'avons pas besoin de cet hypothèse-là.*"

2. "THE BEGINNING OF THE WORLD"

There is something ironical in the fact that, in the days when the man of science was almost sure to be a deist if he had any religion at all, there was no scientific evidence for the fundamental hypothesis of deism, the hypothesis that the world has not always

[1] *Essay on Criticism*, part II.

existed; for in recent years a number of arguments, deriving from very diverse considerations, have converged upon the conclusion that something which it is at any rate possible to interpret as the "beginning of the universe" took place at an epoch which can even be given an approximate date. The first, and most general, of these considerations, was explicitly formulated by Lord Kelvin as long ago as 1852, though its full significance was only realised much later. It is known alternatively as the principle of the degradation of energy or as the principle of increasing entropy, and it was first clearly recognised as applying in the realm of thermodynamics. In that realm it is most clearly exemplified in the common fact of experience that heat tends to flow from hot bodies to cold bodies, and not in the opposite direction. If you put a red-hot poker into a jug of beer, the beer gets hotter and the poker gets cooler. This phenomenon is not accounted for simply by the assumptions that heat is a form of energy and that energy can be neither created nor destroyed. Those assumptions would be perfectly consistent with the iron going off in vapour and the beer freezing into a block of ice. The fact that the movement of heat is such as to make the temperatures of the substances concerned more, and not less, uniform is an illustration of the famous Second Law of Thermodynamics, the principle that, left to themselves, the processes that go on in the universe are in the direction of greater uniformity. Physicists often describe an increase of uniformity as an increase of "disorder", to the mystification of the ordinary reader, who, with memories of the parade-ground in his mind, tends to identify uniformity with order rather than with disorder. From the point of view of the sergeant-major, men standing stiffly at attention in the ranks exemplify uniformity, men rushing at random about the barrack-square do not. From the point of view of the physicist, the reverse is the case; when the men are in order in the ranks the square is not nearly as uniformly covered with men as when they are rushing about at random. It may be well, at any rate in popular discussion, to follow the suggestion of a recent writer and avoid the use of the word "disorder" in this connection altogether.[1] Returning, however, from this digression, let us go on to observe that, with the adoption of the view that the temperature of a body is

[1] J. M. Burgers, *B.J.P.S.*, V, p. 70 (1954).

simply the manifestation of the vibrations and collisions of the molecules composing it, the Second Law of Thermodynamics has been extended from the somewhat narrow realm of heat-phenomena to cover the statistical aspects of the energy-interchanges of material systems in general, and, under the title of the Principle of Maximum Entropy, has become a basic principle governing the process of the universe as a whole. The term "entropy" here denotes a physically definable numerical quantity which provides a measure of the extent to which a system approximates to a state of complete uniformity and homogeneity, of "disorder" in the physicist's sense. What the Principle asserts is that in a closed material system in which interchanges of energy are freely taking place—and it has been generally held that the universe is such a system *par excellence*—there is a steady tendency towards increasing uniformity as time goes on, until in the end there will be a dead-level of undifferentiated homogeneity, the "heat-death" of the universe, in which all process will have ceased for ever. The converse process—a movement to greater differentiation and heterogeneity—is not alleged to be, in the strict sense of the word, *impossible*, but only so overwhelmingly improbable that it cannot be supposed to occur. It would be an event like the freezing of the beer when the red-hot poker is put into it; if you observe that occurring, then, in Eddington's words, "your consciousness is going backwards, and you had better consult a doctor".[1] This is why we recognise as absurd the well-known nursery-rhyme:

> There was a man of Thessaly,
>   And he was wondrous wise.
> He jumped into a quickset hedge
>   And scratched out both his eyes;
> But when he saw his eyes were out,
>   With all his might and main,
> He jumped into another hedge
>   And scratched them in again.

The latter process, unlike the former, would involve an increase in the organisation of the universe.

---

[1] *The Nature of the Physical World*, p. 72.

Now the point with which we are here concerned is this. Since, as time goes on, the universe advances steadily to a condition of greater and greater uniformity, if the universe had been in existence for an infinite time, a state of complete uniformity ought by now to have been reached; the heat-death of the universe ought to have already occurred, and indeed to have occurred an infinite time ago. It is, however, clear at a glance that the universe at the present day is not completely uniform—if it were, we could not exist as physical organisms, for physical organisms are highly differentiated systems. Hence, the argument runs, the universe must have begun a finite time ago. How long ago it is difficult to estimate from purely "thermodynamical" considerations of the present state of organisation of the universe; we shall, however, see later on that several lines of argument converge to suggest that, at a roughly assignable date in the past, a condition existed, or an event occurred, which can reasonably be identified with the "beginning of the world".

Before we pass on to consider these, however, it may be well to recognise that the very general argument which has been outlined above has not gone altogether unchallenged. Dealing with the assertion that as time proceeds the universe proceeds gradually but inevitably to a condition of complete degradation, Sir Edmund Whittaker has written as follows:

It cannot be said, however, that the matter is altogether free from obscurity: the doctrine, though highly probable, is perhaps not established beyond dispute. For the argument is based entirely on the classical or non-relativistic thermodynamics. Now relativistic thermodynamics, which is the true theory, is considerably different from classical thermodynamics. Thus, in classical thermodynamics, a system which is in thermal equilibrium must be at a uniform temperature throughout; but in relativistic thermodynamics, a temperature gradient is necessary to prevent the flow of heat from regions of higher to regions of lower gravitational potential which are in thermal equilibrium. This simple example shows the need for caution, and the importance of using, in any general argument regarding the universe, not the classical laws, but the modified form of them which has been discovered by Professor Tolman of the California Institute of Technology. He has shown that in certain cases a universe expanding or contracting at a finite rate can do so reversibly, without tending to the ultimate "heat-death" which would be predicted by classical thermodynamics.[1]

This passage was written in 1949, but I do not think the position has relevantly altered since that date. Indeed subsequent developments of physics have somewhat underlined the questionable nature of the argument for a steady degradation of the universe. One of the most recent developments has been in the study of the thermodynamics of "open systems", that is to say, systems in which there is ingress and egress of matter across the boundaries, and in the extension of the concept of entropy to systems which are not, in the technical sense, "reversible".[2] There has always been some doubt as to the extent to which thermodynamical considerations can be applied to the universe as a whole, since the concept of entropy was developed in relation to closed systems and it is at least doubtful whether the universe can be considered as having either a boundary or an environment. The whole question is in fact very largely undetermined, but it is important to notice that there are in the field to-day cosmological theories, such as those of Bondi, Gold and Hoyle, which treat the universe as being in a steady state which involves neither a "beginning" at some date in the past nor a "heat-death" at some time in the future.[3] According to these theories, matter is continually receding from our observation as the velocities of the remoter galaxies[4] approach the velocity of light, but the deficiency is continually made up by the spontaneous creation of new matter, at the rate of something like one hydrogen-atom per cubic metre every 300,000 years, which condenses into new galaxies. Thus, in the words of the Astronomer Royal,

---

[1] *From Euclid to Eddington*, p. 46. Whittaker was here applying the argument not to the "beginning" but to the "end" of the world. Cf. also his Riddell Lectures, *The Beginning and End of the World*.

[2] Cf. e.g. R. O. Davies, "Irreversible Changes: New Thermodynamics from Old", in *Science News 28*, p. 41 f. (1953). Cf. also L. von Bertalanffy, *Problems of Life*, p. 126 f. *et al.*

[3] Cf. H. Bondi, *Cosmology*, ch. xii; F. Hoyle, *The Nature of the Universe*, ch. v; H. Spencer Jones, "Continuous Creation", in *Science News 32*, p. 19 f. (1954).

[4] I.e. "spiral" or extra-galactic nebulae; the nomenclature has varied a good deal in recent years. The notion of "recession beyond the observable region" does not seem to be free from ambiguity, as may be seen from a controversy in *The Observatory*, 1953–4.

while galaxies are continually reaching and passing beyond the observational horizon, other galaxies are being born. As the creation of matter is at the rate needed to keep the mean density of matter in the universe constant, the rate at which galaxies are being born just balances the rate at which they are lost to view. The picture of the universe, as revealed by observation, remains much about the same; change in detail is always going on but from the large-scale point of view there is no change. . . .

Thus, he concludes,

the difficulty about the running-down of the universe because of the increase of its entropy to a maximum is avoided because, although the entropy increases in a localised region, the local condensations carry entropy beyond the observational horizon, out of the observable universe. The total entropy within the observable universe remains approximately constant and does not increase with time. The second law of thermodynamics has only a localised application.[1]

It must not be supposed that this "steady-state" theory of the universe has achieved universal acceptance—Dr George Gamow, for example, is a notable opponent of it[2]—but the fact that it has been formulated and has received a good deal of support suggests that it would be rash to build a philosophical or theological edifice upon the contrary view; the more so because, as I have already argued, the question of a temporal beginning of the universe does not seem to have any direct bearing upon theology. It may, however, be of interest to look at the arguments which are alleged to indicate the date of the world's beginning, assuming that it had a beginning at all.

The first and most important indication is provided by the phenomenon of the apparent recession of the extra-galactic nebulae or external galaxies. On the assumption that the "redshift" of the spectral lines in the light received from these galaxies is due to their motion away from the observer (the "Doppler-effect"), it is possible to calculate the numerical value of their velocities of recession. Again, from the observation of the apparent luminosity of the stars of the type known as "cepheid variables" which they contain, it is possible to estimate their

---

[1] H. Spencer Jones, art. cit., p. 29.
[2] Cf. *The Creation of the Universe*, passim.

distance from us; for it is known from observation of the nearer cepheid variables, whose distances can be independently determined, that there is a definite relation between the period of a cepheid variable and its real luminosity. The result of this comparison is that, when minor divergences are allowed for, the galaxies are receding from us at velocities proportional to their distances from us; this does not mean that we occupy a position in the universe specially uncongenial to galaxies, it merely means that the whole system of the galaxies is expanding at a constant rate. The numerical result, accepted as a result of the work of Dr E. P. Hubble, was that the distance between any two galaxies is doubling in about thirteen hundred million years. This suggests that at some time between one thousand million and ten thousand million years ago the galaxies were crowded together in a comparatively small region. "There must have been", writes Sir Edmund Whittaker, "a beginning of the present cosmic order, a creation as we may call it, and we are even in a position to calculate approximately when it happened."[1] In fact, on the basis of the figures given, the age of the universe is conjectured to be about 2,600 million years.

This was a somewhat puzzling result, as evidence from radioactivity seemed to show fairly certainly that the age of the earth was between three and four thousand million years; the earth therefore appeared to be older than the universe. However, the figures were not considered to be very exact, and so this contradiction did not cause a great deal of concern, although it was rather surprising to discover that the age of the earth and that of the whole universe were even of the same order of magnitude; evolution must clearly have been proceeding relatively much faster when the universe was young than when it had got older. The apparent contradiction has in fact been removed by more recent work, involving the new two-hundred-inch telescope at Mount Palomar in California. It appears that the earlier work involved a confusion between two types of variable stars, which are now distinguished as "cepheid-" and "cluster-type". (The latter are also known as "R R Lyrae stars".) As a result of this the previous figures for both the size and distance of the external galaxies and also the "age of the universe" have to be at least

[1] Cf. Whittaker, *Space and Spirit*, p. 116.

doubled. The figures now given are between 2,000 and 3,500 million years for the age of the earth, and about 4,000 million years for the age of the universe;[1] the discrepancy has thus vanished.

Confirmation of this estimate, at any rate as regards order of magnitude, is provided by various considerations. A comparison of the rate at which energy is generated within the stars with the rate at which it is radiated into space leads to the conclusion that the age of a typical star cannot be more than ten or a hundred thousand million years. Again, the fact that there are to be found groups or "clusters" of stars, in spite of the natural tendency of such aggregations to drift apart, suggests that such clusters have an average age of something like three thousand million years, while similar arguments based upon the existence of double stars leads to a figure of the order of five thousand million years.[2] We have already seen that calculations based upon the proportions of radio-active materials in the earth's crust lead to an estimate of the age of the earth which is in the region of two to four thousand million years.[3] Furthermore, a similar analysis of the contents of meteorites, that is to say metallic masses which fall upon the earth and are believed to originate within the solar system, suggests for these meteorites a maximum age of six thousand million years.[4]

The convergence of these results is striking, for both the objects and the methods of investigation are remarkably diverse. Whether we consider the universe as a whole, or star-clusters, or binary systems, or individual stars, or meteorites, or our own earth, in each case the conclusion seems to be that the object with

[1] Cf. *Science News* 29, p. 112 f. (1953), and H. Spencer Jones in *Times Science Review*, Autumn 1954, p. 6. A further correction has been suggested, which would have the effect of quadrupling, and not merely doubling, the original estimates. E. J. Öpik on this basis suggests an "age" for the universe of not more than 6,000 million years (*B.J.P.S.*, V, p. 210, 213 (1954)). It should be remembered that, on any theory, the estimates arrived at are very rough ones.

[2] Whittaker, *Space and Spirit*, p. 116 f. Cf. G. J. Whitrow, *The Structure of the Universe*, ch. vii.

[3] Recent work, allowing for the initial concentration of lead, suggests the higher figure. Cf. Hoyle, *Frontiers of Astronomy*, p. 64.

[4] Whitrow, loc. cit. However, recent work on the production of helium in meteorites by cosmic rays has reduced this figure to one thousand million years (Cf. E. J. Öpik, *B.J.P.S.*, V, p. 206 (1954)).

which we are concerned came into existence some time between one and ten thousand million years ago. Some of these figures would need drastic re-interpretation or even rejection if we adopted the views of Bondi, Gold and Hoyle about the continuous creation of matter; on those views, for example, the universe as a whole did not have any beginning at all. Leaving them over for future consideration, and assuming their falsehood for the time being, the conclusion would seem to be that, in the words of Whittaker, "there was an epoch about 10^9 or 10^{10} years ago, on the further side of which the cosmos, if it existed at all, existed in some form totally unlike anything known to us". What, however, is the ultimate significance of this epoch, and in particular its significance for theology?

Whittaker's answer to this question is enthusiastic. "We may perhaps without impropriety refer to it as the Creation. . . . If this result should be confirmed by later researches, it may well come to be regarded as the most momentous discovery of the age; for it represents a fundamental change in the scientific conception of the universe, such as was effected four centuries ago by the work of Copernicus."[1] The epoch of creation, he maintains, gives us a natural origin of time; "the Creation itself being a unique event is of course outside science altogether".[2] And on the basis of this he attempts to reconstruct and modernise the Thomist proofs for the existence of God.

Whittaker first remarks on the fact which has already been emphasised, that St Thomas believed that without the aid of revelation it was impossible to know that the world had a beginning in time, and that therefore the sequences of moved and mover, of effect and cause, of consequence and ground, which he asserts "cannot proceed to infinity", could not be taken by him as temporal sequences. But, asks Whittaker, if they are not temporal sequences how can we be sure that they are monotonic, that is to say, how can we be sure that they do not form closed chains requiring no first member? If they do form closed chains, we can avoid the infinite regress without postulating that unmoved mover, first cause and absolutely necessary being which, in the words of St Thomas, "all men speak of as God".[3] St Thomas avoided this cyclic impasse by his belief in Aristotelian cosmo-

---

[1] *Space and Spirit*, p. 118.   [2] Ibid., p. 121.   [3] *S. Theol.*, I, ii, 3c.

logy; the cause of events in one of the celestial spheres is to be found in the sphere next above it, so there is no danger of finding ourselves where we began. To-day, however, we know that the Aristotelian cosmology is false. How then can we ensure that the sequence is monotonic?

Whittaker answers: by abandoning St Thomas's assertion that reason cannot show the world to have had a beginning in time, an assertion that modern science has shown to be false. If the world-process had a beginning, then the cause-and-effect sequence, understood now as a sequence in time, is inevitably monotonic; this arises out of the fact, fundamental in relativity theory, that no physical influence can be transmitted at a greater speed than the velocity of light *in vacuo*. The chain of causes and effects cannot be re-entrant. Moreover, St Thomas had difficulty in proving that the chain, even when taken as monotonic, does not regress to infinity. There is, however, no such difficulty for us: "this difficulty now disappears automatically, since the chain cannot in any case be prolonged backwards beyond the Creation. At this point we escape from the order of the Newtonian cosmos, and, as in St Thomas's original proof, the sequence of causes terminates in God."[1] Whittaker adds two final remarks. The first is that no essential difference is made if effects may be the joint results of several causes, and if a cause may produce more than one effect, since the rule still holds that a cause always precedes its effects in time. The second remark is that chains of causation, when traced backwards, need not all terminate at the same point; and this, Whittaker asserts, is sufficient to eliminate from his argument any suspicion of deism.

What conclusion can we come to about this approach to theism? I shall leave until later the consideration of the Bondi-Gold-Hoyle hypothesis, and shall assume that the assertion upon which Whittaker's argument is based is well-founded, that the universe had a temporal beginning. Sir Edmund Whittaker is well known to be a convinced and practising Christian, and one would not readily reject an approach to theism which is clearly the outcome of devout and serious reflection. Nevertheless, I find it very difficult to feel that his argument can bear the weight which he places upon it, and I shall try to indicate why.

[1] *Space and Spirit*, p. 125.

Although he would no doubt hold that the divine activity operates in the world's continual preservation, as well as in its temporal origination, it is of the essence of Whittaker's argument not to base his assertion of God's existence upon the fact of the world's existence, since he thinks that to do so would involve us in the possibility of a closed chain of causes unless we were prepared to cling on to the outmoded cosmology of Aristotle. He does, however, hold that the fact—for he believes it to be a fact —that the world had a *beginning* provides ample evidence of divine activity. Now the difficulty about this position, as I see it, is this. If we already accept God's perpetual and continuous activity, then, although we shall find no difficulty in accepting his activity at the beginning of things (since what is true always is true at any time), that activity will not be essentially different from his activity at any other moment. God is not, in fact, performing a succession of acts at successive moments; he is performing one extra-temporal act which maintains the whole temporal sequence from its first moment onwards. On the other hand, if we are *not* already convinced of God's perpetual activity, why is the first moment of the world's existence a sign of his activity *then*? I cannot help thinking that Whittaker has fallen into the snare of thinking of time as existing from all eternity, and so of the world's creation as a change—the very *mutatio* which St Thomas rejects—taking place in time. At one moment there is no world, at the next moment there is a world; this appears to be the picture. And, just as when a milk-bottle arrives on the door-step I assume it to be due to the activity of the milkman, so when the world arrives I assume it to be due to the activity of God. This type of argument collapses altogether if the beginning of the world is also the beginning of time. It is remarkable that Whittaker should have overlooked this point, for one of the most striking features of the outlook of modern physics is its rejection of the Newtonian view of space and time as receptacles, and its recognition that they are bound up with the process and history of the concrete changing world. We can summarise our objection as follows. If God's activity is continuous, then of course he acts at the beginning of the world as he does at all other moments. But then we need not go back to the beginning of time to discern his activity; we can see it where we are. Whittaker's argument as-

sumes that God's activity at the beginning of the world is qualita-
tively different from his activity at all other moments and that it
can be discerned in a way in which his subsequent activity cannot.
This assumption seems to be totally unfounded except upon the
hypothesis that creation is an act performed in time by a God who
is himself in time, an assumption which seems to be repugnant
alike to science and to theology. Nor can I see that Whittaker's
conclusion differs substantially from deism, in spite of his *démenti*.
For, although he says that the chains of causation need not all
terminate at the same point, the activity of God which he postulates at the various points of termination is purely an activity of
initiating in time, not an activity of continuous conservation. I
do not for one moment suggest that Whittaker himself thinks of
God in a deistic way, but I cannot see that his argument, if it
were valid, could lead to anything but deism.

I do not think, in fact, that it is either desirable or possible to
modernise St Thomas's argument in Whittaker's way. I have
attempted elsewhere to discuss Thomist theism from what I hope
is a twentieth-century standpoint.[1] All I can do here is to emphasise my conviction that St Thomas was entirely right in his
realisation that creation in the philosophical sense has simply
nothing to do with the beginning of the world; and this seems to
me to be all the more significant because, accepting as he did the
interpretation of the Genesis narrative which he had received
from the Church's tradition, he had not the least doubt that the
world had in fact a beginning.

A similar stress to that laid by Whittaker upon the alleged
scientific evidence for a beginning of the world in time appears in
the allocution delivered by Pope Pius XII in November 1951 to
the Pontifical Academy of Sciences.[2] This is an unusual, and in
many ways an impressive, papal utterance and it quotes a fairly

---

[1] Cf. *He Who Is* and *Existence and Analogy*, passim.

[2] Reported in the *Tablet* of Dec. 1st, 1951. The Italian original is in *Acta Apostolicae Sedis*, XLIV, p. 31. In the English version there is a mistranslation; on p. 393, col. 2, l. 26, "combine with" should be "combine into" (*vengono congiunti*). Another translation, with a commentary by Dr P. J. McLaughlin, has been published under the title *Modern Science and God*.

A more cautious exposition of the same thesis will be found in the pamphlet *The Cosmic Drama* by Dr William G. Pollard, a distinguished nuclear physicist who is now a priest of the American Episcopal Church.

long passage from Whittaker's *Space and Spirit*. The august speaker was wisely careful to avoid any direct confusion of philosophical and scientific questions: "The question", he reminded his learned hearers, "is not one of revising philosophical proofs, but rather of enquiring into the physical foundations from which they flow." His purpose was to show that recent developments of physical science, so far from making belief in God more difficult, had noticeably moved in the direction of theism; he referred to "the priceless services rendered by modern science to the demonstration of the existence of God", and there were two chief points on which he laid stress. The first was the mutability of the cosmos; it was pointed out that, in contrast to the physical science of the last century, modern physics, with its discovery of radio-activity and nuclear transformations, has made it impossible to attribute to matter that self-sufficiency and immutability which was one of the main bases of old-fashioned materialism.

The scientist of to-day, directing his gaze more deeply into the heart of nature than his predecessor of a hundred years ago, knows well that inorganic matter is, so to speak, in its innermost being, countersigned with the stamp of mutability, and that consequently its existence and its sub-existence demand a reality entirely different, and one which is by its nature invariable.

Just as in a picture done in chiaroscuro the figures stand out on a background of darkness, and only in this way achieve the full effect of form and life, so also the image of the Eternally Immutable Being emerges clear and resplendent from the torrent which snatches up and carries off with itself all the material things of the macrocosm and the microcosm in an intrinsic mutability which knows no pause.

The Pope thus sees the all-pervasive character of impermanence and change, which modern physics discerns in the universe, as powerfully reinforcing the classical arguments for the existence of God. For classical theism, of course, the existence even of an unchanging world would imply the existence of an immutable and self-sufficient creator, provided that that unchanging world could be seen not to contain the ground of its own existence; but, for many minds, the consideration of the fugitiveness of the things of which the world is composed emphasises their lack of self-sufficiency as nothing else can. This is why in practice St

Thomas's First Way—the argument from "motion" or change—is more useful than the more strictly philosophical Second and Third Ways, though it is more open to theoretical objections. At the least, we may say that the Pope's point is valuable as an argument *ad hominem*, in view of the stress that nineteenth-century materialism laid upon the alleged incorruptibility and eternality of matter. That it does very much to meet directly the secularism of the present day is, perhaps, less certain.

More relevant, however, to our present concern is the Pope's second point, which is concerned with the alleged agreement of physicists and astronomers that the world had a beginning in time. The ultimate cessation of macroscopic processes as a result of the law of increasing entropy is asserted as a fact; and hypotheses, such as that of continuous creation, which try to avoid this conclusion are dismissed as "sometimes unduly gratuitous". And, although it is admitted that the argument from entropy may not hold on the microcosmic scale, it is asserted that the progressive degradation of energy is manifested in the phenomena of radiation and radio-activity. "Thus everything seems to indicate that the material universe had in finite times a mighty beginning, provided, as it was, with an indescribably vast abundance of energy reserves, in virtue of which, at first rapidly, and then with increasing slowness, it evolved into its present state." Then the questions are raised whether science is in a position to state when the process began and what was the initial state of the universe.

In reply to the first of these questions the Pope appeals to the evidence which has been summarised earlier in this lecture, drawn from the recession of the external galaxies, the radio-active content of the earth's crust, the radio-active content of meteorites, and the stability of double stars and stellar aggregations; evidence from very diverse sources which coheres in specifying a figure of between one and ten thousand million years. As regards the second question, that of the initial condition of the universe, brief reference is made to the work of Unsöld and the substantial agreement of scientists that the initial state was one of enormously high density, pressure and temperature. The conclusion of the discussion is stated with almost lyrical eloquence:

With the same clear and critical look with which it examines and passes judgment on facts [the scientific mind] perceives and recognises the work of creative omnipotence, whose power, set in motion by the mighty *Fiat* pronounced milliards of years ago by the Creating Spirit, spread out over the universe, calling into existence with a gesture of generous love matter bursting with energy. In fact, it would seem that present-day science, with one sweeping step back across millions of centuries, has succeeded in bearing witness to that primordial *Fiat lux* uttered at the moment when, along with matter, there burst forth from nothing a sea of light and radiation, while the particles of chemical elements split and formed into millions of galaxies.

The Pope was careful to make it clear that he was not claiming for these arguments from contemporary science an absolutely coercive force. He contrasted them with the proofs drawn from metaphysics and revelation, and asserted the need for further development. Nevertheless he was plainly profoundly impressed by the change that had come over the attitude of scientists in less than half a century, and he explicitly mentioned Whittaker in this connection. His final conclusion was stated in the following words:

> What, then, is the importance of modern science for the argument for the existence of God based on the mutability of the cosmos? By means of exact and detailed research into the macrocosm and the microcosm, it has considerably broadened and deepened the empirical foundation on which this argument rests, and from which it concludes to the existence of an *Ens a se*, immutable by his very nature. It has, besides, followed the course and the direction of cosmic developments, and, just as it was able to get a glimpse of the term towards which these developments were inexorably leading, so also has it pointed to their beginning in time some five milliard years ago. Thus, with that concreteness which is characteristic of physical proofs, it has confirmed the contingency of the universe and also the well-founded deduction as to the epoch when the cosmos came forth from the Hands of the Creator.
>
> Hence, creation took place in time. Therefore, there is a Creator. Therefore, God exists. Although it is neither explicit nor complete, this is the reply we were awaiting from science, and which the present human generation is awaiting from it. . . .

This is indeed a remarkable pontifical utterance, and it would be a pity if it were lost to view in the dark backward and abysm of the *Acta Apostolicae Sedis*. The first part of the allocution, with its stress upon the mutability which modern science discerns in the cosmos, seems, as I have suggested above, valuable, at least as an *argumentum ad hominem.* The second part, however, dealing with the alleged beginning of the universe, while admirable as a popular scientific exposition, seems to me to fall under the same criticism as the discussion of Sir Edmund Whittaker, namely that creation in the philosophical and theological sense has no essential connection with the question of a temporal beginning, and that it is only by a misleading use of the imagination that the beginning of the universe can be seen to have any theistic implications that are not already involved in its mere existence. The Pope was indeed careful to distinguish between scientific and metaphysical arguments; nevertheless he suggested that the scientific arguments had metaphysical consequences, and this is, I think, unfortunate. The opportunities for imaginative exposition that are provided by the notion of a "beginning" of the universe are, of course, undeniable. Nobody could read without a sense of excitement, for example, Dr Gamow's description of the way in which, in his view, there took place about seventeen hundred million years ago a gigantic explosion in a highly concentrated condensation of elementary physical particles. Within the first hour, he tells us, the full complement of the atomic species were formed, and nothing more of interest took place for about the next thirty million years, when there began to form the first nebular masses which later on led, by further condensation, to galaxies, stars and planets. Nevertheless, although his book bears the theologically-sounding title *The Creation of the Universe,* and although he prints on his dedication-page the music (but not the words) of Haydn's famous anthem "The heavens declare the glory of God", he almost ostentatiously avoids giving any theistic interpretation to his narrative. It further appears that, although he looks upon the "Big Squeeze" as setting a lower limit to the period of which we can have any detailed knowledge, he does not consider it to represent an absolute beginning of the physical world. Putting the questions: Why was our universe in such a highly compressed state, and why did it start expanding?, he answers as follows:

> The simplest, and mathematically most consistent, way of answering these questions would be to say that *the Big Squeeze which took place in the early history of our universe was the result of a collapse which took place at a still earlier era, and that the present*

expansion is simply an "elastic" rebound which started as soon as the maximum permissible squeezing density was reached. . . . Most likely the masses of the universe were squeezed together to such an extent that any structural features which may have been existing during the "pre-collapse" era were completely obliterated, and even the atoms and their nuclei were broken up into the elementary particles (protons, neutrons, and electrons) from which they are built. Thus nothing can be said about the pre-squeeze era of the universe, the era which may properly be called "St Augustine's era", since it was St Augustine of Hippo who first raised the question as to "what God was doing before he made heaven and earth".[1]

It would be interesting to speculate about the comment that St Augustine himself might make upon this passage, especially as he explicitly states that the question with which he is credited was raised not by him but by somebody else.[2] We are, however, concerned here only to recognise that the term "creation" is used by Gamow in a very secondary and "improper" sense. For Milne, as we saw in a previous lecture, the epoch $t = 0$ does possess an absolute character and marks an absolute beginning of the universe. It is a transcendental singularity, inaccessible to observation or description: "we can make no propositions about the state of affairs *at* $t = 0$; in the divine act of creation, God is unobserved and unwitnessed, even in principle".[3] But Milne's cosmology depends upon some very special assumptions, which are far from being universally accepted; and, in any case, if we transform our time-reckoning from the scale of kinematic or microscopic time t to that of dynamical or macroscopic time τ, the "epoch of creation" becomes "minus infinity" and its inaccessibility becomes much less mysterious. Many apparent "mysteries" of science lose their glamour when they are subjected to the powerful debunking agency of a logarithmic transformation of variables; this has happened, for example, with the Absolute Zero of temperature, which by the beginning of this century had acquired an august and almost supernatural aura of inaccessibility but which now lies low

And none so poor to do it reverence.

It is in fact quite rash to assume that the notion of time as applied

---

[1] *The Creation of the Universe*, p. 29.   [2] Cf. *Confessions*, XI, xii.
[3] *Modern Cosmology and the Christian Idea of God*, p. 58; cf. p. 121 supra.

to remote cosmological epochs bears any direct relation to the time of our experience, except as an almost wild extrapolation from it. When, for example, we are told by Dr Gamow that the different kinds of atomic nuclei were formed during the first hour after the "great explosion" and that nothing of special interest happened during the next thirty million years, we naturally tend to imagine ourselves as contemporary spectators, observing the dials of our wrist-watches, and we reflect with some astonishment that a process of such fundamental importance in the evolution of the physical universe should have taken place while we might have been consuming a somewhat leisurely meal. Second thoughts, however, remind us that until the universe had got far beyond the stage in question it was impossible, not only in fact but in principle, for either physical bodies, watches or meals to have existed; the reflection loses all its imaginative provocativeness and becomes purely abstract and theoretical.[1] Since *ex hypothesi* neither we nor anyone else could have been observers of the process, it is strictly meaningless to speculate as to what we should have observed if we had been "there".

However, to return to the point, the mere fact that the world as we know it seems to derive from some event in the past behind which we cannot penetrate does not necessarily involve us in considering that event as the creation of the universe. In whatever sense we can attribute time co-ordinates to events in the remote past, it may well be, as Gamow suggests, that the event in question can be conceived as deriving from a previous process of contraction. All such suggestions are, of course, highly speculative and almost desperately difficult to determine, but the mere fact that they can be made by serious scientists shows how unwise it is to allow points of theological importance to depend upon their falsity, the more so since, as we have seen, the whole question whether the world had a beginning or not is, in the last resort, profoundly unimportant for theology.

3. THE STEADY-STATE THEORIES

The preceding discussion has been conducted upon the assumption that, at a roughly specifiable date in the past, an event

[1] Cf. C. F. von Weizsäcker, *World View of Physics*, p. 170.

took place which, if it cannot be regarded as the creation of the universe in the theological sense, may at least be regarded as the beginning of what Whitehead would call "the present cosmic epoch".[1] But in fact, as I have already remarked, there are cosmologists of repute, such as Bondi, Gold and Hoyle, who hold some form of steady-state theory, according to which the universe has been from all eternity substantially what it is now and will remain so *per omnia saecula saeculorum*.[2] These theories do not deny either the degradation of energy in thermal and dynamical exchanges or the recession of the galaxies from the visible realm as their velocities attain the velocity of light; but they consider that this loss is made up by a "continuous creation" of matter throughout space at the rate of roughly one hydrogen-atom per cubic metre every three hundred thousand years, a rate which is of course far too small to be detected by observation or experiment.[3] We should see the converse process happening if we could reverse the direction of time and travel back into the past. As Gamow says,

> if we were to make a motion-picture representing the views of Bondi, Gold and Hoyle, and run it backward, it would seem at firs that all the galaxies on the screen were going to pile up as soon as we reached the date of 1·7 billion years ago. But as the film continued to run backward, we would notice that the nearby galaxies, which were approaching our Milky Way system from all sides, threatening to squeeze it into a pulp, would fade out into thin space long before they became a real danger. And before the second-nearest neighbours could converge on us (at about 3·4 billion years back in time), our own galaxy would fade out too.[4]

There are considerable difficulties in the way of steady-state theories, as Gamow and others have pointed out,[5] but there are

---

[1] Cf. *Process and Reality*, p. 126.

[2] Cf. Bondi, *Cosmology*, ch. xii; Hoyle, *The Nature of the Universe*, ch. v.

[3] It will be clear that, in the strict sense, this is not a doctrine of *continuous*, but rather of steadily and unendingly *repeated*, creation.

[4] Op. cit., p. 32. The billion here is the American billion, equal to a thousand millions or a milliard. These figures do not take into account the proposed "doubling" of the age of the universe referred to on p. 145 above.

[5] Quite recently evidence against the steady-state theories has been alleged from radio-astronomy.

considerable difficulties in the way of other cosmological theories too, and it seems a little sweeping of the Pope to dismiss hypotheses of continuous creation without discussion, as "sometimes unduly gratuitous". Which type of theory in fact makes the fewer special assumptions or unproved postulates can be argued at some length, and the determination of the question is not rendered easier by the almost religious fervour which some of the leading figures on both sides exhibit in the defence of their views. An interesting discussion has recently been given by Dr Milton K. Munitz[1] of the claim made by several of the steady-state theorists that the doctrine of continuous creation purges cosmology of the last remnants of metaphysics and theology and sets it firmly in the domain of scientific accuracy and rigour. Munitz points out that there is in fact nothing to choose between the two outlooks in this respect. Each of them postulates an ultimate, which it glories in refusing to explain. For Milne this ultimate is the scientifically inaccessible point-singularity at the moment $t = 0$; for Bondi, Gold and Hoyle it is the perpetual creation of matter at the rate of one hydrogen-atom per cubic metre per 300,000 years. As Munitz says, "by spreading out creation in time and space, there is no reduction in the mystery, since multiplication of the occasions of creation as contrasted with the single unique event leaves it open to exactly the same objections as the latter".[2] The steady-state theorists are in fact most anxious to insist that no physical cause is to be invoked to explain the continuous creation of matter; it is made "out of nothing",[3] it "simply appears".[4] It is true that Bondi attempts, if not to explain, at least to *justify*, his concept of creation by appealing to what he describes as the "Perfect Cosmological Principle", the principle that "apart from local irregularities the universe presents the same aspect from any place at any time";[5] but this principle is about as "metaphysical", in the pejorative sense, as anything could be. It is certainly not based on observation or experiment; if it were, it would not need to be helped out by the postulation of an

[1] "Creation and the 'New' Cosmology", in *B.J.P.S.*, V, p. 32 f. (1954).
[2] Art. cit., p. 34.
[3] Bondi, *Cosmology*, p. 144.
[4] Hoyle, *The Nature of the Universe*, p. 105.
[5] Op. cit., p. 12.

undetectable creation of matter.[1] In fact, the introduction of the word "creation" is highly revealing, and it will repay a little attention. Its port of origin is, of course, theology, and scientists who used it in the past did so because they believed that the act or activity which it was used to describe was an act or activity of God. Creation was "making out of nothing", not in the sense that "nothing" is a sort of material out of which things are made, but in the sense that, although things are made, they are not made out of anything. To speak about creation, therefore, was to declare yourself a believer in God; if we may so put it, the absence of a material was compensated by the omnipotence of the maker. A non-religious scientist would have felt himself obliged to eschew the word "creation" at all costs. More recently, however, the word "creation" has come to be used in a way which, instead of implying the existence of God, provides a substitute for him. Bergson's "creative evolution", for instance, ascribed the appearance of novelty in the world not to the activity of a transcendent deity but to an immanent characteristic of the world itself. Similarly, when Whitehead, in his great cosmological treatise *Process and Reality*, makes "creativity" his "Category of the Ultimate",[2] this is done not with the intention of describing by this term any activity of God, but in order to assert an inherent principle of all existents, which is found equally both in God (in the highly "Pickwickian" sense in which Whitehead uses that word) and in the actual occasions of the finite world. So it is also with Hoyle. An uninstructed person, when told that Hoyle is a fervent advocate of the view of continuous creation, might not unreasonably suppose that Hoyle was a convinced theist who saw the hand of God in every being and event in the world's history, and who would endorse with enthusiasm St Thomas's assertion that "as it depends on the will of God that he produces

---

[1] There is, we may note, at least one theory postulating continuous creation of matter which is not a "steady-state" theory, namely the theory put forward by P. Jordan in 1947. In this theory the new mass appears not as hydrogen atoms but in the very different form of the exceptionally bright new stars known as *supernovae*. Bondi rejects Jordan's theory on observational grounds (*Cosmology*, p. 164); Dingle, who is slightly more sympathetic, describes it as "in some respects more and in others less heretical than that of Hoyle" (*The Scientific Adventure*, p. 162). Cf. R. O. Kapp on "Hypotheses about the Origin and Disappearance of Matter" in *B.J.P.S.*, VI, p. 177 f. (1955) and comments by Bondi and Lord Halsbury, p. 239 f. [2] Op. cit., p. 28.

things into being, so it depends on his will that he preserves them in being; . . . hence, if he withdrew his action from them, all things would be reduced to nothing".[1] The uninstructed person would, however, be totally mistaken in his supposition. Hoyle does indeed reject the outlook of the people whom he describes as the "out-and-out materialists", and says that "the essence of their game lies in throwing up the sponge".[2] But he also condemns religion as "but a blind attempt to find an escape from the truly dreadful situation in which we find ourselves".[3] Strange as it may seem, Hoyle appears to find in the notion of continuous creation itself something that gives him a quasi-religious satisfaction; it is remarkable to find him saying, "I am sure you would hardly wish me to end without saying something about how the New Cosmology affects me personally".[4] How in fact the New Cosmology affects him personally is a matter about which Hoyle is extraordinarily vague. He rejects both materialism and the Christian religion in a discussion which shows quite remarkable ignorance of what the Christian belief actually is. He is tremendously impressed by the picture of the universe that modern science has drawn: "It is my view", he says, "that man's unguided imagination could never have chanced on such a structure as I have put before you in these talks."[5] Although he thinks that future theories will bring about improvements and modifications of detail, he expects no substantial changes in cosmological theory. About the future of science and of mankind he is on the whole gloomy; and while the final destiny that he would like would be to share the consciousness of half a dozen chosen individuals, he is sceptical about its achievement. "Perhaps the most majestic feature of our whole existence", he concludes, "is that while our intelligences are powerful enough to penetrate deeply into the evolution of this quite incredible Universe, we still have not the smallest clue to our own fate."[6] It is, in fact, in the contemplation of the universe itself that Hoyle gets something like the experience that has been commonly found in religion, and it is clear that in this a great part is played by the traditional psychological associations of the word "creation".

---

[1] S. Theol., I, ix, 2c.
[2] Op. cit., p. 115.
[3] Ibid.

[4] Ibid., p. 111.
[5] Ibid.
[6] Ibid., p. 118.

Dr Munitz's comments are all the more illuminating since he does not himself show any great sympathy with theology. He asserts that historically the notion of creation came into Western thought by way of Platonism, which used the notion of human craftsmanship as the basis of a myth about the fashioning of the universe by a Demiurge out of pre-existent recalcitrant materials. In saying that "theology simply carried forward what Plato had here begun", he ignores altogether the fundamental part played in Christian theism by its Hebraic ancestry; his subsequent remarks are nevertheless illuminating. "What had been [in Platonism] a conscious myth", he writes,

> now became a literally intended mystery. The Creator not only cannot be located in the familiar world, he is no longer merely a symbol. His existence, literally claimed, is a "transcendent" one and basically an article of faith. Similarly the process of creation becomes a divine mystery, the most real of facts but shielded from human understanding. . . . As we turn to the present day, the manner in which we find creation appealed to in the steady-state theory is one which, in effect, carries this progressive mystification to its last stage. For all of the sustaining motives or analogical threads of comparison with art are gone. Scientific cosmology, of course, now not only makes no claims about the designful character of the universe; it also stops short of making any reference to the Creator or the process of his making. It is not even claimed that these are mysteries whose existence is to be believed in even though not understood. All that it would retain is the fact that matter in an elemental form is created continuously. But if the Maker, the process of making, and the purpose are gone, *what is there left to the concept of creation?* Doesn't the very description of the appearance or presence of matter as one which is due to creation lose *all* its significance? Isn't it a case of its having lost not merely its primary meaning, but even its various attenuated analogical modifications as in metaphysics and theology?[1]

I should quarrel with Munitz's description of the Christian doctrine of creation as "mystification". However mysterious they are in themselves, the function of the Christian mysteries is not to mystify but to illuminate; and I should myself argue that, by its application of the principle of analogy, Christian theism raised the notion of creation from the status of a myth to that of a meta-

[1] Art. cit., p. 40 (italics in original).

physic. But with the rest of this passage I fully agree. Whether in fact the quantity of matter in the universe does or does not increase at the rate of about one hydrogen-atom per cubic metre per 300,000 years is, I should say, a purely scientific question and one which, from the scientific point of view, is of great interest. But to suppose, as the steady-state theorists do, that this hypothesis has an ultimate metaphysical character for which it is almost impious to demand any further reason, seems to me to rest upon the quite ungrounded assumption that, when the notion of a personal God has been thrown overboard, we can retain the metaphysical ultimacy and the emotional associations which belonged to the notion of creation when it was conceived as the freely willed activity of a personal God. So far from the notion of creation shedding its last trappings of myth when the notion of God is taken away from it, it becomes altogether unintelligible. It is almost amusing to reflect that, whereas in the last century the notion of the continuous creation of matter would have been highly embarrassing to an atheistic or agnostic scientist, Hoyle hails it with enthusiasm as finally eliminating God from the picture of the universe, in somewhat the same way in which one might eliminate Newton from the *Principia* on the ground that the results were all really due to mathematics.

4. CONCLUSION

Whatever we may think about steady-state theories of the physical universe, it would be foolish in the extreme to stake the truth of Christian theism upon their falsehood, or to construct, with some of the manualists, an "entropological argument" for the existence of God. Reference, for example, to a recent symposium[1] on "The Age of the Universe" by six authorities in the field of cosmology will reveal how little agreement there is as yet on the question. The preceding discussion should serve to underline our previous conclusion that, interesting as they undoubtedly are in themselves, cosmological theories as such are of no ultimate theological importance. Whether matter is continually coming into existence or not, whether the world has an infinite past or had a first moment a finite number of years ago,

[1] *B.J.P.S.*, V, p. 181 f. (1954).

makes no difference to the question of the ground of the universe's existence. So far as I can see, almost any cosmological theory can be interpreted either religiously or atheistically, according to the general metaphysical position of the interpreter. Whether the universe had an infinite past or not, the theist will insist that its existence is due to an extra-temporal act freely exercised by a transcendent God. Whether he believes that matter came into existence with a "big bang" or is continually arriving by innumerable "little pops", the atheist will postulate the bang or the pops, as the case may be, as ultimates for which no transcendent cause is required. I believe, in fact, that there are very substantial arguments for theism, and I have tried to expound and discuss them elsewhere,[1] but they are metaphysical arguments, not physical ones. And it seems to me that both theists and atheists have allowed themselves to be far too much influenced by a lingering feeling that there is something peculiarly substantial, in the metaphysical sense, about physical matter. This leads the atheist to assume that matter can be taken as something ultimate and self-explanatory. But it also leads the theist to assume that the character of finite existence, upon which metaphysical arguments for the existence of God have traditionally been based, is to be identified with that measurable characteristic of physical matter which the physicist calls "mass". In consequence, if he has reason to suppose that mass is being conserved, he tends to interpret this as a direct indication of God's love and care for his creatures, while if he finds that mass is increasing, he tends to interpret this as a direct indication of the creative activity of God. This equation of physical mass with metaphysical substance seems to me to be simply a hang-over from the nineteenth century. Dr Herbert Dingle writes as follows:

The basic assumption of the scientists of 1851 was that there was lying before them a world of material objects, moving about in space and time. . . . It is important to realise the strength and the essentially metaphysical nature of this belief in the existence or reality or substantiality, or whatever you care to call it, of matter, because in these days of return to the strictly empirical basis of science, those more at home with the modern outlook (fortunately

---

[1] Cf. *He Who Is* and *Existence and Analogy*.

for my purpose now, they are not numerous) might not realise exactly what it meant. . . . Whewell expresses the matter very clearly.

There follows a passage from Whewell, in which the appearances and qualities of things are contrasted with the substances or substrata which lie behind the appearances and qualities. Dingle then continues:

> But "substance" is clearly metaphysical; only these inessential qualities are observed. How, then, are we to know from them that a substance exists in any particular case? Clearly there must be at least one specially accredited quality for this purpose, and Whewell found this in weight. . . . The weight of a body (or its inertia—Whewell was prepared to accept this as an alternative) was exempt from the liability to deceive that besmirched the honour of qualities in general. The senses might be misled in any other way, but when they apprehended the descent of a balance-pan they were infallible. . . This, of course, was not only Whewell's belief; it is implicit in the writings of almost any scientist of the time. . . . They looked out upon a real external substantial world of material bodies whose content was measured by its mass or weight.[1]

Mass was indeed not the only concept that the nineteenth-century scientist tended to reify; energy was another. I can vividly remember reading, as a boy of about sixteen, a battered and obsolete volume on the philosophy of science in which the author had stated the three fundamental laws of the universe as follows:

> Matter is indestructible, and is measured by mass.
> Energy is indestructible, and is measured by work.
> Intelligence is indestructible, and is measured by adaptability.

I do not think it ever occurred to me to wonder what were the units in which adaptability was measured, but I remember attempting, during the course of Morning Prayer at church on a festival, to reconcile science with religion by interpreting this statement as an up-to-date equivalent of the trinitarian formulas of the Athanasian Creed; I am glad to say that this, my first essay in the subject of the present lectures, failed dismally. However, to return to our point, the conservation of mass has, if

---

[1] "The Scientific Outlook in 1851 and in 1951", in *B.J.P.S.*, II, p. 86 f. (1951).

anything, gained in prestige as a result of the turmoils through which physics has passed in the last half-century; for it has survived a storm in which many idols were destroyed. Admittedly it has undergone a certain metamorphosis in the process. Mass and energy are considered to be mutually convertible, but with this convertibility the conservation-law persists even in relativity and quantum mechanics;[1] and its most startling manifestation is in the hydrogen-bomb. Only in the steady-state theories of the universe is the conservation of mass-energy repudiated, and it is significant that in order to describe this "formation of matter not out of radiation but out of nothing"[2] the steady-state theories pay homage to the idol which they destroy by borrowing from theology the august term "creation".

Now at the risk of appearing paradoxical I wish to suggest that the adornment of matter with a halo of substantiality in the metaphysical sense, even when the qualification is made that energy is a kind of matter or matter a kind of energy, is a superstition that ought to be abandoned. That we live in a universe composed of what St Thomas Aquinas would have called *beings* (*entia*), whose existence can be accounted for only by the free creative activity of a transcendent God, I should obstinately assert. But that these beings are to be identified *tout court* with the physical concepts to which scientists give the names "matter" and "energy", in such a way that their existential status can be measured in grams or ergs, seems to me to be highly questionable. It leads to the conclusion that a mere increase of mass, if it is unaccompanied by a corresponding decrease of energy, can (if one is a theist) be viewed only as a direct and immediate intervention of the primary causality of God's creative activity, or else (if one is not a theist) can be viewed only as a fundamental and inexplicable emergence of something from nothing, which is to be described, in however secularised a sense, by the word "creation". There is, in fact, felt to be something ultimate about uncompensated increases of energy or mass which is not felt about increases of other physical entities or concepts. The Second

---

[1] Cf. Eddington, *Nature of the Physical World*, pp. 236, 241; *New Pathways in Science*, pp. 108, 305; Born, *Natural Philosophy of Cause and Chance*, pp. 19, 119; Bondi, *Cosmology*, pp. 73, etc. There is a very interesting discussion in C. F. von Weizsäcker's *World View of Physics*, ch. iii.

[2] Bondi, op. cit., p. 144.

Law of Thermodynamics, as commonly understood, asserts that the entropy of the universe continually increases, but, however useful it may be for certain purposes to reify entropy and to speak, for example, of entropy-flux and so on, no one asks, "Where does this entropy which was not here before come from?" No theologian, however audacious, has argued that there must be a God to create all this new entropy. If the volume or the pressure of a gas increases, we do not speak of pressure or volume having been "created". Mass and energy after all are simply operationally defined quantities like any others; their conservation may be of considerable interest to physicists but it has no metaphysical significance. It would perhaps be well for us to remember Bridgman's point that "the existence of conservative functions is involved in the possibility of describing natural phenomena with differential equations";[1] when we solve a differential equation or a system of differential equations, there inevitably appear in the solutions so-called "constants of integration", which can be interpreted as corresponding to conservative properties and in many cases as the numerical magnitudes of conserved entities.[2] The degree of universality of the "law of conservation" will depend on the range of applicability of the original differential equations. It is thus extremely hazardous to assume that any conceptual entity which appears as the subject of a conservation-law has in consequence some kind of metaphysical substantiality; and this is as true of mass and energy as of anything else.

The conclusions which I find myself drawing at the close of this lecture will, I fear, seem to many to be disappointingly negative. When we get rid of the ambiguities with which the question has been frequently bedevilled there appears to be no particular relation between the concepts which in theology on the one hand and in science on the other are commonly denoted by the name "creation". But I do not think this should cause either the theologian or the ordinary Christian the least alarm. There are perfectly good reasons for holding that the world in which we live, and we ourselves who live in it, are the creatures of a trans-

[1] *The Logic of Modern Physics*, p. 113.
[2] Ibid., p. 111. Cf. H. Margenau: "Laws lead automatically to conservation principles; they are equivalent to conservation principles" (*Nature of Physical Reality*, p. 183).

cendent and free God; those reasons are metaphysical and not scientific, and have a permanence that no purely scientific argument could have. I can think of no greater disservice that could be done to the Christian religion than to tie it up with arguments based upon verbal confusions or with scientific views that are merely temporary. No doubt, for one who is a Christian theist, the picture of the world which is put before him by the scientists of a particular epoch may be inspiring and stimulating as providing impressions, even if only ephemeral impressions, of the world which God creates and conserves. The Christian may well rejoice in the fact that the heavens declare the glory of God and the firmament sheweth his handiwork, while adopting an attitude of extreme detachment towards arguments that attempt to prove the existence of God from the Second Law of Thermodynamics or the recession of the extra-galactic nebulae. So far as they are reliable, the findings of modern science tell us a great deal for which we should be grateful about the nature of the universe that God has made, but we shall be wise if we build our conviction that God has made it upon other foundations than those of modern science. In any case, for Christianity, creation, in the sense of the communication of existence to the world by God, is only the less important half of a story which culminates in the re-creation of the world in the mystery of the Word made flesh. The Christian message is that the Creator is also the Redeemer, that God has been pleased in the fullness of the times to sum up all things in Christ, the things in the heavens and the things upon the earth.[1] If the Creator is the Redeemer, the Redeemer is also the Creator; and it is God the Word, whom men have known in the flesh as Jesus of Nazareth, by whom the world was made, though the world knew him not.

[1] Eph. i. 10.

Chapter Five

MODERN PHYSICS AND INDETERMINACY

Laqueus contritus est et nos liberati sumus.—Psal.
cxxiv. 7.

I. OBJECTIVITY AND DETERMINISM

TOWARDS scientific theories, as towards other things,
familiarity tends to breed, if not contempt, at least a certain comfortable informality of attitude. They commonly
appear as far more sensational and revolutionary in their youth
than they appear in their domesticated maturity, when we have
had time to get used to them and they to us. Not least is this
true of the Theory of Relativity, which, when it burst upon a
startled public in the early decades of this century, seemed to have
achieved an all-time record for novelty and paradox. To the
production of this effect both its serious exponents and its less
responsible popularisers contributed. Minkowsky's oft-quoted
assertion that "henceforth space and time separately have vanished
into the merest shadows, and only a sort of combination of the
two preserves any reality" must have caused the spines of many
people to tingle, in spite of the fact that the world went on looking very much the same as before. And the discovery that "time
turns into space if you multiply it by the square root of minus
one", while it can have done little to enlighten the uninstructed,
did much to enhance the prestige of the scientist, to whom, it was
believed, such mysteries were as clear as the day.

As time has gone on, however, Relativity has lost a good deal
of its mystagogic aura. Dr Martin Johnson has warned us against
"finding philosophical profundity in geometrical convenience",
pointing out that "the fact that time becomes 'imaginary' in this
system has no metaphysical significance, and we recollect that
multiplication by $\sqrt{-1}$ in a physical diagram merely means a
turning of the picture from horizontal to vertical".[1] Such vivid

---

[1] *Time, Knowledge and the Nebulae,* p. 64; cf. L. De Broglie, *The Revolution
in Physics,* p. 89. An entertaining exploitation of the "mystagogic" attitude can
be found in the popular writing of Eddington and Jeans.

phrases as "curvature of space-time" and "absolute elsewhere", however picturesque and stimulating to the imagination, lose much of their occult eeriness when they are replaced by the austere equations from which they have been derived. Even the famous limerick about the misadventure of the young lady named Bright loses some of its sparkle when it is realised that the velocity of light is a limiting velocity which no material body can in fact attain. And, although in relativity theory measurements of time and distance vary from one observer to another, there is no reversal of causal order; "The limit to the velocity of signals", writes Eddington, "is our bulwark against that topsy-turvydom of past and future, of which Einstein's theory is sometimes wrongfully accused."[1] Event A cannot precede event B when observed by one percipient and follow it when observed by another. Furthermore, the objectivity of the physical world and its independence of the fact that we are observing it are preserved. Prince Louis De Broglie, after referring to the so-called "unification" of space and time in relativity theory, goes on to say: "Despite this essential modification of the concepts of space and time, the relativist is in accord with his predecessors in asserting that each observer can represent the totality of physical phenomena in a framework of space and of time which is well defined and completely independent of the nature of the entities which enter into it. . . . Moreover", he continues, "for the relativist, as for the physicist of the preceding epoch, the entire evolution of the phenomena is governed by an inexorable play of differential equations which determine the entire future. . . . By his affirmation of the possibility for each observer to localise events exactly in space-time, by the spatialisation of duration, and the negation of all becoming, that the very conception of space-time implies, the theory of relativity, while pushing them to their extreme consequences, retains the guiding ideas of the old physics. Thus", De Broglie concludes, in a way which would have been most deflating to the earlier relativists, "it can be said that, despite the so-new and almost revolutionary character of the Einsteinian

---

[1] *The Nature of the Physical World*, p. 57. Bridgman writes: "It appears then, that the fundamental postulate of relativity (that the form of natural laws is the same in all reference systems) demands that the temporal order of events causally connected be the same in all reference systems" (*Logic of Modern Physics*, p. 87).

conceptions, the theory of relativity is in some ways the culmination of classical physics."[1]

This passage perhaps betrays a tendency on the part of De Broglie to take rather too literally the conceptual machinery of relativity physics—to forget, in fact, that a model is only a model—but this only makes the more striking his assertion of the fundamental homogeneity of relativity and classical physics. Whether we consider the picture of world-lines extended through space-time as anything more than a vivid expository device or not, the fact remains that the world of Einstein is every bit as deterministic as that of Laplace. Most competent judges would agree that the heroic attempt of Whitehead, in his formidable work *Process and Reality*, to interpret the world of relativity in terms of a fundamental spontaneity, avoids determinism only at the cost of unintelligibility and incoherence, when all is said and done. The quantum theory, however, as De Broglie emphasises, is far more radically revolutionary. There are various ways of stating its essential character and of giving it mathematical formulation; and it is not immediately obvious that they are all equivalent. Our task is made more difficult than in the case of relativity, and is at the same time made safer, by the fact that the quantum conceptions do not nearly so easily lend themselves to expression in pictorial or quasi-pictorial form. We may state them in terms of Bohr's "principle of complementarity", according to which the full description of any phenomenon requires the successive use of concepts which are in a sense irreconcilable, since they can never be simultaneously applicable *in toto*; an example of such a pair of concepts is provided by the notions of "wave" and "particle", applied to either radiation or matter. Alternatively we may postulate Heisenberg's famous "uncertainty-principle", which asserts a linkage between the kinematic and the dynamical characteristics of a material system, in such a way that it is impossible to determine with complete precision both the position and the momentum of a particle, since the determination of either quantity changes the other one by an unspecifiable amount. Or again we may say that the fundamental laws of physics are purely statistical; that is, that as applying to individual micro-

---

[1] *The Revolution in Physics*, p. 100.

scopic[1] events they state merely the probability of these events occurring, and that the apparent regularity that is observed in the macroscopic realm is merely due to the smoothing-out that always happens when we take averages over a very large number of individuals. Furthermore, we may note, although this is not immediately relevant to our present interest, that there are several ways of formalising the quantum concepts mathematically. Schrödinger's wave-mechanics, Heisenberg's matrix-mechanics and Dirac's non-commutative algebra, though they are now recognised as formally equivalent, appeared in the early twenties very much in the guise of competitors. As Dr Henry Margenau has written:

> With the discoveries of Heisenberg and Schrödinger there were available two tools, matrix mechanics and wave mechanics, which performed in different ways the same function and achieved the same ends. This curious duplicity, which stood in violation of basic metaphysical principles, disappeared in a remarkable flash of illumination which allowed the whole new territory to be seen at once. For it was discovered that the matrix and the wave calculus were *isomorphic*, were two different forms of the same fundamental set of constructs, and the discovery of this equivalence exposed that basic structure to view. Isomorphic calculi are not uncommon in mathematics.[2]

When all due care has been taken to avoid the conceptual idolatry which so often dogs the physicist, and which consists in identifying his conceptual models of physical events with the events themselves, we may say that the quantum theory raises two important questions for the philosopher and the theologian; the first is concerned with the objectivity of the physical world, the second with the determination of physical events. I shall discuss them in order.

First, then, the question of the objectivity of the physical world. The notion that the world of our experience derives all

---

[1] The word "microscopic" in this context denotes something that may be very much smaller than the objects which we commonly observe under a microscope.

[2] *Nature of Physical Reality*, p. 330. This is the reverse of the situation referred to on p. 22 above. Here we are concerned with one physical fact-complex having several models; there we were concerned with one model for several physical fact-complexes.

or many of its observable characteristics from the process of perception is by no means a new one. As far back as Galileo the distinction was drawn between the primary qualities, which a body is alleged to have even when it is not being perceived, and the secondary qualities, which we attribute to it as a result of perceiving it. The astounding success of Newtonian physics was largely due to the convenient way in which the primary qualities, such as extension, location and mass, lent themselves to mathematical formulation and treatment; and the physicist continued to attribute objective reality to the world of space, time and matter long after the philosopher, under the guidance of Berkeley and Hume, had decided that all qualities were really secondary ones. The subjectivising of the world of our experience reached its climax with Kant, who was under the extraordinary delusion that he was providing Newtonian physics with its appropriate metaphysic. The previous subjectivisms were, on the whole, limited in their depth, even when they were not limited in their scope. Even when they asserted that all qualities were secondary ones, they tended to assume that the subjective character of the qualities arose from the physiological and psychological mechanism of perception. For Kant, however, the subjectivism was epistemological, in the narrowest sense of the term; it was not through perceiving them by our peculiar physiological and psychological make-up that we endowed the objects of our perception with their characteristics, but through the mere fact of knowing them at all. As Kant's critics pointed out, for a consistent Kantianism the thing in itself, the *Ding-an-sich*, would be not merely unsensable but unknowable; even the statements that Kant makes about it really involve an abandonment of his own doctrine. In any case, whatever the philosophers might say, scientists have almost always been healthy realists, and have gone about their work in the confidence that they were investigating and not merely constructing a world; and, as De Broglie says in the passage which I have already quoted, this was as true of relativity as of classical physicists. If he is right, however, it is not true of the quantum physicists. Commenting on Heisenberg's uncertainty principle he writes: "It is in no way evident that an operation of measurement purely and simply makes the pre-existent state known to us: it might very well be that the operation of measurement results in the creation of a new state by extracting from the pre-existent state one of the possibilities contained in it. And now", he concludes, "we must try to formulate precisely the role of measurement as it is conceived in this new light."[1]

Whittaker has given an amusing illustration of this notion. "Suppose", he writes,

> that a child with a penny comes to an automatic machine which supplies chocolate when the penny is put in one slot, and sweets when the penny is put in the other slot. Since he has only one penny, he can get either chocolate or sweets, but not both; from the fact that he can get either at will, is he justified in concluding that they are both present in the machine? Not necessarily; for it is possible to imagine that there is a kind of paste in the machine which is converted into chocolate by his inserting the penny into one slot, and into sweets by his inserting the penny into the other. If this latter explanation is correct, then it is possible to imagine the machine fitted with a number of other slots, such that by inserting the penny into any one of them a confection is obtained which is intermediate in some proportion between chocolate and sweets. This is analogous to the situation which exists in atomic physics. If we consider one of the elementary entities—electrons, protons, and so forth—which are the ultimate constituents of nature, we can have an accurate knowledge of its position combined with complete ignorance as to its momentum, or we can have an accurate knowledge of its momentum, combined with complete ignorance as to its position, or we can have a simultaneous partial knowledge of both, but there is no justification for assuming that the entity is a particle in the old sense, possessing simultaneously an exact position and an exact momentum. We have no right to postulate the existence of entities which lie beyond the knowledge actually obtainable by observation, and which have no part in the prediction of future events. Thus the classical concept of a particle must be discarded: in its stead there has been introduced a new fundamental element in the description of the external world, which is called a *state*.[2]

This ingenious analogy would, I think, be taken as substantially accurate by most quantum physicists. What, however, does it in fact imply about the reality of the physical world?

The answer to this question will depend very largely upon the precise analogical character which we ascribe to the paste in

[1] *The Revolution in Physics*, p. 200.   [2] *From Euclid to Eddington*, p. 145.

Whittaker's parable. On a literal interpretation, the paste has just the same kind and degree of reality as the chocolate or sweets which are made out of it; the process of decoction which is initiated by placing the coin in the appropriate slot merely brings about certain chemical changes in the uncooked material. If we removed the front from the machine we could presumably find the paste there in a container, and the paste would be apprehended by our senses in the same way as the finished product. I do not think, however, that Whittaker or any other quantum physicist would have understood the parable in precisely this way. It is of the essence of the quantum theory that only the finished product can be apprehended, whether as chocolate or sweets or in one of the intermediate forms. The status of the paste thus becomes somewhat ambiguous. A physicist with a hearty realistic outlook may assert that the paste is as real as the chocolate or the sweets; that is to say, translating the parable into terms of physics, that there is a world existing independently of our experience and composed of material which is fundamentally like the objects of our senses, though in some mysterious way less determinate in its details. On the other hand, a physicist who is more of an idealist (in the philosophical sense of that somewhat protean word) may say that the only realities are realities which we perceive, and that the paste is a purely conceptual and theoretical entity which it is useful to hypothecate in order to give concreteness to our thought; that it is in fact something like the packet of notes with my name on it which I tend to imagine when I think of my bank balance, because it provides a more concrete image than the entries in the relevant account-books in the Bank. I suspect that in practice most physicists, not being philosophers, go as far as they can along the former of these two ways, and only console themselves with idealist reflections when the realist picture breaks down. For there are points at which it does break down, and at which it seems to break down irreparably. This is the reason for De Broglie's assertion that quantum theory is far more revolutionary than relativity theory. Much of the attractiveness of relativity theory to the general public has been due to the fact that, although it requires the acceptance of such novel notions as time being space multiplied by the square root of minus one, and gravitational fields being puckers in a four-dimensional continuum, once these notions have been accepted the familiar concepts of extension, continuity and causal ordering remain; relativity in fact possesses the same kind of charm as a well-written ghost-story, in which the unfamiliar and eerie is combined with the commonplace and cosy. The fundamental concepts of quantum theory, on the other hand, seem to lend themselves to no such marriage of the *outré* and the domestic, although Einstein consistently rejected the doctrine of a fundamental indeterminism in the universe and has been recently joined somewhat hesitantly by Louis De Broglie. Where the views of the experts are so diverse and the subject itself is so obscure, it may seem the height of rashness for the outsider to intervene. Nevertheless there are, I think, some things that can usefully be said.

The simple physical realism which I have described as the view that the paste has the same kind of reality as the chocolate or the sweets does seem to me to be quite unacceptable if one takes the quantum theory seriously. A real universe which has the characteristics involved in such generalisations as Bohr's principle of complementarity or Heisenberg's uncertainty-principle cannot simply replicate the characteristics of the sensible world. But to say this does not involve us in the view that the world of the quantum theorist, with its inherent discontinuity and indeterminacy, is nothing more than a useful conceptual model or map in the sense of Braithwaite or Toulmin. That the *theories* of the physicist are models or maps I should be ready to admit, but I would not conclude from this that what they are models or maps of is simply the sensible characteristics of our experience; I should wish to add that they are models or maps of a real intelligible world which we, as intelligent beings, perceive through the medium of our sensations. I must recall here the point which I made in my second lecture, that intelligibility has a wider range than sensibility, and that the essence of perception consists not in sensing objects but in intellectually apprehending them, even if we can only apprehend them through the mediation of the senses. The paradigm of a real world, I argued, is not its sensible imaginability but its intellectual apprehensibility. The world does not lose its claim to reality by ceasing to be imaginable as an infinite Euclidean receptacle, populated by tiny passive lumps drifting uniformly down the stream of time, and only recover that claim by becoming imaginable as a four-dimensional non-Euclidean space-time continuum, in which what used to be thought of as material objects are now seen to be wrinkles or puckers. Nor, we may now add, does the world lose its claim to reality by ceasing to be a world in which position and momentum can be simultaneously specified, or by becoming one in which the ultimate laws of physics are statistical or probability laws. The only difference between these two cases is that quantum theory has not been as successful as relativity theory in producing a technique for recovering the world's sensory imaginability. Whether it will succeed in doing this later on is irrelevant to our present point. That point is that, although the physicist knows the objective world only through the mediation of sensation, the essential character of the objective world is not sensibility but intelligibility. Its objectivity is not manifested by different observers having the same sensory experiences of it, but by their being able, through their diverse sensory experiences, to acquire a common *understanding* of it. If some such account as this is accepted, there is no need for us to feel that, with its principles of complementarity and indeterminacy and with its view of physical laws as purely statistical, the quantum theory has cut away the ground of reality from under our feet and left us falling through a bottomless abyss of subjectivism.[1] What it has done, supposing its assertions to be sound, is to show what *kind* of intelligible nature that part of the intelligible universe which is the concern of physical science possesses. And if the quantum theory is correct as we now understand it, one of the consequences seems to be that the intelligible universe is not structurally isomorphic with our sensory continua or with any complex made from them, although rules can be specified by which the characteristics of our sensory continua can be derived from it.

I have quoted above De Broglie's remark that it may well be that the operation of measurement does not simply make known to us a pre-existent state of the object but creates a new state by actualising what was previously a mere possibility. It may be

---

[1] At this point I feel bound to depart from the modified Kantianism of C. F. von Weizsäcker's *World View of Physics*, a book for which in general I have great admiration.

well, therefore, to emphasise that, if this suggestion is correct, it does not provide any support for a subjectivist epistemology of the Kantian type, as some writers have claimed. In Kantianism, it is the act of apprehending the world that is held to impress upon it its perceptible characteristics, not the act of measuring it. This has been very lucidly expressed by Dr Hans Reichenbach in his *Philosophic Foundations of Quantum Mechanics*. "Some philosophers", he writes,

> and some physicists as well [have seen] . . . in Heisenberg's principle a statement that the subject cannot be strictly separated from the external world and that the line of demarcation between subject and object can only be arbitrarily set up; or that the subject creates the object in the act of perception; or that the object seen is only a thing of appearance, whereas the thing in itself forever escapes human knowledge; or that the things of nature must be transformed according to certain conditions before they can enter into human consciousness, etc. We cannot admit that any version of such a philosophical mysticism has a basis in quantum mechanics. . . . The disturbance by the means of observation . . . is an entirely physical affair which does not include any reference to effects emanating from human beings as observers.
>
> This is made clear by the following consideration. We can replace the observing person by physical devices, such as photoelectric cells, etc., which register the observations and present them as data written on a strip of paper. The act of observation then consists in reading the numbers and signs written on the paper. Since the interaction between the reading eye and the paper is a macroscopic occurrence, the disturbance by the observation can be neglected for this process. It follows that all that can be said about the disturbance by the means of observation must be inferable from the linguistic expressions on the paper strip, and must therefore be statable in terms of physical devices and their inter-relations.[1]

And, as Reichenbach goes on to point out,

---

[1] Op. cit., p. 15. This point seems to have been overlooked by Henry Margenau when he writes about the uncertainty principle as follows: "According to this principle, the act of observation has an important effect upon the observed; indeed the act of *knowing* has an important effect upon the *known*" (*Nature of Physical Reality*, p. 38, italics mine). Similarly Herbert Dingle writes: "The whole of the physical world is unknowable because the act of *knowing* necessarily changes it in an unknowable way" (*The Scientific Adventure*, p. 242, italics mine).

the disturbance by the observation, in itself, does not lead to the indeterminacy of the observation. It does so only in combination with the principle of indeterminacy.[1]

Reichenbach's own position is a professedly positivistic one, and on the basis of it he discusses his subject in logical and linguistic terms. The realist conclusion of his book is thus all the more striking. "The relation of indeterminacy", he says, "is a fundamental physical law; it holds for all possible physical situations and therefore involves a disturbance of the object by the measurement."[2] He devises three languages for the description of the physical world and shows that they all contain deficiencies. For a description of them the reader must be referred to Reichenbach's book; it will be sufficient here to note that both the "wave-language" and the "corpuscle-language" involve causal anomalies, while what he calls the "neutral language" avoids causal anomalies only by the adoption of a three-valued logic, in which truth and falsehood need to be supplemented by a third truth-value of indeterminacy. And here is Reichenbach's conclusion:

> The stated deficiencies are not due to an inappropriate choice of these languages; on the contrary, these three languages represent optima with respect to the class of all possible languages of quantum mechanics. The deficiencies must rather be regarded as the linguistic expression of the structure of the atomic world, which thus is recognised as intrinsically different from the macro-world, and likewise from the atomic world which classical physics had imagined.[3]

I should like to make it plain at this point that, although the view of perception upon which my own discussion has been based seems to me to be in essence, though not in every detail, that of St Thomas Aquinas, I do not want to claim for it any more authority than that to which its own qualities entitle it. In particular I wish to avoid any suggestion that the truth of Christian theism is tied up with the truth of St Thomas's doctrine of perception, and still more that it is tied up with the truth of my own. My own conviction is that some such doctrine of perception is true, and that it is thoroughly coherent both with the outlook of modern science and with the outlook of Christian theism; more-

---

[1] *Philosophic Foundations of Quantum Mechanics*, p. 17.   [2] Ibid., p. 176.
[3] Ibid., p. 177.

over I find it very difficult to conceive that Christian theism could be compatible with any doctrine of perception that differed notably from it. Nevertheless I would rather that a man who rejected my views on perception as unspeakably ridiculous continued to believe in Christian theism than that he abandoned Christian theism as incompatible with any other doctrine of perception. It is, in fact, both disquieting and salutary to reflect on the doctrines that Christians have sometimes believed to be compatible with, and even necessary to, Christian theism. Roman Catholic scholars have sometimes commented with emphasis upon the theological inadequacy of a Church which could both beget and commend the philosophy of a Berkeley; but, in view of the philippics—and, as I believe, the quite justified philippics —directed against Cartesianism by Catholic writers such as Gilson and Maritain, it is interesting to remember that Roman Catholic theology and philosophy was for two centuries and more inspired by the tremendous figures of Descartes and the ultra-Cartesian Père Malebranche. So difficult is it to avoid bewitchment by the spirit of the age!

This much, then, for the bearings, such as they are, of the quantum theory upon the objectivity of the physical world. I shall now turn to the other question, that of the determination of events; this will need to be treated at greater length.

Nineteenth-century physics was overshadowed by the grim and unrelenting figure of the Laplacean demon or calculator, a kind of mythological personification of the determinism of Newtonian mechanics, a super-mathematician who from the configuration of the universe at any one moment could calculate its history in every detail from eternity to eternity. "An intelligent being", wrote Laplace in the year 1812,

> who at a given instant knew all the forces animating Nature and the relative positions of the beings within it would, if his intelligence were sufficiently capacious to analyse these data, include in a single formula the movements of the largest bodies of the universe and those of its lightest atom. Nothing would be uncertain for him: the future as well as the past would be present to his eyes.[1]

There are two remarks upon this statement which are, I think,

[1] *Oeuvres Complètes* (1886), VII, p. vi; cit. E. W. Barnes, *Scientific Theory and Religion*, p. 578.

worth making, though they do not substantially affect the point at issue. The first is that, in order to trace in detail the course of development of the material universe, the calculator would need to know not only the initial configuration of the bodies of which it was composed, but also the value from moment to moment of the forces acting upon them. Laplace himself would not have felt troubled by this objection, as in his view of the universe all the forces to which any body was subject would be mechanical or gravitational forces, arising from the action of other bodies upon it, and would therefore be calculable from the configuration. If, however, forces were impressed upon the bodies by some external agency whose scheme was unknown to the calculator, his power to foretell the future would be gone. A Laplacean demon who could only calculate would be powerless against a demon—or a god—who could plan.

The second remark is concerned with the fact that the initial data with which the calculator must be furnished in order to perform his task comprise not only the positions but also the velocities of the individual particles or bodies. (Strictly speaking, we should say "momenta" rather than "velocities", but the difference is irrelevant in cases when the mass is conserved.) This arises directly from the fact that the Newtonian laws of motion state how the rate at which the velocities change depends upon the impressed forces, but say nothing about the values of the velocities themselves. Now, although we are accustomed to speak of the velocity of a body *at a particular instant,* the determination of this quantity requires that we shall know the position of the body throughout an interval containing the instant and not merely at the instant itself. If we confine our attention simply to the instant, it will be impossible to discern whether the body is in motion or at rest. It is true that the interval may be as small as we please, but there must be an interval of some extent or other. The notion of "velocity at an instant" is in fact an example of a *limit,* in the mathematical sense of the word; it can be made intelligible only by first defining the concept "average velocity during an interval containing the instant" and then applying to the latter concept the technique by which a mathematical limit is defined.[1] The upshot

---

[1] If the co-ordinates of position at instants t_0 and t are denoted by x_0 and x, then "the average velocity during the interval from t_0 to t" is defined as the

is that it is not enough for the calculator to know the configuration of the universe at the initial instant; he must know its configuration at all the instants of some subsequent interval as well, although this interval can be as short as he likes. And the configuration during this interval will be entirely unpredictable from the configuration at the initial instant, save only for the fact that the shorter the interval is, the more nearly will the configuration during it approximate to the configuration at the initial instant. So far as this consideration has any importance, it is that even in a Laplacean universe some extraneous activity seems to be demanded other than the mere activity of positing its material content, though this additional activity can be limited to an arbitrarily small stretch of time. In any case the fact remains that, for the typical post-Newtonian scientist, whatever might have happened when the universe first came into existence, its subsequent course of development could be completely deduced, from the initial positions and velocities of the individual massive particles, by the application of the Newtonian laws of motion and gravitation and any similar laws that it might be necessary to formulate in order to include subsequently discovered phenomena such as those of electricity and magnetism. For him, as for Fitz-Gerald's Omar Khayyám,

> the first Morning of Creation wrote
> What the Last Dawn of Reckoning shall read.

The only assumptions that needed to be made were that no fresh matter would be created and that the laws would invariably hold.

This last assumption was, of course, not logically necessary, and it provided a loophole by which the theistically-minded scientist could make room for the intervention of God in the world's history. I have previously quoted the great mathematical physicist Sir George Gabriel Stokes to this effect. "Admit the existence of a God, of a personal God," he wrote in his Gifford Lectures in 1891, "and the possibility of a miracle follows at once. If the laws of nature are carried on in accordance with his will, he

---

quotient of $x_0 - x$ by $t_0 - t$. If there is a quantity v_0 which is such that the difference between this quotient and v_0 can be made less than any assigned quantity by taking t sufficiently nearly equal to t_0, then "the velocity at t_0" is defined as being equal to v_0. The notion of an interval, and indeed of an infinite set of intervals, is essential to the definition.

who willed them may will their suspension. And if any difficulty should be felt as to their suspension, we are not even obliged to suppose that they have been suspended; it may be that the event which we call a miracle was brought about, not by any suspension of the laws in ordinary operation, but by the superaddition of something not ordinarily in operation, or if in operation, of such a nature that its operation is not perceived."[1] The logician may find it difficult to distinguish between the suspension of a law of nature and the superaddition of something not ordinarily in operation; but for the mathematician it will presumably correspond to the difference between the removal of a term from an equation of motion and the addition of a new term to those already there. In any case, the distinction is of little importance. The essential point remains that, for the nineteenth-century physicist, any activity of God which was not just the necessary working out of the constitution with which he had originally endowed the world could only be conceived as some sort of interference from outside. There was no room *within* the equations of physics for spontaneous activity, whether creaturely or divine; that could only be expressed by altering them. The initial conditions plus the physical laws were logically sufficient to determine the state of the universe at any subsequent time.

2. DETERMINISM IN CLASSICAL AND QUANTUM PHYSICS

Before we go on to consider how this conception of the physical world has been altered by quantum physics, it may be interesting to notice one or two caveats that have been entered in recent years against the conclusion that even classical physics necessarily entails a deterministic view of the world.

In a long article published in *The British Journal for the Philosophy of Science* in 1950,[2] Dr K. R. Popper has argued that, quite apart from the indeterminism which is peculiar to quantum physics, there is a fundamental type of indeterminism which obtains in classical physics as well. Popper begins by considering the Laplacean "demon" or "calculator" but, in order to avoid such psychological irrelevances as the difficulty of supposing that

---

[1] *Natural Theology*, p. 24; quoted on p. 7 supra.
[2] *B.J.P.S.*, I, pp. 117 f., 173 f.

any intelligence, even if "superhuman", can attain infinitely precise and complete knowledge, he replaces Laplace's disembodied spirit by a "predictor" or physical predicting machine, which, just because it is physical, is itself a member of the physical world which it is used to predict. As he is discussing classical mechanics, he assumes that the machine is itself subject to classical mechanical laws. Now the essential point which Popper makes is that, before it can start to perform its calculations, the predictor must provide itself with information about the positions, velocities and masses of the physical particles within a certain finite spatial region or "environment"; it can do this by making explorations with tentacles, measuring-rods and the like. However, in general this process of probing will alter the state both of the predictor and of its environment, and unless the whole process of prediction is to be overthrown two conditions must be fulfilled. The first is the obvious one that the predictor must only interfere very weakly with its environment. The second is that the environment must interfere fairly strongly with the predictor; the reason for this is that minute differences in the environment at time t_0 may give rise to considerable differences at a later time t_1 and that, in consequence, if the predictor is to predict the later state with any accuracy, it must be highly sensitive to differences in the earlier one. Now Popper's conclusion, after a long and elaborate argument, is that, while a predictor is theoretically constructible for the performance of any specified prediction task, nevertheless, if we construct it for the task of predicting, to some assigned degree of accuracy, the state of its environment (including itself) at any specified future time, it will only be able to produce the answer after the arrival of the time in question. We set the machine on Monday to calculate what the state of affairs will be on Tuesday, and it triumphantly produces the right answer on Thursday evening! There is nothing wrong with the "prediction", except that it turns out to be not a prediction but a historical statement. Even if we exclude the predictor's own state from what is to be predicted, the same conclusion is alleged to hold, so long as we include the predictor's nearer environment. There is an inherent delay, which cannot be overcome, and it arises from the interaction between the predictor and its environment, in the derivation from the environment of information about the environment. In order to be sufficiently accurate the record must be so complicated that its implications can never be worked out fast enough; no technical improvement can remove this disability, since among the factors of which the calculator has to take account are the results of its own preceding calculations. Thus, if Popper's argument is correct—and it does not seem to have been successfully questioned—although the future states of the world of classical physics are a logical consequence of its past state plus the laws of Newtonian mechanics, it is inherently impossible to devise a machine by which a future state could be even approximately calculated before it had in fact occurred. A vital state in the argument is the assertion that none of the members of a society of predictors can predict the future states of another or of the society as a whole; for if X discovers Y and tries to predict its future, Y will be unable to predict X, since X's future behaviour will become dependent upon the future behaviour of Y, which Y cannot predict. A one-way membrane cannot work both ways.

What then are Popper's final conclusions? First, that "even if any prediction task given is capable of being carried out by some predictor, there will be no predictor capable of carrying out every task, since no predictor can fully predict its own closer environment". And, secondly, that "classical mechanics is not deterministic, but must admit the existence of unpredictable events".[1] "If this is correct", he says,

> then Laplace's determinism, and that of others who were influenced by the *prima facie* deterministic character of classical mechanics, is based upon a misinterpretation. I suggest that this misinterpretation is due to the tendency of attributing to Science (with a capital S) a kind of omniscience; and that this theological view of science ought to be replaced by a more humanistic view, by the realisation that science is the work of ordinary humans, groping their way in the dark. In doing so, we may sometimes find something interesting; we may be astonishingly successful; but we shall never get anything like "the whole truth".[2]

Popper's discussion is of great interest, but I doubt whether it really meets the demands of belief in either human freedom or

---

[1] Art. cit., p. 193.   [2] Ibid.

divine intervention. What his argument seems to amount to is simply that, given the Newtonian physics as a complete specification of the behaviour of the universe, the future is completely determined, although we cannot, even in principle, predict it. A positivist might maintain that the distinction just made is meaningless, that determination and predictability are simply synonyms; nevertheless it is, I think, obvious that, if Newtonian physics has the last word, the future is logically entailed by the past, and freedom is an illusion even if the future is unpredictable. In fact, there appear to be certain loopholes even in Popper's own account. He admits that if an observer could make his observations without disturbing the objects of his observation and without himself being observed, he could fulfil the requirements of a Laplacean demon. Popper even suggests a physical example of this possibility. If the system under observation is a purely mechanical one, and if the demon makes his observations by optical means or by radar (in which case the disturbance of the system by the process of observation can be made negligibly small), and if he himself contains no moving parts, he can make his observation without being himself observed, there is no interaction between him and the system, and the task of prediction is in principle possible. The demon can predict what goes on in the system, because he himself stands outside it; if, however, we demand that physics shall include electro-magnetic as well as mechanical phenomena, then the demon becomes part of the system and prediction becomes impossible. In Popper's words, "there are miracles in a purely mechanical world, as it were—electro-magnetic miracles".[1] Furthermore, although Popper does not make this point, even in a physical world which included electro-magnetic as well as mechanical processes, prediction would presumably be possible for a demon who was a pure spirit; who, consequently, could observe without causing even electro-magnetic disturbances, and who could observe without being observed even electro-magnetically. And this, I think, makes it clear that to prove, as Popper claims to prove, that the universe is not physically predictable is not to prove that it is fundamentally undeterministic. It should be added that Popper goes out of his way to insist that he does not believe that human

[1] Art. cit., p. 131.

beings or human brains are only a kind of calculating machine. In so far as man *is* a predictor, Popper maintains that his results are applicable to man and the human society. But he adds that man, while he is a predictor, is something more. "In so far as we are calculators, we are miserably bad ones ... and we construct electronic brains because we have no such brains ourselves. Thus we are not calculators. But we are constructors of calculators. ... Our fundamental intellectual impulse is that of searching for difficulties; it is even one of inventing difficulties, in order to overcome them."[1]

The upshot of his discussion is described by Popper as the restitution of the naïve or commonsense view of the world, the view that there are some events which can be predicted and some which cannot. But he adds that his considerations even suggest something like a reconciliation between this view and the other— "the 'more sophisticated' view that it is as a rule only lack of knowledge which makes us believe that events are unpredictable". "This reconciliation", he concludes, "can be brought about if we realise that it is the existence of knowledge in the physical world which creates the kind of indeterminism we have been discussing."[2] But all that this comes to, as far as I can see, is the assertion of a kind of indeterminism which leaves no room for either free will or divine intervention, and it is indeed obvious that this is the only kind of indeterminism that there can be in a world which is wholly specifiable by the laws of Newtonian physics. As Stokes pointed out in the passage already quoted,[3] even a Newtonian universe cannot escape from its Creator, but he can only intervene by overruling his own laws; there is no place for his intervention *within* them.

A very different approach from that of Popper is found in the lectures given in 1943 by the father of wave-mechanics, Professor Erwin Schrödinger, and published under the title *What is Life? The Physical Aspect of the Living Cell.* Schrödinger begins by insisting that, even in classical physics, the fundamental laws describing the behaviour of individual atoms or molecules ought to be taken as purely statistical; that is to say, not as specifying precisely how any individual atom or molecule will behave under given conditions, but only as specifying the probability that it

[1] Art. cit., p. 194.   [2] Ibid., p. 195.   [3] Cf. p. 181 supra.

will behave in any particular way. Physicists have, of course, known for a long time that the regularity of behaviour of bodies of visible and tangible dimensions can be explained as due to the averaging out of the individual random idiosyncrasies of the immense number of individual atoms and molecules of which they are composed, in the same way in which it is possible to forecast with considerable accuracy how many people will be killed on the roads of England in the course of the year without knowing anything at all about the fate of any specified person. The classical statistical mechanics, however, always assumed that our inability to describe the behaviour of any individual entity was due merely to our human limitations. There were simply too many of these entities for us to know their individual positions and velocities and the forces acting upon each of them, and if we did know these facts life would be too short for us to work out their motions; the number of molecules in a cubic centimetre of a gas under normal conditions of temperature and pressure is something like twenty-seven million million million. It was never doubted that each of these molecules was in fact governed by the same laws as had been found to hold in the case of tangible bodies. Indeed, somewhat paradoxically, it came to be assumed that it was to these microscopic[1] entities that the laws of mechanics primarily applied; the individual molecule seemed to be a closer approximation to the massive point-particle about which Newton's second law of motion spoke than was a lump of sulphur in the laboratory. Thus, although the laws had been verified, directly or indirectly, for bodies which the physicist could handle and had only by a process of extrapolation been extended to the world of microscopic entities, whose very existence was largely inferential and even conjectural, the classical statistical physics came to view the microscopic entities as the objects to which the laws immediately applied and then extended the laws to the tangible world by considering tangible objects as assemblages of vast numbers of the microscopic entities and applying the techniques of statistical averaging. Now Schrödinger does not deny the existence of microscopic entities, the individual atoms and molecules; but he does deny, at least by implication, that they are the objects to

[1] I am again using the word "microscopic" to mean something very much smaller than the objects which we commonly observe through a microscope.

which physical laws primarily apply. The laws of physics have been established by observations of large-scale objects, and large-scale objects are therefore what they are about.[1] However, since large-scale objects are now known to be assemblages of microscopic entities, the conclusion is drawn that the laws of physics are essentially statistical; they do not describe the determinate behaviour of large-scale individuals, but the statistically averaged behaviour of aggregates consisting of enormous numbers of randomly moving microscopic entities. The appearance of determinism in the large-scale world is due simply to the smoothing-out effect of the averaging process; as regards the individual atoms or molecules, the most we could do, even in principle, would be to state the probability that any one of them was behaving in any particular way.

Schrödinger illustrates his point by taking three examples, picked, as he says, "somewhat at random out of thousands". The first is the phenomenon of paramagnetism in gases. The molecules of a gas are tiny magnets, but under ordinary conditions no magnetic effects are detectable, since the heat-motion of the molecules produces a random orientation in which at any moment as many molecules are pointing in one direction as in any other. When, however, a magnetic field is applied to the gas, although the molecules continue to move in a chaotic manner, there is at any moment a slight preponderance of acute angles over obtuse angles between the magnetic axes of the molecules and the field; the consequence is that the gas now behaves like a weak magnet. There is, at it were, a balance between the randomising tendency of the heat motion and the aligning tendency of the superimposed magnetic field; if the heat-motion is lessened by lowering the temperature, or if the aligning tendency is increased by strengthening the field, the induced magnetisation will increase. This is a purely statistical phenomenon, in which all that can be stated is the proportion of molecules that are orientated towards the field rather than against it. Nothing whatever can be said about the orientation of any individual molecule; although all the molecules are precisely alike and are under the influence of a uniform field, any one of them may at any moment be pointing in any direction whatever.

[1] Cf. A. D. Ritchie, *Reflections on the Philosophy of Sir Arthur Eddington*, p. 24.

Schrödinger's second example is that of the so-called Brownian movement. If a fog of minute droplets is introduced into a vessel containing air and the movements of the individual droplets are observed by means of a microscope, they are seen not to fall steadily to the bottom of the vessel but to perform a very irregular motion indeed. Although there is on the average a definite and predictable rate of sinking, at any moment an individual droplet may be moving upwards or sideways; it follows a zig-zag course and its motion is incessantly changing by fits and starts. The physicist's explanation of this is that, although the droplets are not single molecules, they are small enough and light enough to be affected by the impacts of individual molecules of the air. The motion of any droplet is thus quite incalculable, although the motion of the fog as a whole can be calculated.

Schrödinger remarks in passing that there exist bacteria and other organisms which are so small that they are affected by the Brownian phenomena; they are tossed to and fro by the heat-motion of the surrounding medium. Dr J. W. N. Sullivan has suggested that, if our universe was peopled by intelligent bacteria, they would have no need of the second law of thermo-dynamics,[1] for that law is, from the standpoint of statistical mechanics, the result of averaging the behaviour of a tremendous number of individual randomly moving particles. Such organisms would provide living embodiments of Clerk Maxwell's demons, the mythical characters (not to be confused with Laplace's demon) which were small enough to observe and utilise the movements of individual molecules. It might, of course, be answered that an organism small enough to be affected by the individual impacts of surrounding molecules must consist of so few molecules itself that it could not have a physical structure sufficiently complicated to provide the material basis of intelligent mentality; and this reply is in essence given by Schrödinger himself, when he argues that our brains must consist of an enormous number of atoms, since "a physical organism, to be in close correspondence with thought . . . must be a very well-ordered organisation, and that means that the events that happen within it must obey strict physical laws, at least to a very high degree of accuracy".[2] I

---

[1] *The Bases of Modern Science*, p. 85.
[2] Op. cit., p. 8.

shall, however, return at a later stage to this question of the relation between statistics, thermodynamics and life.

The third example which Schrödinger gives to illustrate his point is concerned with the limits of accuracy of measuring by the use of any physical instrument. He takes the case of the torsion-balance, in which a light body is suspended by a long thin fibre; forces are measured by allowing them to impinge upon the suspended body in such a way as to twist it round against the resistance which the fibre offers. The angle of twist provides a measure of the magnitude of the applied force. Now if we wish to increase the accuracy of the instrument we have to make the suspended body lighter and the fibre longer and thinner. There is, however, a limit to the accuracy that can be reached, quite apart from the limitations of the craftsman. This limit is set by the fact that when a certain degree of sensitivity is reached the balance begins to respond to the Brownian movement of the surrounding medium and this disturbance may quite swamp the deflection due to the force which it is desired to measure. Schrödinger comments that our sense-organs would become equally useless if they became too sensitive.

Thus, for Schrödinger all the laws of classical physics are essentially statistical. Although he believes that the individual microscopic entities exist, and indeed that they manifest their individual activities in such phenomena as have just been described, he insists that the laws of physics say nothing about these individual entities but only about the large-scale averaged activities of aggregates of enormous numbers of them. He concludes this part of his discussion by referring to the importance of the "root-n rule", which specifies the degree of inaccuracy to be expected in any statement about an aggregate of any number of particles. This rule, which is one of the basic theorems of statistical mathematics, states that the probable error involved in asserting that the number of individuals in an aggregate is n, is itself of the order of the square root of n. Thus, if n is 100, $\sqrt{n}$ is 10, and the relative error is 10/100 or 10%. If n is 1,000,000, $\sqrt{n}$ is 1000, and the relative error is 1000/1,000,000 or 0·1%. Thus the probable relative error decreases very rapidly as the number of entities in the aggregate increases; this is why the large-scale laws of physics hold to such a very high degree of accuracy. The relevance of this to living phenomena will be seen later.

It might perhaps be thought that Schrödinger, like many other physicists, has a somewhat naïve conception of the reality of the microscopic entities of physics, and that if one holds, in the manner of Braithwaite and Toulmin, that physical theories are merely models or maps, his conclusion as to the fundamentally indeterministic character of physical laws will not hold. I do not think, however, that the objection can be sustained. For even if the theories are models or maps, they are presumably good ones, in the sense that they work. They give the right experimental results. Now phenomena like the Brownian movement are *facts*. Observable phenomena take place *as if* matter were composed of randomly moving minute particles, even if it is not in fact composed of them, and even if the statement that it is composed of them is, when judged by some positivistic canon, strictly meaningless. And this is all that is necessary for the root-n rule to apply. The classical view that the microscopic laws were deterministic rested upon two suppositions: the first was the belief that, when experimental errors were allowed for, the large-scale physical laws were absolutely, and not merely approximately, deterministic; the second was the assumption that this determinism could be extrapolated from the macroscopic into the microscopic realm. However, the first of these suppositions is, so far as one can see, empirically false, and the second is logically baseless. I do not think it is inconceivable that the microscopic realm should be deterministic, as the classical physicists believed it to be, but I think that Schrödinger has shown that, on its own grounds, classical physics had no right to this belief. *De facto* the classical physics was indubitably deterministic; whether it was so *de jure* is highly doubtful.

If we accept Schrödinger's point that even the classical physics has an essentially statistical basis, a remarkable conclusion follows. It is that in certain important cases classical physics approximates far less closely to determinism than quantum physics does. Schrödinger illustrates this point by reference to the inheritance of biological characters in living organisms. Modern genetical research has established that hereditary features are dependent upon the chemical nature of certain minute constituents of the living cell. These constituents, which are known as "genes" and which appear to be large protein molecules, are strung out along fibrous structures called "chromosomes" and their positions on the chromosomes can in many cases be very accurately mapped. "They control all hereditary characters, from trifling minutiae, hardly bearing on the process of living, such as the colour and shapes of pea seeds or the colours of eye and hair in man, to serious defects, such as deaf-mutism or epilepsy, up to highly intellectual characters like musical talent or scientific aptitude."[1] It seems clear that a gene cannot consist at most of more than a few million atoms. We are not concerned here with the details of the fascinating story of the way in which the chromosomes divide and rearrange themselves in cell-division and associate them-selves with chromosomes from another individual in fertilisation; many excellently written popular accounts of these processes are readily available.[2] What is important here is to recognise that the inheritance of biological characters from one generation to another depends upon the chemical nature of the genes concerned persisting unchanged through the various cell-divisions and unions that are involved. When, as in fact happens from time to time, a change in a gene in a germ-cell does occur, we get one of those abrupt alterations in a physical characteristic with which biologists are familiar under the name of "mutations" and which are the raw material for the selective processes which condition organic evolution. Mutations are inherited as the original un-mutated characters were; in Schrödinger's words, "a mutation is definitely a change in the hereditary treasure and has to be ac-counted for by some change in the hereditary substance".[3] Now Schrödinger's point is concerned with the comparatively small number of atoms of which a gene is composed, a few million at most. (Later on, in fact, he suggests, on the bases of work on the production of mutations by X-rays, that a thousand may be nearer the right number.) "That number", he says,

is much too small (from the $\sqrt{n}$ point of view) to entail an orderly and lawful behaviour according to statistical physics—and that

<hr/>

[1] L. von Bertalanffy, *Problems of Life*, p. 72.
[2] E.g. Wilma George's *Elementary Genetics*, H. Kalmus's *Genetics*, Anthony Barnett's *The Human Species*, and E. B. Ford's article on "Heredity" in *Chambers's Encyclopaedia*.   [3] *What is Life?*, page 34.

means according to physics. It is too small, even if all these atoms played the same role, as they do in a gas or in a drop of liquid. And the gene is certainly not just a homogeneous drop of liquid. It is probably a large protein molecule, in which every atom, every radical, every heterocyclic ring plays an individual role, more or less different from that played by any of the other similar atoms, radicals, or rings.[1]

In other words, if the constitution and behaviour of genes was governed by the statistical laws of classical physics, biological mutations would occur very much more frequently than they do; the persistence in the Habsburgs throughout the centuries of the peculiar disfigurement of the lower lip which is characteristic of the family, and which has been shown to be due to a definite gene-modification or "allele", would be so unlikely as to be virtually impossible. "The gene", writes Schrödinger, "has been kept at a temperature around 98° F. during all that time. How are we to understand that it has remained unperturbed by the disordering tendency of the heat motion for centuries?"[2]

By the fact, he replies, that the laws which are operating are not classical but quantum laws. Mutations have been shown to be due to changes in the molecule that are governed by the probability functions of the quantum theory. Whether and when a mutation will occur in a particular gene-molecule, theory is powerless to predict; what it can say is how likely any gene-molecule is to mutate in any given time or, what is mathematically equivalent, the number of gene-molecules in any large aggregate which will mutate in that time. And this probability turns out to be very much less than it would be if it was governed by the classical root-n law. It is well for living organisms that this is so: "if [mutations] were so frequent that there was a considerable chance of, say, a dozen of different mutations occurring in the same

---

[1] *What is Life?*, p. 30. The article on "Biological Individuality" by G. M. Wyburn in *Science News 34* (1954) gives a more up-to-date account of contemporary views of the structure of nucleoproteins. "Nucleoproteins are formed by a salt-like union of a nucleic acid and a basic protein. . . . Recent work suggests that the desoxyribonucleic acid molecule is made up of two backbone chains, coiled round a common axis, each chain consisting of alternating sugar and phosphate groups. The two chains in this construction are held together by connecting horizontal rods, representing pairs of bases, one from each chain (a purine and a pyrimidine) united by a hydrogen bond" (art. cit., p. 75).

[2] Ibid., p. 47.

individual, the injurious ones would, as a rule, predominate over the advantageous ones and the species, instead of being improved by selection, would remain unimproved, or would perish".[1] It is, indeed, well known that one of the most alarming features of large-scale operations in nuclear fission or fusion arises from the fact that the mutation-rate of genes is very considerably raised when the genetic substance is irradiated with intense X-rays or gamma-rays. Leaving out of account such abnormal stimulants, whose effect is equivalent to an enormous rise of temperature within the gene, the likelihood of an energy-change occurring of the magnitude involved in an isomeric transformation of the gene-molecule is comparatively small. (The mathematical reason for this is that the expression for the time of expectation of a mutation is an exponential function of a fraction which contains the threshold-energy of the mutation in the numerator and the absolute temperature in the denominator; the time of expectation thus increases enormously with any increase in the threshold-energy or decrease in the temperature.) We may sum up this discussion by saying that, although it would be unwise to put too much confidence in the conclusions that seem to follow from the contemporary situation of so rapidly changing a science as that of genetics, it is interesting, in view of the common feeling that quantum theory has reduced the world to a condition of flux and disintegration, to find one case at least in which quantum theory seems to provide a more solid foundation than could be legitimately provided by classical physics. Ludwig von Bertalanffy has summed up the matter as follows:

> The "quantised" character of mutations is at the basis, first, of their discontinuity, secondly, of the great stability of the gene and the relative rarity of mutations, and thirdly, it follows that the number of possible mutations is not infinite, since only certain stable states are "allowed".[2]

And again:

> The induction of mutations is subject to the statistical laws of microphysics; these microphysical events, however, are amplified by the organisation of the living system to a macro-effect, and thus a mutation induced by radiation will become manifest at the macro-

[1] *What is Life?*, p. 41.   [2] *Problems of Life*, p. 95.

physical level, say, in a change of the shape of wings or the colour of eyes in a descendant of the fruit fly submitted to the treatment.[1]

It will be interesting, in concluding this section of the present lecture, to turn for a few minutes to the exposition which is given by Dr Hans Reichenbach at the beginning of the book to which I have already referred, *Philosophic Foundations of Quantum Mechanics*. Like Schrödinger, Reichenbach insists that the classical physics was, without knowing it, fundamentally statistical in nature, and he sees the reason for this in that imprecision in all our measurements which the classical physicists glossed over with the comfortable phrase "experimental error". "Whenever we speak of strictly causal laws", he says,

> we assume them to hold between idealised physical states; and we know that actual physical states never correspond exactly to the conditions assumed for the laws. This discrepancy has often been disregarded as irrelevant, as being due to the imperfection of the experimenter and therefore negligible in a statement about causality as a property of nature. With such an attitude, however, the way to a solution of the problem of causality is barred. Statements about the physical world have meaning only so far as they are connected with verifiable results; and a statement about strict causality must be translatable into statements about observable relations if it is to have a utilisable meaning.[2]

The consequence of this is that even in classical physics we can never, even in principle, specify exactly the measure of a physical quantity. Instead of specifying a definite value q we can only specify a probability-density function $f(q)$, such that the probability of the measured value falling within a small range dq will be given by the quantity $f(q)dq$ calculated for the values of q and dq corresponding to the range in question. In most cases the function will be a Gauss-function, giving, when plotted on a graph against q as independent variable, a bell-shaped curve. Now in classical physics the distribution-functions for two different physical quantities will be quite independent of each other; the two quantities can be measured independently and the measurement of one will have no effect upon the measurement of the other. In quantum physics, however, this is no longer so, if one

[1] *Problems of Life*, p. 166.   [2] Op. cit., p. 1.

of the quantities is a generalised co-ordinate q and the other is the corresponding generalised momentum p; if $f(q)$ is represented by a high and narrow bell-shaped curve, $f(p)$ will be represented by a low and broad one, and *vice versa*. That is to say, if the value of q is determined to a high degree of accuracy, the value of p becomes correspondingly vague; hence, for example, we can never determine with near accuracy both the position of a particle and also its momentum or velocity. There is a "cross-section" law which is a limitation of measurability.

It states that the simultaneous values of the independent parameters cannot be measured as exactly as we wish. We can measure only one half of all the parameters to a desired degree of exactness; the other half then must remain inexactly known. There exists a coupling of simultaneously measurable values such that greater exactness in the determination of one half of the totality involves less exactness in the determination of the other half, and vice versa. This law does not make half of the parameters functions of the others; if one half is known, the other half remains entirely unknown unless it is measured. We know, however, that this measurement is restricted to a certain exactness.[1]

This law, it must be noted, rests upon purely empirical evidence and has no logical necessity. It is formulated in the famous uncertainty-principle of Heisenberg.

I shall not attempt to enter more deeply into the technicalities of Reichenbach's discussion. I shall simply remark that it is important for two main points. The first is his insistence that classical physics, no less than quantum physics, was essentially, if unconsciously, statistical; the second that the ultimate basis of quantum physics is empirical and not logical. I remarked upon the latter point earlier in this lecture.

3. CAUSALITY IN PHYSICS AND THEOLOGY

I shall say something later on about the remarkable and highly disputable theological conclusions which Schrödinger draws in the concluding chapter of his book. At the moment I shall consider the effect of the supersession of classical by quantum physics

[1] *Philosophic Foundations of Quantum Mechanics,* p. 4.

upon our notions of causality in the physical world. It has sometimes been suggested that, for practical purposes, no change has
been brought about; quantum physics, it is said, is concerned
only with microscopic and unobservable events, and the large-
scale events which are of practical importance are governed by
those statistically averaged laws in which the quantum idiosyncrasies of the individual atom or nucleon are swamped in the
crowd. This is not, however, the case. We have already seen how
an individual quantum phenomenon occurring in one particular
gene-molecule may radically change a hereditable character and
so influence the future of the species concerned. Take for example the case of haemophilia, a condition in which trivial injury
causes excessive bleeding, and blood-coagulation is abnormally
slow. This disease is due to what is technically known as a sex-
linked recessive gene; it is manifested exclusively in males, but
transmitted mainly by females. "If a man with haemophilia has
children, all his sons will be normal and all his daughters will be
transmitters. It is nevertheless true that only a small proportion
of haemophiliacs live long enough to have children. As regards
the female transmitter, it may be noted that half her sons will be
haemophiliacs and half her daughters will be transmitters."[1] Now,
"a famous case was Queen Victoria's. She had no haemophilic
ancestors, but she handed the condition on to the former Russian
and Spanish dynasties through her daughters, but not to the
reigning English house. Thus the mutation must have arisen in
her body or in the gonads of either of her parents."[2] If we consider how the course of history was influenced by the hold which
the pseudo-monk Rasputin exerted upon the parents of the
haemophilic Tsarevitch, we can see how even an isolated quantum phenomenon may have very far-reaching results. Nor is it
true that individual quantum phenomena cannot be detected;
very frequently they can. In any well-equipped physical laboratory to-day it is possible to hear from a loud-speaker an irregular
sequence of clicks, each of which announces the arrival of an
alpha-particle in a Geiger counter. Now the emission of an alpha-
particle from a radio-active atom is a typical quantum pheno-

[1] L. J. Witts, *Chambers's Encyclopaedia*, II, p. 371, s.v. "Blood, Diseases of
the". This assumes that the other parent is normal.
[2] H. Kalmus, *Genetics*, p. 94.

menon. If we know the design of the apparatus we can specify the average number of alpha-particles which will arrive in the counter in a given time; but we cannot say whether and when any particular atom will eject an alpha-particle. Nor can we say, even in principle, whether a click will be heard in the loud-speaker at any particular moment or not; we can only calculate the average number of clicks that will be heard over an extended period of time. In other words, from the point of view of modern physics, any particular click is an entirely unpredictable phenomenon, for which no physical cause can be assigned other than the equally unpredictable disintegration of the particular atom from which the alpha-particle that produced it came. And it would be perfectly possible for the arrival of a particular alpha-particle to produce effects much more far-reaching than a mere click. Let us suppose, for example, that the design of the apparatus was such that on the average one alpha-particle would arrive in the counter every ten minutes. Let us also suppose that for a period of one minute the counter was connected not to a loud-speaker but to an apparatus for detonating a hydrogen bomb. Then it would be altogether impossible for a physicist, even in principle, to predict whether the bomb would explode or not; all he could say would be that the odds against the explosion were nine to one. In other words, the destruction of a great urban population might be made to depend upon a purely physical event whose occurrence was entirely unpredictable.[1] The fact that physics is as successful as it is in predicting and designing physical occurrences is mainly due to the further fact that very few physical events depend upon individual quantum occurrences.

Such examples as these will serve to indicate how far the old-fashioned views of physical causality have been abandoned. It is true that only physicists whose philosophical ideas were very crude ever identified physical causality with causality in the metaphysical sense. The causality with which physics was concerned was simply the invariable correlation, under specified conditions, between phenomena of different types, a correlation which was never absolute, since the totality of conditions holding on one

---

[1] Cf. Margenau's example of the neutron and the plutonium block: "The fate of the globe, as a single event, may hide itself within atomic uncertainty" (*Nature of Physical Reality*, p. 420).

occasion could never be exactly replicated upon another.[1] It was, however, assumed that, if metaphysical causality had any meaning at all, there was a one-one correspondence between physical and metaphysical causation. This conviction was the basic assumption of the physical determinism which so oppressively dominated nineteenth-century science. If there was a physical law that B followed A, then it was metaphysically necessary that B should follow A, allowance being made for what were somewhat circularly called "disturbing factors". It must, of course, be recognised that, in contrast to the physicists, the majority of philosophers, following in the steps of Hume, rejected the notion of metaphysical causality altogether; for them causality simply *was* the invariable sequence of the physicist, though, strangely enough, this did not in most cases lead them to abandon their determinism. They still managed to make the transition from invariable connection in the past to inevitable connection in the future, though it is notorious that the justification of induction has been one of the most obstinate problems for the positivist philosopher. It will perhaps clear the air if we set the matter against an earlier and more venerable background.

The main tradition of classical Christian philosophy, while it insisted upon the universal primary causality of God in all the events of the world's history, maintained with equal emphasis the reality and the authenticity of secondary causes, both necessary and voluntary. Whatever the speculative difficulties involved, it had far too vivid a conviction of the generosity with which God had bestowed existence and activity upon his creatures to view

---

[1] There is not, we must note, complete agreement among physicists in their use of the word "causality" even in its physical application. Thus for Margenau causality is identical with the invariability of physical laws with time; it means that in so far as the conditions of a phenomenon can be replicated the phenomenon will be replicated too. "*Causality holds if the laws of nature (differential equations) governing closed systems do not contain the time variable in explicit form*" (*Nature of Physical Reality*, p. 405). Thus theories, such as those propounded by Dirac and Pascual Jordan, in which the so-called "constants of nature" change with time, are described by Margenau as rejecting the principle of causality. They are, however, none the less deterministic, so long as the time-variable enters into the laws in a determinate functional form. And, as Margenau goes on to point out (p. 409), a law which is, in his sense, non-causal can frequently be reduced to a causal law, e.g. by a sufficient number of differentiations. In any case, what we are interested in in the present chapter is not causality as Margenau defines it, but determinacy.

either them or their operations as mere phantom-appearances masking the activity of the transcendent First Cause. It is well known that intractable problems arise in the reconciliation of divine omnipotence with the reality of secondary causes, especially when the secondary causes are voluntary ones and when the discussion is extended from the realm of nature to that of grace. The names of Calvin, Jansen and Molina are a sufficient reminder of the passions which the question has aroused, and its intricacy is indicated by the fact that the only concrete result of the sessions held for fifteen years from 1592 onwards by the celebrated Congregation *de Auxiliis* was the papal decree of 1611 forbidding any further disputation on the subject.[1] We are not concerned with its details here, but only with the fact that, whatever problems this raises for the intellect, the main tradition of Christian theism has firmly held that, in their different modes of primary and secondary causality respectively, both God and created agents are active in all the processes of nature.

It is well to stress that Christian theism is concerned to maintain the reality of the secondary causality of creatures no less than that of the primary causality of God. It is not Christian doctrine that what seems to be the activity of finite beings is, when we get behind the curtain, the lonely activity of God. For Christian theism, creatures are not phantoms or illusions, but dependent beings, and God is dishonoured if his creatures are treated as phantoms or illusions no less than if they are treated as being self-existent and independent. There is an order of nature in which real beings exert real activity, even though those beings and their activity depend wholly upon the incessant creative and conserving action of God. The very notion of the miraculous depends upon the notion of an order of nature; for if there is no order of nature everything that happens is as miraculous as everything else, since everything that happens happens by the naked *ad hoc* act of God. (In themselves, of course, miraculous occurrences are no more the result of divine activity than are non-miraculous ones; traditional theology has steadily maintained that the existence of the natural world itself provides the basis for the demonstration of the existence of God. It is only *quoad nos*

[1] Cf. e.g. E. L. van Becelaere, *Encyc. of Religion and Ethics*, VI, p. 369 f., s.v. "Grace, Doctrine of (Roman Catholic)".

that miracles are specially indicative of God's existence and action.) My present point, however, is simply this, that, while Christian theism insists that the world is dependent, it no less emphatically maintains that it is real. In every event that happens we see in operation both the primary causality of God who is the world's creator and the secondary causality of the creatures which he maintains.

I have already remarked that there are physicists who are convinced that the present dominance of physical science by the concept of indeterminacy is only temporary and that sooner or later the fundamental laws of the physical universe will once again take a deterministic form. Such nonconformists are few in number, and in any case it should be of interest to see how Christian theism will interpret the indeterminist view.

We can, I think, put the matter quite briefly in the following way. If the standpoint of classical physics is accepted, with its deterministic outlook, the theist will see every physical event as the effect of the secondary causality of finite agents. He will not, of course, deny that the primary causality of God is involved; indeed he will emphatically affirm this. But he will see the primary causality of God as involved in the act by which God creates and conserves the finite agents and their causality. There will be a one-one relation between the divine and the created causality in virtue of which it will be possible to give an account, which on the physical level is complete, in terms solely of the finite agents and their activities. (Of course, if we want to give an account on the *metaphysical* level we shall have to introduce a reference to God, but that is another matter.) If now we abandon the classical standpoint and adopt that of quantum physics, we cannot give a complete account, even on the physical level, simply in terms of finite causes. The degree of autonomy with which God has endowed the finite agents is sufficient to specify the relative frequency or probability with which specified types of event occur, but nothing more. Even this is perhaps too much to say, as the probabilities are not numerically fixed from the start; the degree of indeterminacy that attaches to a measurable quantity is affected by the previous measurement of its dynamical conjugate. The situation in fact is as if, while conferring a certain degree of autonomy upon his universe and giving his creatures a certain freedom in sharing out that autonomy between them, God has reserved to himself the final decision as to whether a specified event occurs or not. That there is a ten per cent chance that a click will be heard during the next minute in a loud-speaker which is connected to a particular Geiger-counter may be a fact that follows from the precise degree and type of determinacy with which God has endowed the finite world; that a click will—or alternatively will not—be heard at a specified instant may be due solely to the primary causality of God. Of course, a positivist will say that there is no cause whatever for the occurrence of the click at the specified instant—it "just happens". But this is the one thing that a theist cannot say; for the theist, nothing ever "just happens". If some such account as I have given is acceptable, I think that the relation between the primary causality of God and the secondary causality of his creatures becomes somewhat easier to envisage than it used to be. On the classical view, the primary and the secondary causality were co-extensive, and although they could be theoretically distinguished their effects were simply identical. On the view which I have just developed, the primary and secondary causality are equally concerned with the act, and with the whole of it; there is no partitioning of the act in the Molinist manner, as if part of the act was solely due to the primary cause and part of it solely to the secondary. But the primary and secondary causes are concerned with the act in different aspects. To the secondary cause it belongs merely to determine that there is a certain probability of the event occurring, and even this it does only as a result of its conservation by the primary cause which is God. To the primary cause alone it belongs to determine whether the event shall occur, and when and where; the secondary causes have no part or lot in this. Thus the relative autonomy which God has given to his creatures does not in the least diminish his sovereignty; whether a particular event happens or not depends in the last resort upon his choice and upon it alone.

The preceding argument, it should be observed, does not depend upon the assumption that atoms, alpha-particles and the like have necessarily anything more than a purely theoretical status. We can imagine an objector saying that we had no right to treat the emission of an alpha-particle from an atom as an event undetermined by the laws of physics, on the ground that we had no right to treat it as a physical event at all. The whole paraphernalia of electrons, nucleons, alpha-particles and quantum-jumps, he might complain, is merely a model in the Braithwaitean sense; it provides concepts and rules which are convenient for talking about the phenomena, but the words which it employs are not the names of entities which are real in the sense that tables and spectroscopes and loud-speakers are real. The objection is, however, irrelevant, for the argument does not need to be expressed in terms of theoretical concepts at all. Its starting-point is not the physical impredictability of the emission of an alpha-particle from an atom—that may very well be a useful scientific fiction—but the physical impredictability of a particular click in a loud-speaker. It is the indeterminacy of perceptible sensory occurrences with which we are concerned, not the hypothetical indeterminacy of hypothetical unobservables.

At the risk of being wearisome, I must once again add that I am not in any way trying to use the concept of physical indeterminism as a foundation on which to build Christian theism. If Einstein's belief that indeterminism is only a passing phase should turn out to be correct, the withers of the Christian theologian will remain unwrung. Nevertheless, it has been, I think, of interest to enquire how the traditional doctrine of the relation between the primary causality of God and the secondary causality of his creatures will interpret the new outlook which is characteristic of current physical theory. As in one or two other cases which we have examined, the outcome of the enquiry has been that the current physical theory is somewhat more congenial to the Christian doctrine than was the theory which it has displaced. This is a welcome conclusion, but its significance ought not to be exaggerated. And this, I think, is all that there is to say about it.

4. THE PANTHEISM OF SCHRÖDINGER

Having made as much use as I have in this lecture of Schrödinger's stimulating little book *What is Life?*, it will only be fair to conclude by seeing where his thought subsequently takes him. We shall, I fear, find ourselves confronted with one more of those all too frequent examples of the way in which even a brilliant thinker can become inconsequent when he gets outside his own special subject. The discussion which I have outlined above leads to an investigation of the relation of living organisms to the Second Law of Thermodynamics, the law of entropy-increase. This law, to which I have already referred and which has commonly been looked upon as one of the most widely pervasive principles in the whole of physical and biological science, may be briefly formulated in the statement that the effect of the energy-interchanges which are constantly going on in the universe, and of which the flow of heat from hotter bodies to colder ones is the most obvious example, is to produce a condition of greater and greater uniformity, or of less and less organisation, as time goes on. Stated in this form, the law strictly applies only to a system which is isolated from its environment; and one of the difficulties of knowing whether it applies to the universe as a whole arises from the uncertainty as to whether the universe, which *ex hypothesi* has no environment, can be considered as isolated from the environment which it has not got. To a system which is not isolated the law need not apply. Such a system may well maintain or even increase its organisation at the expense of the organisation of its environment. This is, in fact, what happens, broadly speaking, when we eat our meals. In Schrödinger's words, "the device by which an organism maintains itself stationary at a fairly high level of orderliness . . . really consists in continually sucking orderliness from its environment. . . . In the case of higher animals we know the kind of orderliness they feed on well enough, viz. the extremely well-ordered state of matter in more or less complicated organic compounds, which serve them as foodstuffs."[1] A precise numerical measure of the degree of organisation of a system can be given in terms of the quantity known as "entropy" or the closely related quantity "thermodynamic probability";[2] since entropy increases as organisation decreases, the organism can be said to maintain its organisation by "feeding upon negative entropy", or upon the reciprocal of

[1] *What is Life?*, p. 75.

[2] The relation between the entropy S and the thermodynamic probability W is given by the expression $S = k \log W$, where k is "Boltzmann's constant", equal to $3.2983.10^{-24}$ cal./°C. Since, from this, $- S = k \log (1/W)$, $1/W$ can be taken as a direct measure of order.

thermodynamic probability. Now for Schrödinger the striking fact about living creatures is the way in which, as a result of the stability of the patterns of the gene-molecules, the orderliness of the organism persists.

> It is simply a fact of observation that the guiding principle in every cell is embodied in a single atomic association existing only in one (or sometimes two) copy—and a fact of observation that it results in producing events which are a paragon of orderliness. Whether we find it astonishing or whether we find it quite plausible, that a small but highly organised group of atoms be capable of acting in this manner, the situation is unprecedented, it is unknown anywhere else except in living matter.[1]

In spite of this, Schrödinger does not think it necessary to suppose that living organisms need for their description an essentially different type of physical law from that which applies to non-living matter. After all, he points out, there are inorganic machines, such as clocks, which maintain a high degree of organisation over long periods. If we ask how they manage to do this in spite of the disorganising effect of the Second Law of Thermodynamics, the answer is to be found in the facts that at the absolute zero of temperature (the inaccessible dead level approximately equal to $-273\,°C.$) all thermal motion would cease, and that in many cases room-temperature may be a close enough approximation to it. If, on the other hand, we raise the temperature of the clock above the melting-point of the materials of which it is composed, its organisation will be suddenly and drastically reduced. Thus, in spite of the remarkable difference in degree, there does not seem to be any essentially different principle involved in the orderliness of living and of non-living structures.

All this is interesting and plausible, but the psychological and theological sequel which Schrödinger appends to it is glaringly debatable. In striking contrast to the distinguished neuro-physiologist Professor J. C. Eccles, whose exposition I shall discuss in the next lecture, he denies that quantum indeterminacy plays any part in the physical events in a living body which correspond to the activity of mind. Such events are, for

---

[1] Op. cit., p. 79.

Schrödinger, determined by the statistical averaging-out of the individual microscopic processes in exactly the same way as any other events in the physical world. "To the physicist," he says, "I wish to emphasise that in my opinion, and contrary to the opinion upheld in some quarters, *quantum indeterminacy* plays no biologically relevant role in them, except perhaps by enhancing their purely accidental character in such events as meiosis, natural and X-ray-induced mutation and so on—and this is in any case obvious and well recognised." [1]

No reason is given for this opinion so confidently stated, but its function in the argument becomes immediately evident. It is to produce a contradiction, which is to be resolved into pantheism. Far from denying the validity of our introspective consciousness of free will, Schrödinger maintains it. He states explicitly the following two premises:

(i) My body functions as a pure mechanism according to the Laws of Nature.

(ii) Yet I know, by incontrovertible direct experience, that I am directing its motions, of which I foresee the effects, that may be fateful and all-important, in which case I feel and take full responsibility for them.

How, then, is the antinomy to be solved?

The only possible inference from these two facts [writes Schrödinger] is, I think, that I—I in the widest meaning of the word, that is to say, every conscious mind that has ever said or felt "I"— am the person, if any, who controls the "motion of the atoms" according to the Laws of Nature. [2]

What is the precise force of the words "if any" in this astonishing sentence I am quite at a loss to determine, but that Schrödinger is defending pantheism is made unambiguously clear. In spite of what he describes as its "blasphemous and lunatic" sound in Christian terminology, he defends the statement "Hence I am God Almighty". He appeals for support to the Upanishads, with their identification of *Athman* with *Brahman*. He insists that the experience of the mystics of many centuries is to be condensed in the phrase *Deus factus sum*. He invokes both Schopenhauer and "those true lovers who, as they look into each other's eyes,

[1] *What is Life?*, p. 87.   [2] Ibid., p. 88.

become aware that their thought and their joy are *numerically* one—not merely similar or identical".

It would be monstrous to ridicule a conviction which is held with such evident passion and sincerity and which has clearly been felt as a precious and liberating power. I cannot, however, see that it in any way follows from the premisses upon which it professes to be based. The conclusion of the argument is that "I" am the source of the deterministic laws by which natural processes are governed. But the second premiss was that I am conscious that, at any rate as regards my own acts, the laws of nature are not deterministic at all. And this, so far from providing a basis for the conclusion, is flatly contradictory to it. The argument seems to be that "I" have created the world, endowed it with deterministic laws of behaviour, and then forgotten that I have done so; then this forgotten memory turns up again in the quite delusory form of a feeling that I am now able to alter its working. Is this really plausible? And has any reason whatever been given for supposing it to be true? Again, what is the relation of the universal "I" to its innumerable conscious manifestations? The "I" of the second premiss is the individual personal experient— Schrödinger knowing that Schrödinger is free, Crippen knowing that Crippen is free, Mascall knowing that Mascall is free. But in the conclusion Schrödinger, Crippen and Mascall and countless other people—in fact, "every conscious mind that has ever said or felt 'I'"—turn out to be one and the same person, who is moreover the controller of the universe; and all this follows from the fact that our bodies are pure mechanisms. In further confirmation of the conclusion, it is pointed out that consciousness is never experienced in the plural, only in the singular, but so far from confirming the conclusion this undeniable fact seems only to weaken it. That consciousness is experienced in the singular means that Schrödinger is conscious of being Schrödinger, Crippen is conscious of being Crippen, and Mascall is conscious of being Mascall. This, so far as it indicates anything, would seem to indicate that Schrödinger, Crippen and Mascall are three distinct persons. What in fact Schrödinger deduces from it is that Schrödinger is really Crippen and Mascall as well, and Crippen is really Schrödinger and Mascall as well, and Mascall is really Schrödinger and Crippen as well. If we were really all one mind, as Schrödinger maintains, consciousness would presumably be experienced not in the singular, but in the plural. As St Thomas argued against the Averroists, if there is only one passive intellect for the whole human race, then I am it and I ought to think simultaneously the thoughts of every human being.[1] Schrödinger asserts that pluralisation of consciousnesses or minds has seemed a "very suggestive hypothesis" to people who have allowed themselves to be misled by the plurality of bodies. I think that it is in fact a very suggestive hypothesis and that it is true. It is at least clear that Schrödinger's view is a very unplausible alternative. If his experience of other people does not lead a man to believe that they are individual conscious beings like himself, I should expect him to believe them to be hallucinations. I cannot see any reason why he should believe that they are really himself having experiences of which he is not conscious.

Schrödinger seems in fact to be dogged by an inability to distinguish between any form of union between persons and sheer individual identity. This is a fault to which mystics have been notoriously prone, though Christian mysticism has consistently repudiated it. What is amazing is not that Schrödinger should maintain it, but that he should claim to deduce it from his two premisses. As he states them, those premisses are simply contradictory, and it is idle to draw deductions from them. All that we can validly conclude is that one of them must be false. Either our bodies are not pure mechanisms, in the deterministic sense, or our impression of freedom is an illusion. Schrödinger has given no reasons for his first premiss, but simply affirms it without argument. In the next lecture we shall, I hope, see, at least in general terms, the kind of way in which the quantum mechanics, which no one has done more to establish than Schrödinger, dovetails in with our experience of freedom of choice. And in doing this we shall not be led to the view that we are all really identical, and still less to the view that we are all of us God. But to return to the main subject of this lecture, let us register our gratitude for the supersession of the determinism with which post-Newtonian physics had for so long bound the bodies and the souls of men. The snare is broken and we are delivered.

[1] Cf. *S.c.G.*, II, lxxiii.

Chapter Six

THE BODY AND THE SOUL

Quid est homo?—Psal. viii. 5.

I. BODY AND SOUL IN MAN

IN 1780 Mrs Sarah Trimmer dedicated to the Lady Charlotte Finch the first edition of her *Easy Introduction to the Knowledge of Nature and Reading the Holy Scriptures, adapted to the Capacities of Children*; in 1817 there was published the fifteenth edition "with considerable Additions and Improvements". In this work, which is written in the form of monologues delivered by a governess to her charges, the young Charlotte and Henry are addressed as follows:

Mankind, my dear children, are rational creatures, they have immortal souls, and God designed them to be angels hereafter, and to live happy for ever and ever in heaven. . . . The great difference between mankind and the inferior animals consists in their having *immortal souls*. The soul is that part of a human creature which thinks. You wish me to describe the Soul to you, Henry; this, my dear, I cannot do, any farther than that it is of a spiritual nature, and consequently invisible, for a spirit has not bodily parts, and therefore cannot be seen with the eyes; but I am convinced that I have a Soul by what passes within myself, and that human creatures have Souls by what I observe in other people. . . . Do you think with your eyes, your ears, your hands, your feet, or any part of you which can be seen? What can it be then that thinks? Your Soul, to be sure. It is by means of the Soul that mankind have so many ingenious contrivances. . . . And it is by means of the Soul, my dear children, that mankind are capable of knowing God, and of paying that tribute of prayer and praise which is due to the great CREATOR.

I told you, my dears, that the Soul is immortal, and so it certainly is, it will live for ever; the Body is condemned to die, but the Soul will remain alive to everlasting ages. Every human creature dies sooner or later; the Soul leaves the Body, and the Body turns to corruption, but the Soul cannot die, for the CREATOR has said it shall live.[1]

[1] Op. cit., p. 168 f.

Many people, even at the present day, would take this passage as an accurate exposition of orthodox Christian teaching about the nature of man. It is what any number of Christian children have been taught at home and in Sunday-school. Nevertheless this doctrine that man is a pure spirit and that his body is a temporary integument, from which he may hope ultimately to get free, is plainly contradictory both to the Bible and to the central Christian tradition. Although the temptation to retreat into a purely spiritual realm has recurred throughout the history of the Christian Church, it was left to Descartes in the seventeenth century to give explicit expression to the view of man which has been characterised in M. Maritain's phrase, "an angel driving a machine",[1] and in Professor Gilbert Ryle's phrase, "the ghost in the machine".[2] It is true that the Platonic setting in which the Christian religion found itself when it emerged from the Jewish into the Gentile world led many early Christian writers to speak, and occasionally even to think, as if it was the soul that was the real man and as if the body was only a temporary encumbrance. Even St Augustine, in defining man as "a rational soul *using* (*utens*) a terrestrial and mortal body",[3] might appear to have capitulated verbally to this tendency. He had, however, far too profound a grasp of the Christian verity to yield to it in reality, and he commends the philosopher Varro for "calling the essence composed of body and soul, man, and denying the appellation to either of them, being separately considered".[4] What made it really impossible for any intelligent Christian to forget for long that the body was not the integument of a human being but an integral part of him, was the central conviction of the Faith that the Second Person of the Holy Trinity had united to himself a complete human nature, flesh as well as spirit, and in that human nature had died and risen from the dead and ascended into heaven. For the resurrection of Christ in the totality of his human nature was the firstfruit and the pledge of our resurrection in the totality of ours. This is expressed with complete lucidity in the fragmentary work *De Resurrectione*:

> God calls even the flesh to the resurrection and promises it eternal life. To announce the good news of salvation to man was in

[1] Cf. *Religion and Culture*, p. 24.
[2] *The Concept of Mind*, p. 15.
[3] *De moribus eccl.*, I, xxvii, 52.
[4] Aug., *De Civ. Dei*, xix, 3.

effect to announce it to the flesh. For what is man if not a reasonable being composed of soul and body? Shall we say that the soul in itself is the man? No, it is the soul of the man. And the body alone— is that the man? By no means; we should rather say that it is the body of the man. Since, then, neither soul alone nor body alone are man, but the thing called man arises out of their union, when God called man to the resurrection and the life, he called no mere part of man, but the whole man, body and soul together in one.[1]

M. Gilson has pointed out that the Christian Fathers were so little concerned to identify the human being with his soul that some of the earliest of them were quite ready to believe that the soul ceased to exist between death and the resurrection.

A Christianity without the immortality of the soul is not, in the long run, absolutely inconceivable, and the proof of it is that it has been conceived. What really would be absolutely inconceivable would be a Christianity without the resurrection of the Man. The man dies, his body dies, but nothing would be irretrievably lost, the Good News would not be rendered vain, if the soul died also, provided always that we were assured of a resuscitated body and soul, so that the entire man might rejoice in eternal beatitude. There is no occasion therefore for surprise if certain fathers admitted the death of soul and body pending the resurrection and the judgment.[2]

As Gilson goes on to remark, this represented only a passing hesitation in the history of Christian anthropology; it was soon realised that the immortality of the soul was indispensable to Christian doctrine. Nevertheless the conviction persisted, in spite of the domination of Christian thought by Platonism, that, even if a human soul continues to exist when it is separated from the body, it continues to exist as something less than a complete human being until it receives a body once more at the resurrection. A clear formulation of this truth was not in fact achieved until the thirteenth century, when St Thomas Aquinas, in a brilliant and profound synthesis, christianised the Aristotelian doctrine that the soul and the body of a man are related to each other as form to matter, by uniting it to a baptised Platonism, in which the soul, while incomplete by itself, nevertheless possesses

[1] *De Resurrectione*, viii (Migne, P. G., vi, 1586), cit. Gilson, *Spirit of Medieval Philosophy*, p. 171.
[2] Gilson, op. cit., p. 172.

substantiality and confers it upon the concrete composite human being. Aristotle had said definitely in one place: "Probably it is wiser not to say that the soul pities or learns or thinks, but rather that the man does it by the soul."[1] St Thomas says categorically: "It is manifest that a man is not the soul alone, but is something composed of soul and body."[2] And elsewhere, as if to refute in advance both Descartes and Mrs Trimmer, he denies that an angel and a soul belong to the same species.[3] (Incidentally, we may remark how Mrs Trimmer's Cartesianism is emphasised in the assertion that "the soul is that part of a human creature which *thinks*". "What then am I?" Descartes had asked; and replied, "A thing that thinks."[4])

It would take us far from our present subject if we were to relate in detail how St Thomas dealt with the difficulties which were raised for Aristotle's doctrine of the hylemorphic constitution of man by the Christian belief in the immortality of the soul, and to show how his determination to plumb the question to its depths resulted in a transformation of the Aristotelian doctrine which is remarkable for its originality and penetration. It is, however, relevant to emphasise the significance of the Angelic Doctor's decision to undertake the vast labour of transforming the Aristotelian doctrine, when he might with so much less trouble have taken over Platonism ready made. For the whole point is that Platonism, even Christian Platonism, while abundantly providing for the immortality of the soul, could never take quite seriously the Christian assertion that the body is part of the man. Aristotle was at least clear about that, even if he thought that men die like brute beasts; Aristotle, then, had to be christianised, even at the cost of war with his Arab interpreters, and the result was the Thomist doctrine of the human soul as a substantial form. All this helps to bring out the fact that a human being, as Christianity understands him, is neither a brute beast nor an angel, but a highly complicated creature, consisting of body and soul, of matter and spirit, interpenetrating each other in an almost unbelievably intimate and complicated way. There is no need for us

[1] *De Anima*, I, iv, 408*b*.
[2] *S. Theol.*, I, lxxv, 4*c*. Cf. the penetrating remark of the brilliant psychologist Roland Dalbiez: "*Our body is a part of our ego*" (*Psychoanalytical Method and the Doctrine of Freud*, II, p. 19).
[3] Ibid., 7.   [4] *Meditations*, II.

to express this fact in the way in which St Thomas expressed it, but it is vital that we should take it as literally and whole-heartedly as he took it, for it is a natural corollary of the fundamental Christian belief in the Incarnation of the Son of God. That it is essential for a Christian understanding of the discoveries of modern psychology and physiology is a matter which is of less importance in itself, but is of considerable moment for our present purposes.

2. DETERMINISM AND SCEPTICISM

Many Christians feel a vague sense of dismay when they are confronted with some new discovery of the endocrinologists about the influence of our glandular secretions upon our behaviour, or with some new machine invented by the electronic engineers in order to mimic some human function in the sole possession of which we had formerly believed ourselves to be secure. Such a sense of dismay is no doubt frequently due to a fear that human freedom is gradually but irresistibly being proved to be a delusion, that one range after another of human activity is being shown to be predictable by scientific laws. For this reason, it is equally likely to arise when we contemplate the alleged discoveries of psychologists, for psychological complexes are asserted to be as compulsive of human behaviour as are the secretions of the ductless glands. Whether, and in what way, even mechanical laws can be considered as absolutely deterministic is a question which I have discussed already;[1] at the moment I shall only observe that one of the necessary conditions of fruitful and constructive free action is to know what are the limits within which one's freedom can be exercised. A man who holds the humiliating but true belief that he cannot fly like a swallow is likely to be more successful as regards locomotion than a man who holds the gratifying but erroneous belief that he can, by flapping his arms, sail through the air at fifty miles an hour. Human freedom has never meant that we can do anything that we wish; what it does mean is that we can do some things that we wish, and it is very important for us to know what those things are. For everything that science can tell us about the limits of our

[1] Cf. ch. v supra.

freedom we can only be grateful; for we can then proceed to act successfully within those limits and even, it may be, by taking appropriate action, to widen them.

There is, of course, one conceivable type of determination of our beliefs and actions which would be devastating. Suppose, for example, it was the case that the necessary and sufficient condition for me to be convinced that an argument which I was considering was valid was that an event of some particular type A should occur in my cerebral cortex, and that the necessary and sufficient condition for me to be convinced that an argument which I was considering was invalid was that an event of some other particular type B should occur in the cortex. Suppose, moreover, that a type-A event was just as likely to occur whether the argument was in fact valid or invalid, and that the same was true of a type-B event. Then it is clear that my conviction that an argument which I had been considering was valid would provide no evidence for the argument's validity,[1] but only for the occurrence of a type-A event. And my conviction that an argument which I had been considering was invalid would provide no evidence for its invalidity, but only for the occurrence of a type-B event. Again, suppose that the necessary and sufficient condition for me to be convinced that I was performing a free action was that an event of some particular type X should occur in my cortex, and that the necessary and sufficient condition for me to be convinced that I was acting under pure compulsion was that an event of some other particular type Y should occur in it. Suppose, moreover, that a type-X event was just as likely to occur whether I was acting freely or compulsively, and that the same was true of a type-Y event. Then it is clear that my conviction that I was acting freely on a particular occasion would provide no evidence that this was in fact the case, but only for the occurrence of a type-X event. And my conviction that I was acting compulsively on some other occasion would provide no evidence that that was the case, but only for the occurrence of a type-Y event. Such a radical scepticism is, however, self-destructive, not in the comparatively mild sense of being self-refuting (this is true of every *reductio ad absurdum*), but in the much more drastic sense of being self-

[1] By "P provides evidence for Q" I mean here that, when P occurs, Q is more likely to occur than not, i.e. there are more cases of P and Q than of P and not-Q.

stultifying. I mean by this that the mere statement of the position deprives it of any claim for acceptance. For I shall only accept an argument for any position if I am convinced that the argument is valid. However, this position itself asserts that my conviction that an argument is valid is no evidence of its validity. When the proponent asserts that the necessary and sufficient condition for the existence of conviction of the validity of an argument is the occurrence of a type-A event in the cortex of the person concerned, and that such an event is equally likely to occur whether the argument is valid or not, he has presumably formed his belief in this assertion by going through certain arguments, whether *a priori* or empirical in their character, which seem to him to be valid. However, if the assertion is itself correct, his conviction of the validity of these arguments provides no evidence for their validity, but only for the occurrence of a type-A event in his cerebral cortex. (Admittedly, if I recite to him the last two sentences which I have written they will not convince him, if he applies his own principles consistently. For, on his theory, even if they seem convincing to him, all that this shows is that type-A events are happening in his cortex.) If the theory is true, then no arguments against it have any force. But then, if it is true, no arguments in its favour have any force either. It is pretty clear that no one in normal society in fact holds this position in its fullness, for its consistent adoption would lead to insanity. What, I think, frequently happens is that it is held in a mitigated form. The second half of the position, which denies that acts which seem free are really free, is asserted, while the first half, which denies that arguments which seem valid are really valid, is not. This, however, seems very arbitrary, for it is difficult to see why one type of mental operation should be held to bear genuine credentials if another type is held to bear forged ones. It was the failure to see that a consistent determinism must result in an intellectual scepticism as well as a denial of human freedom that, in my opinion, vitiated the criticisms which Miss G. E. M. Anscombe made of Dr C. S. Lewis in a paper read to the Oxford Socratic Club, which acquired some celebrity in 1947. Dr Lewis, in his book *Miracles*, had argued that Naturalism—the doctrine that Nature is a closed, interlocked system—is self-contradictory: "no thought is valid", he asserted, "if it can be fully explained as the result of irrational causes".[1] Miss Anscombe in reply accused Dr Lewis of confusing the relation of ground and consequent with the relation of cause and effect,[2] and implied that we can always examine an argument in order to see whether it is valid or not, whatever may be the causes, physical or psychological, which have led a particular person to accept its conclusions. Her reply is, I think, a good one, but only so long as we exclude from the sphere of application of the naturalistic theory the examiner's conviction of the validity of his examination. I will illustrate this point by a simple parable.

There is, we will suppose, a man who has a violent antipathy to the Bishop of Capaccio-Vallo, which he is accustomed to justify by the following argument:

> Some ecclesiastics are dipsomaniacs;
> The Bishop of Capaccio-Vallo is an ecclesiastic;
> Therefore the Bishop of Capaccio-Vallo is a dipsomaniac.

A friend, who is not only a logician but also a psychologist, analyses the man's mind and discovers that his readiness to believe the worst of the bishop is due to the fact that he was badly frightened by the local vicar when he was two years old and has felt a horror of ecclesiastics ever since. The patient, when this is explained to him, replies: "You are no doubt perfectly right about this, and I am grateful for your help. It doesn't, however, affect my views about the Bishop. Cause-and-effect is one thing, ground-and-consequent is another. Whatever the psychological cause of my sense of repugnance, I have given you a perfectly good syllogistic argument for the belief which I have formed about the Bishop." "But", the friend rejoins, "your syllogism is invalid; it contains an undistributed middle. And it is obvious on a moment's thought that no syllogism with an undistributed middle is valid." "Is it?" the patient answers; "it may be so to you, and I confess that there are times when it seems so to me.

---

[1] Op. cit., p. 27. The same point had been stated by J. E. McTaggart as follows: "If materialism is true, all our thoughts are produced by purely material antecedents. These are quite blind, and are just as likely to produce falsehood as truth. We have thus no reason for believing any of our conclusions—including the truth of materialism, which is therefore a self-contradictory hypothesis" (*Philosophical Studies*, p. 193).

[2] *Socratic Digest*, No. 4, p. 7 f.

But after all, you have just assured me that all our beliefs are the effects of psychological and physical causes. In all probability the widespread belief in the invalidity of syllogisms with un-distributed middles is simply caused by something in people's genetic inheritance, and if a mutation occurred in the right gene on one of their chromosomes a line of human beings would arise to whom such syllogisms appeared indubitably valid. Such a mutation may in fact have happened more than once in the world's history. It might perhaps have very little survival value, but that would have nothing to do with the truth or falsehood of the belief. We must not be sentimentalists. After all, as one of your own poets has said:

> Truth for ever on the scaffold,
> Wrong for ever on the throne.

In fact, to be quite honest, I suspect that this mutation did take place in one of my parents and that it is dominant to the non-mutated form."

It is, I think, clear that a radical determinism about our mental processes is self-stultifying in the sense that I have tried to explain. If it is consistent, it must be applied not only to our volitions and our attitudes, but to our reasoning processes as well. Such plausibility as it has is due, I would maintain, to the fact that when it is asserted an escape-clause is either explicitly included or, more often, implicitly assumed. It is held to apply to volitions and attitudes, but not to ratiocination; or, if it does apply to ratiocination in general, it does not apply to the ratiocination which its propounder makes use of in arguing for its truth. In the psychological, as distinct from the cerebral, realm this criticism seems to apply to the psychoanalytical doctrine of Freud. He is not interested in the cerebral cortex, but he is interested in the unconscious, and his view has been summarised in the following words:

Psychoanalysis considers mental "events" as determined by a strict and inexorable law of causality. This causality is conceived according to the pattern of causality in physics. (Or as physics used to conceive of causality, before the idea had been born that the notion of causality had to be given up and that it was "dissolved" by the latest discoveries of the physicists.)

For the psychoanalyst, every mental fact, be it a dream or an action, an inspiration or a sentiment, an idea about chemistry or the plan of a book, is strictly determined by causal factors. These causal factors are of two kinds; they are rooted either in the bodily constitution of the individual or in his past history. Every experience, whether conscious or not, leaves lasting traces. Nothing is "forgotten", nothing ever disappears from the mind.[1]

According to Freud, the convictions which we hold have rarely, if ever, been formed as a result of our consideration of the arguments which we afterwards use to justify them; the arguments are merely rationalisations of our unconscious desires and are usually in fact invalid, though we cannot see this. If all that Freud was asserting was that we sometimes form our beliefs over-hastily, his theory would be harmless and indeed useful; more careful examination would enable us to sift out those beliefs which had a rational justification from those which were mere wish-fulfilments. Freud, however, asserted his position in the most uncompromising way. Once he had explained how, on his theory, a belief had been formed it ceased to have any interest for him. As soon as he had convinced himself that the idea of God was the projection of a father-image in a wish-fulfilment, he could discuss the whole subject of religion in twenty thousand words under the title *The Future of an Illusion*. No arguments were exempt from his diagnosis, except presumably the arguments, if any, on which his own position was based. It only needs the escape-clause to be ruled out of court for the whole argument to collapse under its own weight; this is what in fact was done by one of Freud's severest critics, Dr Rudolf Allers, in his book *The Successful Error*, in which time after time he turns Freud's own weapons against him and points out that Freud's views are just the views which on Freud's own principles a person with the background of Freud would be expected to have developed. As an *argumentum ad hominem* this is brilliant, but Allers makes, I think, an even stronger point when he asserts that Freud is in fact so loyal to his own theory that he bases it not upon argument, but upon dogma. "Psychoanalysis", he writes,

[1] R. Allers, *The Successful Error*, p. 64. In this passage "psychoanalysis" is used in the strict sense as referring to the system of Freud, as distinct from other schools of psychology.

has become entangled in a truly difficult situation. Since its statements really rest, not on facts but upon previously introduced views —the very same views that the facts allegedly demonstrate—the method itself and the accordance with the theory is no sufficient proof. All these reasonings move in the same fatal circle which they cannot escape except by a radical change of tactics. If the truth of the propositions of psychoanalysis could be made evident by observations based on totally different methods, the viciousness of the circle would disappear. But this is the one thing impossible to do.[1]

It should be added that it is quite possible to approve of psychoanalysis as a technique of investigation and as a therapeutic method while rejecting it *in toto* on the philosophical side. This is the position taken up in the two massive volumes of M. Roland Dalbiez on *Psychoanalytic Method and the Doctrine of Freud*; he is followed by M. Maritain in his essay on "Freudianism and Psychoanalysis"[2]. On the other hand, Dr Rudolf Allers, in the book already quoted, rejects Freudianism root and branch with great vigour, and Fr Victor White, while questioning some of his arguments, agrees with his conclusion.[3] One of the most balanced of Catholic writers on psychology, Fr Joseph Nuttin of Louvain, while avoiding a direct condemnation of Freudianism as a therapeutic method, criticises it at so many points as virtually to supersede it.[4]

We can thus reject with confidence the view that our convictions of valid argumentation and of freedom of volition are alike illusory, being simply the effects of physical or psychological causes acting in a purely deterministic way. I must, however, make it clear that in denying that these convictions are illusory, I am not maintaining that they are infallible. It is not necessary, in order to avoid the sceptical outcome of the determinist view, to maintain that we are *never* mistaken when we think that we have argued validly or acted freely. What is necessary is to hold, with common sense, that, although we sometimes make mistakes, we are usually able to correct them. Our minds are not infallible but they are self-correcting. Error is the exception, correctness the rule. To use an Aristotelian phrase, correct-

[1] Op. cit., p. 44.
[2] In *Redeeming the Time*. The French original is in *Quatre essais sur l'esprit*.
[3] *God and the Unconscious*, p. 48.
[4] *Psychoanalysis and Personality*, I, i.

ness and error are not two species of the same genus but are related as the perfect to the imperfect;[1] the normal is not simply a special case of the pathological; truth is not just a special case of error.[2]

3. THE PHILOSOPHERS AND THE PHYSIOLOGISTS

It should be sufficiently clear by now that the Christian religion is in no way committed to the Cartesian doctrine of man. It is not, however, thereby committed to the views which that strenuous anti-Cartesian, Professor Gilbert Ryle, has expounded in his celebrated book *The Concept of Mind*. Few, if any, philosophers have repudiated as explicitly as he has the theory which he describes, with what he himself calls "deliberate abusiveness", as "the dogma of the Ghost in the Machine".[3] The reason for this is, however, not that he believes human beings to consist of two parts, namely body and mind, in an intimate and mysterious union, but that he does not think that it is meaningful to use the term "mind" to refer to any "thing" at all. His view of man is not a "mechanistic" one, for he thinks that the behaviour of men differs in important ways from the behaviour of machines. Nor does he consider that it is illicit or misleading to use the word "mind" or the words which are commonly used to denote mental activities or characteristics; on the contrary, he uses them repeatedly. "Men are not machines," he writes, "not even ghost-ridden machines. They are men—a tautology which is sometimes worth remembering."[4] Again he says:

> I am not . . . denying that there occur mental processes. Doing long division is a mental process and so is making a joke. But I am saying that the phrase "there occur mental processes" does not mean the same sort of thing as "there occur physical processes", and, therefore, that it makes no sense to conjoin or disjoin the two.[5]

It is very important for the understanding of Ryle's views to see precisely what he means by the last sentence quoted. To say that

---

[1] Cf. A. M. Farrer, *Finite and Infinite*, p. 103.

[2] Cf. E. Gilson, "Vade mecum du débutant réaliste", in *Le Réalisme méthodique*, p. 96. Nuttin repeatedly makes this point against Freud: "The professional bias of the psychopathologist often leads Freud to look upon *normal* phenomena as *deviations from the abnormal*" (op. cit., p. 170; cf. pp. 27, 67, 162 f.).

[3] Op. cit., p. 15.   [4] Ibid., p. 81.   [5] Ibid., p. 22.

'There occur mental processes" does not mean the same sort of thing as "There occur physical processes" might mean that there were mental processes and there were physical processes, but that they were not the same kind of process. Such an interpretation would, however, be for Ryle an instance of the Cartesianism which he is concerned above all else to deny; it would suggest that the body and the mind were two different kinds of substance. What Ryle in fact means is that, in the sense in which physical processes are said to occur, mental processes do not "occur" at all. For Ryle the words which are commonly taken to denote mental processes do nothing more than describe the way in which certain physical processes occur, or certain of their observable characteristics. "To find that most people have minds", he says, "(though idiots and infants in arms do not) is *simply* to find that they are able and prone to do certain sorts of things, and this we do by witnessing the sorts of things they do."[1] And again: "Overt intelligent performances are not clues to the workings of minds; they *are* those workings".[2] It is in fact clear that Ryle's doctrine is really a form of behaviourism, and at the end of his book he admits this.[3] But it is a highly sophisticated behaviourism which, as he rightly points out, is in sharp contrast to much that has generally gone by that name. The traditional behaviourists were people who wished to eliminate from the description of human and animal activity all use of mental terms and concepts; ideally the description should be given in purely physical terms. Ryle, on the other hand, believes description by mental terms and concepts to be highly advantageous, and he himself makes great use of it; his command of "psychological" epithets is the envy of all his readers. But for him mental acts and dispositions are not acts and dispositions of a substance called the mind; description in terms of mental terms and concepts is simply description of certain characteristics of bodily behaviour. To say, for example, that a man was avaricious would not, in Ryle's view, assert any continuously persisting characteristic of the man's inner self; it would merely indicate what his observable physical behaviour would be like under certain conditions. "It must be noticed from the start", Ryle says,

---

[1] *Concept of Mind*, p. 61 (italics mine).   [2] Ibid., p. 58 (italics mine).
[3] Ibid., p. 327.

that it is one thing to say that certain human actions and reactions exhibit qualities of character and intellect; it is, by an unfortunate linguistic fashion, quite another thing to say that there occur mental acts or mental processes. The latter expression traditionally belongs to the two-worlds story, the story that some things exist or occur "in the physical world," while other things exist and occur not in that world but in another, metaphorical place. Rejection of this story is perfectly compatible with retaining the familiar distinction between, say, babbling and talking sense, or between twitching and signalling; nor does acceptance of the two-worlds story in any degree clarify or consolidate this distinction.[1]

Ryle's doctrine about the use of mental terms and concepts seems, so far as I can understand it, to provide a fairly good example of Braithwaite's view of the nature of scientific theories. Ryle does not hold that the mind or any mental concept is simply a logical construct out of sensible data; that is to say, he does not hold that some form of words can be given, in which the only non-logical words are the names of sensible particulars, and which, if it is substituted for the word "mind" in any sentence in which that word occurs, will reproduce the sense of the sentence unchanged. What he does apparently hold is that rules can be given, at least in principle, by means of which the conclusion of any argument that has been conducted with mental terms and concepts can be translated, without loss or gain of meaning, into terms that directly refer to observable behaviour. Thus for Ryle the mind seems to have the same kind of nature as the elastic ether in the physical theories of the last century; it is not a substance that exists in the sense in which observable physical phenomena exist, but it provides a model that has considerable explicative power and results in considerable economy of thought in the discussion of a large range of important phenomena.

This is perhaps all that would need to be said in description of Ryle's view of the mind if he were perfectly consistent. He does not, however, deny, as the old-fashioned behaviourists for the most part denied, that people at any rate think that they have a direct introspective awareness of their own minds which shows these to be of a quite different nature from the objects which are perceived by the senses. This is discussed in his chapter on "Self-

[1] *Concept of Mind*, p. 135.

knowledge". He denies that we obtain any kind of privileged access to our own selves either by consciousness or by introspection, but he offers us the consolation that "on the account of self-knowledge that I shall give, knowledge of what there is to be known about other people is restored to approximate parity with self-knowledge".[1] Whether, in view of the extremely spectral character which Ryle ascribes to our knowledge of other people, this consolation will in fact be very consoling is, I think, highly doubtful. He seems to hold that our awareness of ourselves is the same in kind as our observation of the physical behaviour of other people, though it is considerably fuller. "I come", he writes,

> to appreciate the skill and tactics of a chess-player by watching him and others playing chess, and I learn that a certain pupil of mine is lazy, ambitious and witty by following his work, noticing his excuses, listening to his conversation and comparing his performances with those of others. *Nor does it make any important difference if I happen myself to be that pupil.* I can indeed then listen to more of his conversations, as I am the addressee of his unspoken soliloquies; I notice more of his excuses, as I am never absent when they are made. On the other hand, my comparison of his performances with those of others is more difficult, since the examiner is himself taking the examination, which makes neutrality hard to preserve and precludes the demeanour of the candidate, when under interrogation, from being in good view.[2]

I do not know how this passage strikes other readers, but I can only record my impression that it is extremely inadequate as a description. I suspect that Ryle has been led into it by a failure to realise that there can be any doctrine of the soul as a real entity other than that of Descartes. The view which I myself should maintain—and which I believe to be, in its main outline if not in detail, that of St Thomas Aquinas—would hold that, while we are not ever, or at least are not normally, aware of either our own or other persons' minds except when we are engaged in sense-perception (the soporific effect of shutting the eyes is a well-known fact of experience), we can and do achieve a real, though extremely obscure, awareness of them through and in our acts of sensation. I should also add that the kind of knowledge

---

[1] *Concept of Mind*, p. 155.   [2] Ibid., p. 169 (italics mine).

which we achieve of ourselves in this way is, in its fundamental character, very different from the kind of knowledge which we achieve of other persons in this way; to know myself as what lies on *this* side of my sensible phenomena is very different from knowing you as what lies on the other side of them. It is, however, clear that for Ryle awareness of this kind simply does not count. However vigorously he may have repudiated the Cartesian doctrine of the ghost in the machine, he has accepted wholeheartedly the Cartesian doctrine of clear and distinct ideas. What is not known with the immediacy of sensation or the transparency of logical implication "isn't knowledge". Now the ambition to think clearly is a laudable one, and anyone who questions it is in danger of condemnation as an advocate of mental fuzziness. Nevertheless it is relevant to point out that, if there are any realities, whether human or divine, which by their very nature cannot be known by us clearly and distinctly, then the requirement that knowledge must be clear and distinct will result in these realities slipping out of our grasp altogether. Ryle is far too much of a realist to ignore the mental aspects of our experience entirely. But time and again while reading his brilliant book I have had the feeling that he was trying to bring within his framework elements of our experience which, while they are undoubtedly real, do not naturally fit into it, and that he has therefore had to submit them to violent distortion in order to get them in. The passage last quoted seems to me to provide a striking example of this. Ryle has written an interesting passage upon "the systematic elusiveness of 'I'",[1] but I suspect that we are all of us somewhat more systematically elusive than he makes out. We may agree with him that "if the doctrine of the ghost in the machine were true, not only would people be absolute mysteries to one another, they would also be absolutely intractable". But it is with a sense of surprise that one reads the subsequent words: "In fact they are relatively tractable and relatively easy to understand."[2]

It is in this connection somewhat amusing to observe that a great many physiologists are convinced that there is a real problem about the relation between body and mind, however difficult it may be to formulate it satisfactorily, while the most fashionable

[1] *Concept of Mind*, p. 195.   [2] Ibid., p. 114.

school of philosophers at the present day, namely the school of the linguistic empiricists, is convinced that the alleged problem is really no problem at all and that it is only thought to be a problem in consequence of an easily exposed logical fallacy. In 1950 there was published under the title *The Physical Basis of Mind* a series of broadcast talks in which some of the most distinguished living British physiologists took part. The concluding broadcast consisted of brief reflections on the symposium by three philosophers, two of them being professionals and one a well-known amateur. The physiologists had almost uniformly shown themselves to be much preoccupied with a real problem which they believed to exist about the relation between the body and the mind. The two professional philosophers, on the other hand, were equally convinced that there was really no such problem and that it was only through sheer mental confusion that the physiologists had thought that there was one. Professor A. J. Ayer wrote as follows:

> If this is a genuine problem, it is hard to see why further information about the brain should be expected to solve it. For however much we amplify our picture of the brain, it remains still a picture of something physical, and it is just the question how anything physical can interact with something that is not that is supposed to constitute our difficulty. If what we are seeking is a bridge across a seemingly impassable river it will not help us merely to elevate one of the banks.[1]

In fact, for Ayer the scientists had simply fallen into the snare which had previously entrapped Descartes, who, having divided substances into two entirely disparate types, namely matter and mind, was faced with the impossible task of trying to find a link between them. For Ayer there are simply two sets of observations, those made by the physiologists and those made by the psychologists, and the only question that can arise about their relations is the question how they are empirically correlated. "There is nothing especially mysterious", he writes, "about the fact that two different sets of observations are correlated; that, given the appropriate conditions, they habitually accompany one another.... To ask *why* something occurs, if it is not simply equivalent to asking *how* it occurs, is to ask what other things are associated

[1] Op. cit., p. 70.

with it. Once the facts are fully described, there is no mystery left."[1] Professor Ryle, who followed Professor Ayer, simply drove home his point by an entertaining exposure of the myth of the ghost in the machine; there can be no problem of the relation between two things called the body and the soul, because there is no such *thing* as a soul. Language that employs mental terms and concepts is merely describing certain features of the observable behaviour of a certain type of material object. This is, as we have already seen, the thesis that Ryle has developed at length in *The Concept of Mind.*

The comments of Ayer and Ryle are highly typical of the philosophical school to which they belong. For them, in the words of Wittgenstein, "Philosophy simply puts everything before us, and neither explains nor deduces anything.—Since everything lies open to view there is nothing to explain".[2] We may indeed be grateful to them for refusing to bog themselves down in the morasses of traditional idealism. Nevertheless, even if the scientists whom Ayer and Ryle criticised had failed to state with full philosophical rigour the question which was troubling them, it is difficult to believe that they were quite as simple-minded as their critics made out. It may well be that the question of the relation between mind and body is only to be answered by examining their correlation, but it is also possible that the nature of that correlation may be extremely revealing about the way in which they act upon each other. This is something which only investigation can show, but it is at least striking that a great many physiologists, whose professional concern is with the functioning of the body, feel impelled to postulate the existence of the mind as an active entity, although Professor Ryle, whose occupation is logic, has persuaded himself that they have no need to do this.

4. THE NEUROPHYSIOLOGICAL APPROACH

The most interesting discussion of this question that I have seen is that which is given by Professor J. C. Eccles in his Waynflete Lectures of 1952 on *The Neurophysiological Basis of Mind.* From the point of view of the general reader, it is unfortunate that he introduces many technical terms without definition, for

[1] Op. cit., p. 73.   [2] *Philosophical Investigations*, I, 126.

the substance of his exposition and discussion is by no means difficult to follow once one has penetrated the lexicographical barrier. The relevant matter for our present purpose is to be found in his last two chapters, and I shall try to give a simple statement of the argument which I hope, in spite of the simplification, will be substantially accurate.

I shall take it for granted that the reader is familiar with the general picture which modern physiology puts before us, of the structure of the brain and its relation to the sensory-motor system of the body. A succinct and authoritative account can be found in the broadcast talk by Professor W. E. Le Gros Clark which forms the third chapter in the symposium on *The Physical Basis of Mind* to which I have already referred. A fuller, but still popular, account is given in Lord Adrian's book *The Physical Background of Perception*. Very briefly, and neglecting irrelevant refinements, the essential facts are as follows. The human brain is a massive organ weighing about fifty ounces and consisting of something like ten thousand million nerve-cells or neurones. These are interconnected by an almost incredibly complicated network of fibres. The receiving areas of a cell are known as "dendrites", the output-channel as the "axon". Upon the dendrites there impinge multitudes of nerve-fibres, each of which terminates upon the neurone in one or more "synaptic knobs". Into the brain there come from the sensory nerves of the body electric impulses whose ultimate source is the stimulation of the sense-organs. Out of the brain there pass electric impulses along the motor nerves; and it is as a result of these impulses that the muscles and other organs are stimulated to do their work. In Dr W. Grey Walter's words, "the current of a nerve impulse is a sort of electrochemical smoke-ring about two inches long travelling along the nerve at a speed of as much as 300 feet per second".[1] The mere arrival of a nerve-impulse in the brain is not, however, a sufficient condition for the occurrence of the corresponding sensation. For this it is necessary that the impulse should be relayed through the network of brain-cells to the appropriate area of the surface-layer or "cortex" of the brain. Unless there takes place this stimulation of the sensory cortex, which is situated at the back half of the brain, the sensation will not occur. Similarly,

[1] *The Living Brain*, p. 25.

with an impulse transmitted to a muscle along a motor nerve. Unless this impulse originates in the appropriate area of the cortex, whose location is in the front half of the brain, there will take place the corresponding stimulation of the bodily organ concerned, but it will not be experienced as a consciously willed act. A great many of our sensory-motor reactions take place through a process of stimulus and response which never reaches the cortex at all, or even never reaches the brain; the sensory-motor arc is completed by a shorter route, and this is in fact the case with that whole body of unconscious reactions and reflexes upon which the greater part of our physical existence depends. It is only when the cerebral cortex is active that we have consciousness; "it can be stated", writes Professor Eccles, "that all other systems, e.g. the circulatory system or the endocrine system, produce their effects on the 'mind' or 'self' secondarily to their direct or indirect action on the brain".[1]

Some further points must be added. One is that there is no direct relation between the strength of a nerve-impulse and the intensity of the corresponding sensation; a more intense sensation is produced not by a stronger impulse, but by a train of impulses of greater frequency. Another point is that the sensory cortex is highly differentiated as regards its relation to the different types of sensation and as regards the parts of the body to which it assigns their origination, so much so that if an impulse from a taste-organ gets relayed, by a wrong link-up, to the part of the cortex which is concerned with the sensation of sound, what will be perceived will be not a taste but a noise.[2] Furthermore, it is not only when impulses are coming into or going out from the brain that the brain cells are in a state of electrical activity; electro-encephalography, the measurement of the electric potential of the various regions of the brain-surface, has shown that the brain is the subject of incessant rhythmical activity, the main types of which have been distinguished, according to their wave-frequency, by the Greek letters alpha, beta, delta and theta. Some idea of the complexity of the electrical processes in the cortex may

[1] Op. cit., p. 261.
[2] It is, I think, unfortunate that no reference is made to points such as this by Professor Gilbert Ryle in his discussion of perception in his Tarner Lectures, *Dilemmas*.

be gathered from the fact that it is estimated to contain something like fifty thousand nerve-cells to the square millimetre,[1] each of which cells is the centre of a complicated pattern of afferent and efferent pathways.

Let us turn now to Eccles' discussion of what he frankly describes as the Mind-Brain Problem. It is interesting to notice that he insists categorically that our mental experiences are just as immediate and public as are our experiences of the physical world. By the medium of language, he says,

> the private observation of one's "self-consciousness" achieves public status, and may therefore be ranked as a fact of experience. . . . Thus we report our mental experiences to others and discover that they have like experiences to report to us. Such procedures serve to assure us that our private experiences are not hallucinatory, or more strictly we may say that hallucinatory experiences are discovered by this procedure. . . . The above argument establishes that mental experiences have the same validity that attaches to our perceptual experiences of "things". Hence the observations relating to mind, i.e. mental phenomena, are part of the experiences that a scientist should recognize as providing problems which are suitable for scientific investigation.[2]

With this introduction, Eccles passes on to consider the body-mind problem, and it is interesting to notice that he understands it as something quite different from the nonsensical pseudo-problem which is all that it means to Professor Ayer. He is not concerned to find some mysterious mechanism, made of a substance neither physical nor mental, whose function is to "bridge the gap" between body and mind. What he is concerned to do is to find out what kind of correlation there is between physical and mental processes and to discover at what stage in the physical process the interaction of body and mind may be conceived to occur. He admits that Descartes' explanation was crude and mechanical, but he attributes this to the lack of scientific knowledge of the brain in the seventeenth century. He recognises that many philosophers, of whom he instances Burtt, Stout and Ryle, reject both dualism (by which he means the view that body and mind are both of them "substances", though of vastly different

[1] Cf. Eccles, op. cit., p. 229.   [2] Ibid., p. 263.

natures) and also the interactionist view of brain-mind liaison. He quotes other philosophers, however, such as Broad and Popper, as holding the opposite view and adds to these the weighty scientific names of Eddington, Sherrington, Adrian and Le Gros Clark. He formulates under four headings hypotheses that have been formulated about events that occur in the brain when it is in liaison with mind; these all claim the support of experimental evidence. The first hypothesis is that mind-brain liaison occurs primarily in the cerebral cortex, though diencephalic centres may also be concerned, particularly as continued bombardment by impulses from these inner regions is necessary for sustaining cortical activity. The second hypothesis is that only when there is a high level of cortical activity is liaison with mind possible. The third is that any thought-pattern in the mind has a counterpart in a specific spatio-temporal pattern of neuronal activity. The fourth is that memory of any particular event depends on a specific reorganisation of neuronal associations (the engram) in a vast system of neurones widely spread over the cortex. In this connection he quotes K. S. Lashley as arguing that any act of memory-recall involves the activity of millions of neurones, that any particular memory-trace or engram has multiple representation in the cortex, and that, on the other hand, each neurone, and even each synaptic junction, is built into many engrams. Eccles then goes on to enquire how it comes about that liaison with mind occurs only in special states of the matter-energy system of the cerebral cortex. He answers that the dynamic patterns of neuronal activity that occur in the cortex during conscious states are of a radically different character both from the rest of the matter-energy or natural world and also from the condition of the cortex itself when it is not in the state associated with consciousness. He then argues that it is by means of this special condition that the brain enters into liaison with mind, having in consequence a sensitivity of a different kind and order from that of any physical instrument. What then is this unique type of activity?

Eccles reminds us that the cortex contains some ten thousand million neurones, each of which is the meeting-point of a multitude of fibres which together form a network of indescribable intricacy. He then directs our attention to the rhythmic wave which electroencephalography detects in the cerebral cortex when its owner is inattentive but awake; this is the so-called "alpha-wave", of frequency about ten vibrations a second. When it is remembered that nerve-impulses are transmitted by the successive electric discharge or "firing" of a sequence of neurones and that it takes a neurone about a tenth of a second to recharge itself for further action, it follows, from the fact that a nerve-impulse would take about a thousandth of a second to travel a distance equal to the average length of an interneuronal link, that, assuming the truth of the neurone-circuit theory, each circuit involved in the maintenance of the alpha-rhythm must contain about a hundred neurones. This does not mean, however, that these circuits are isolated from each other; Eccles has already shown, by means of a simplified scheme, that each link in any circuit may be held in common with a number of other circuits. There appears, in fact, to be a loose coupling of a large number of neurones, adopting on the whole the dominant alpha-rhythm. It is remarked that unconsciousness accompanies a neuronal net which, as shown by the electroencephalogram is either at rest, as in sleep, or compulsively driven, as in an epileptic convulsion or shock-therapy; in these cases the net *as such* is not in liaison with mind. Eccles quotes his predecessor in the Waynflete Lecturership, Lord Adrian, as suggesting that the part of the neuronal net that gives the alpha-rhythm is itself not in liaison with mind;[1] when there is such liaison there is a rapid, irregular and low-voltage electroencephalogram, and it is upon this that attention must be directed. From this standpoint Eccles now goes on to develop his hypothesis of the mode of operation of "will" on the cerebral cortex.

He begins this exposition by insisting upon the authenticity of our conviction of the freedom of our wills. "It is a psychological fact", he writes,

> that we believe we have ability to control or modify our actions by the exercise of "will", and in practical life all sane men assume that they have this ability. By stimulation of the motor cortex it is pos- sible to evoke complex motor acts in a conscious human subject. The subject reports that the experience is quite different from that occurring when he "willed" a movement. The distinction arises not

[1] Op. cit., p. 271; cf. Adrian, *The Physical Background of Perception*, p. 77.

in the differences between the movements, but in their different antecedents. In the one case there was the experience of having "willed" an action which was missing in the other.[1]

Eccles is careful to add at this point that this does not mean that all our activity is willed, not even all the activity that devolves from the cerebral cortex. But he points out that much of the activity that is normally unconscious and automatic can be controlled by willing when we wish to do this, as for example the activity of breathing. He then gives a simple schematic example of the way in which, in full consistency with what is known from both physics and psychology, the will may be assumed to change the processes which would otherwise occur in the cortex. He assumes that the immediate effect of the act of will is to shut down one synaptic outlet from a circuit in the cortex and to open another, with the consequence that there is a redistribution of the impulses in adjacent branches. The material entity or "node" in which any branch makes contact with a neurone is sufficiently small for the difference in energy distribution involved to fall well within what is allowed by the quantum theory in virtue of the Heisenberg "uncertainty-principle",[2] so there is no question of any "violation of the laws of physics". The only question is whether such minute effects as this could give rise to cortical excitation of the intensity required to bring about the bodily changes which our acts of willing are capable of producing. Eccles answers this question in the affirmative. The deciding factor is the extreme elaborateness of the neuronal network, as a result of which a discharge along one of the branches of a neurone will in a very brief time have affected a very great number of other neurones. On the conservative assumption that on the average each neurone has three afferent and three efferent branches, and on the further assumption that the activation of one synapse is sufficient to cause a neurone to "fire", it is shown that the number of neurones activated within a fiftieth of a second by a single discharge from one neurone will be of the order of ten thousand. If each neurone has five afferent and five efferent branches, the number of neurones activated within the same brief period will be something like eight hundred thousand.

In applying this simplified model to the actual case of the

[1] Op. cit., p. 271.   [2] Cf. p. 169 supra.

human brain, Eccles is careful to make the necessary qualifications. The first is that the empirical evidence shows that for "will" to be operative a considerable part of the cortex must be at a relatively high level of excitation. He next notes that in fact the number of synaptic contacts made by one neurone is more like a hundred than like four or five, but, in view of the facts that more than one impulse may be needed to cause a neurone to discharge and that it is necessary in any case for the recipient neurone to be within a somewhat narrow range of excitability,[1] he considers that it will be safe to assume that four or five of the synaptic contacts made by any neurone with adjacent ones will (when summed with synaptic impulses from elsewhere) actually cause one of the latter to discharge. The conclusion is that within a fiftieth of a second an impulse from one neurone will have contributed directly or indirectly to the excitation of hundreds of thousands of others. This is confirmed by the measurement of the velocity of an excitation-wave spreading through the cortex from an artificially stimulated focus. This velocity is found to be twenty centimetres per second, which, in conjunction with the observed cortical density of roughly fifty thousand neurones per square millimetre, results in the invasion of about four million neurones in a fiftieth of a second.

The above calculation was based simply upon the assumption of the initial discharge of one neurone. If we now assume that what is immediately affected by an act of will is not one single node in the network, but a whole field of nodes in some kind of spatio-temporal pattern, it is evident that in a few thousandths of a second a vast modification of the condition of the motor cortex may be brought about, with the corresponding subsequent results in the bodily organs. This is the justification that Eccles urges for his claim that the condition of the brain when it enters into liaison with mind is radically different from that of any physical instrument. "It can be claimed", he says,

> that no physical instrument would bear comparison with the postu-
> lated performance of the active cerebral cortex as a detector of

---

[1] The reason for this last condition is that if the recipient neurone is not sufficiently excited the impulse received will not be sufficient to discharge it, while if it is too highly excited it will discharge itself without stimulation by the impulse in question.

minute "fields of influence" spread over a microscopic pattern and with temporal sequences of milliseconds. The integration, within a few milliseconds, of "influences" picked up at hundreds of thousands of nodes would be unique. . . .

Thus, the neurophysiological hypothesis is that the "will" modifies the spatio-temporal activity of the neuronal network by exerting spatio-temporal "fields of influence" that become effective through this unique detector function of the active cerebral cortex.

He concludes with the remark that "this hypothesis assumes that the 'will' or 'mind influence' has itself a spatio-temporal patterned character in order to allow it this operative effectiveness".[1]

A materialist might object at this point that electronic digital computers have already been designed which can be programmed in such a way as to reproduce many of the characteristic operations of human mentality, and that scientists such as Thomas Ross, R. A. Wallace, W. R. Ashby and W. Grey Walter have constructed toy animals which, by a skilful application of the principle of negative feed-back, can be made to imitate much of the behaviour of living animals.[2] It is not, I think, entirely sufficient to reply, as one might be tempted, that these machines would never have come into existence except as a result of the ingenuity of human brains which already existed. Nor is it strictly relevant to point to the extreme efficiency of the human brain in comparison with these machines, although it has been amusingly remarked that, whereas a human brain costs about five thousand pounds to produce and has a power-consumption of twenty-five watts, a machine containing the same number of cells (roughly ten thousand million) adequately interconnected would cost over a million million million pounds, would consume a million kilowatts of power and would occupy about one and half million cubic feet of housing space.[3] All this might be true without the operation of the human brain being in principle different from that of a highly complicated machine. What is much more to the point, I think, is Eccles' remark that the physical execution of an act of will involves the co-ordinated activity of a vast number of

---

[1] Op. cit., p. 277. The sentence last quoted seems to me to be misleading if it suggests that the mind is itself extended in space in any other sense than that it can produce immediate effects at more than one point of space. But this is, I think, all that Eccles means.

[2] Cf. e.g. W. Grey Walter, *The Living Brain*.   [3] Ibid., p. 76.

nodes in some kind of spatio-temporal pattern, for, although the discharge of any particular synaptic element may be, from the physical point of view, a perfectly normal quantum phenomenon taking place in strict accordance with Heisenberg's uncertainty-principle, the co-ordinated functioning of a vast number of elements in the way required would be an occurrence of such extremely low probability that some explanation other than the merely physical one would seem to be required for it. This is, by the nature of the case, not an absolutely conclusive argument; nor, it must be emphasised, does it involve any supersession of physical law by mental volition, since the physical laws themselves are only stated in terms of probability. To illustrate the point by a simple parallel, if, on a particular day, all the Welshmen in Liverpool named Jones were run over by motor-scooters ridden by Irishmen named Cassidy, it would be quite possible to explain this occurrence as due to the normal hazards of life in one of our great cities. People do on occasion get run over by motor-scooters, and if they do, both they and the riders of the vehicles have names and nationalities. There is nothing contrary to the laws of nature in a Welshman named Jones being run over by a motor-scooter ridden by an Irishman named Cassidy. Nevertheless, if such an explanation was offered of the incident in question, an intelligent police-officer would feel that there was still something that needed investigating; and it would be something involving description not in terms of physical law but in terms of human volitions and intentions. Eccles' view of the relation of the will to the brain is of this latter type; and he illustrates it by referring to some remarks made by Sir Arthur Eddington in 1939 in his book *The Philosophy of Physical Science*.

In the discussion referred to, Eddington outlined two ways by which, in accordance with the quantum theory, the action of the mind upon the brain could be conceived to take place.[1] The first way, which he called "hypothesis A", would be by an influence exerted by the mind upon individual quantum events within the limits laid down by the uncertainty-principle. This hypothesis seemed to Eddington to be unlikely, because of the difficulty of seeing how the extremely minute effects permitted by the uncertainty-principle could be amplified in such a way as to pro-

---

[1] Op. cit., p. 182 f.

duce large muscular movements. Eccles remarks, however,[1] that Eddington was presumably thinking of objects as large as a neurone, whereas present-day neurologists would think of the much smaller "synaptic knob"; and he argues, on the basis of the actual physical magnitudes involved, that a disturbance of the synaptic knob that was well within the quantum limits might in fact lead to a synaptic discharge which would be ultimately effective over a large area of the cortical network. Eddington's chief reason, however, for disfavouring hypothesis A was that it seemed to him to involve a fundamental inconsistency in that it first of all assumed the behaviour to be restricted by the hypothesis of non-correlation or "law of chance" and then to be further restricted by the non-chance factor of volition. I am not myself convinced that this objection to hypothesis A would hold unless one accepted Eddington's highly questionable epistemological theory of "selective subjectivism"; but the matter need hardly be discussed here, as his second hypothesis seems on other grounds to be more plausible. Hypothesis B is in fact the view which, on the balance of the experimental evidence, Eccles himself favours, the hypothesis of a correlated behaviour of the individual quantum effects when matter is in liaison with mind; we have already treated it as fully as is necessary for our present purposes.

Having discussed in this way the influence exerted by the mind on the body, Eccles next goes on to consider the converse influence exerted by the body on the mind, and in particular the question of perception. As we have already seen, the necessary and sufficient physical precondition of any perceptual experience is simply the electrical stimulation of the appropriate areas of the sensory cortex of the brain; whether the stimulus in fact originates in the sense organ from which it normally comes is irrelevant to the perceptual experience. If, by some form of short circuit, the stimulus from an organ of taste is diverted so that it arrives at the hearing-area of the cortex instead of the tasting-area, we shall experience not a taste but a noise; and the same is true if the cortex is stimulated directly and not by a stimulus originating in any sense-organ at all. "The only necessary condition", writes Eccles,

[1] Op. cit., p. 278.

for an observer to see colours, hear sounds, or experience the existence of his own body is that appropriate patterns of neuronal activity shall occur in appropriate regions of his brain . . . It is immaterial whether these events are caused by local stimulation of the cerebral cortex or some part of the afferent nervous pathway, or whether they are, as is usual, generated by afferent impulses discharged by receptor organs.[1]

It is as the result of these purely private stimulations of the appropriate cortical areas that we come to believe in the existence of an external objective world. The words which Eccles uses to describe the process by which the transition is made are "projection", "interpretation" and "inference". The first step in the process is that, by conventions both inherited and acquired, which are, as it were, built into the structure of the cortex, the observer experiences a private perceptual world; the second step is that, as a result of communication with other observers, he learns to interpret part of his private perceptual experience as events in a single common public physical world. It is added that science builds a progressively more valid or real physical world, by establishing rules by which numerically specifiable quantities of which the real physical world is composed may be correlated with the sensible qualities of the private perceptual worlds and so the "symbolic bias" of the perceptual worlds may be eliminated.

It is easy to see the kind of havoc that an ill-disposed philosopher can make of an argument such as this. "You say", he will point out, "that what you immediately perceive is a world of private perceptions. You add that you have these perceptions simply as a result of the stimulation of certain areas of your cerebral cortex, and that so long as the appropriate areas are stimulated the appropriate perceptions will follow. You also assert that, normally though not always, the cortex is stimulated by impulses that ultimately derive from the sense-organs, and that when this is so the perceptual experience or part of it can be built into a common public world which you share with other

---

[1] Op. cit., p. 280. This does not mean that the pattern on the cortex must be geometrically similar in structure to the pattern of the percept. As Sir Russell Brain remarks, in connection with binocular vision, "when we perceive a two-dimensional circle we do so by means of an activity in the brain which is halved, reduplicated, transposed, inverted, distorted and three-dimensional" (*Mind, Perception and Science*, p. 9).

percipients. But how do you know that your perceptions are produced by the stimulation of your cortex? How, in fact, do you know that you have a cortex at all? Presumably as a result of observations that other people claim to have made of cortices or that you claim to have made of other people's cortices. But how do you know that there are other people or other cortices, or indeed any beings that exist outside your own mind? You yourself have admitted that you would believe yourself to be perceiving these external objects even if they did not exist at all, so long as your own cortex was appropriately stimulated. But now it appears that you cannot be sure even that you have a cortex. Is all this elaborate paraphernalia of cortices, nerves, sense-organs, external objects, other people and the rest nothing more than a model which makes it possible for you to give a compact account of your own subjective experience but which there is no reason to endow with independent existence? That would at least be a coherent position, but it does not seem to be what you are in fact asserting. For you allege that the perceptual world consists of symbolic data from which a real physical world can be inferred, and you also allege that other people have perceptual worlds which have the same claim to consideration as your own. Admittedly your theory might conceivably be true, in the sense that there is nothing in it which is self-contradictory or inconsistent with experience. The trouble is that, if the theory is true, it follows that the evidence which you allege in its favour turns out to be valueless. Why, then, should you expect us to accept it?"

Now there is, of course, no conclusive logical argument against solipsism or scepticism, but I think we can do better for Eccles than he does for himself. As he states it, his argument undoubtedly seems to be circular, and the type of criticism of it which I have just outlined destroys it. What he is in fact trying to assert is the commonsense view that, although we sometimes make mistakes, we normally have genuine experience of a world that is independent of our own experience. This is a manly and robust position, and I heartily sympathise with it. Eccles cuts the ground away under his feet, however, by an unnecessary capitulation to Cartesianism. He assumes that all he directly experiences is his own private perceptual world and that the external physical world is known only as a "projection", "interpretation" or "inference" from it. But if all that he directly experiences is his own private perceptual world how can he know that this projection, interpretation or inference is anything more than one of the activities that go on in his own mind? He is in fact landed in the perennial predicament of the idealist, that of being locked up in his own mind and finding that he has thrown away the key. I think it is clear that, in spite of the misleading language which he uses, Eccles is not trying to be an idealist at all. He knows very well that, although perception can sometimes go wrong, it does give a genuine knowledge of the external world and that although the mind sometimes makes mistakes, it is able to correct the mistakes that it has made. What the mind does is not to project or infer the physical world from the perceptual world, or to interpret the perceptual world in terms of it, but to apprehend the intelligible characteristics of the physical world through the sensible percepts by means of which it presents itself. In the Thomist sense—which is very different from the modern sense—of the word, it *abstracts* the intelligible essence from the sensible species. It is, I think, unwise to describe perception by using words like "symbol", as for example Sir Russell Brain does when he says that "there is knowledge depending upon perceptual symbols, aroused by stimuli reaching the body from outside itself, and which we call perception, and there is knowledge by means of conceptual symbols derived from perception by a process of inference" so that "the perceptual world must reproduce the structure of the physical world".[1] This suggests that the perceptual data are substitutes for the physical world and that from them we deduce the existence and character of the latter; I would prefer to describe them as media through which, or by means of which (*objecta quibus*) we come to apprehend the physical world in its intelligible nature. We need not, therefore, be worried by the fact that the object we perceive may have ceased to exist long before we perceive it, as when the eye receives light which has taken five hundred million years to reach us from an extra-galactic nebula;[2] the sensible pattern which we sense at any moment does not have to be a *contem-*

[1] *Mind, Perception and Science*, pp. 67, 68.
[2] Cf. Russell Brain, op. cit., p. 15.

poraneous replica of the external world in order to be a medium
through which the external world is known. I would add that it
is quite wrong to talk about hallucinations as is often done, as
if they were due to well-behaved perception of misbehaved
objects; they are due to disorder in perception itself. If a drunkard
"sees rats that are not there", this does not mean that there is a
special species of rat, the *rattus inexistens*, which the drunkard
has a peculiar capacity for observing, co-ordinate with but less
common than the more familiar *rattus rattus* and *rattus nor-
vegicus*; it means that there is no such thing as the drunkard's
rat at all, he only "thinks there is". Misperceptions are not due
to awareness of a "wild" sense-datum; it is the awareness that is
wild, otherwise the percipient would not suppose he was perceiving a sense-datum at all. As Gilson has remarked, "Taine
rendered a great service to common sense when he defined
sensation as *hallucination which is true*, for he thus showed where
logic inevitably lands idealism. Sensation becomes what a hallucination is when a hallucination isn't one."[1] Eccles observes that,
if an impulse from an organ of taste gets switched to the auditory
area of the sensory cortex, what we are conscious of is not a
taste but a noise; there is nothing, however, to get worried about
in this, except for the man to whom it happens. If tastes were not
normally perceived as tastes, and sounds as sounds, we should
not even comment on this fact. In spite of the idealist language
in which he writes, it seems clear to me that Eccles is a thoroughly
healthy realist, for only on realist principles does his account
hang together. Gilson has told us that "the first step on the road
of realism is to recognise that you have always been a realist;
the second is to recognise that, however much you try to think
otherwise, you will never succeed; the third is to notice that
people who try to think otherwise, always think as realists when
they forget to play a part".[2] And it is only when we interpret him
realistically that Eccles' explanation makes sense.

[1] "Vade mecum du débutant réaliste", in *Le Réalisme méthodique*, p. 96; cf.
ch. ii, p. 77 f. supra.
[2] Ibid., p. 87. It may be added that only on a realistic view can we accept in
their full force the assertions of scientists that there are features of the real world
which, owing to the limited nature of our sensory equipment, we fail to perceive
but which are of precisely the same kind as those which we do, e.g. radiation
whose wave-length is too long or too short for it to be perceptible by our eyes.

One or two final observations may be made before we leave this part of our discussion. It is interesting to note that, although the excitation of a considerable area of the cerebral cortex appears to be necessary for conscious experience to occur, no special area seems to be involved. Even when a large part of the cortex has been removed the mind-body liaison can persist, and in fact less than a tenth of the total area of the cortex seems to be needed. Eccles suggests that the so-called psi-capacities which Professor Rhine claims to have demonstrated (telepathy, clairvoyance and psychokinesis) may be explained in a way substantially similar to that in which he himself has explained the normal interrelation of body and mind. It is perhaps wise to exercise a certain reserve about these phenomena, and in any case it is difficult to see how the particular phenomenon of precognition could be brought within this principle of explanation. The suggestion is, however, interesting and ought to be further explored.

It is time to sum up this somewhat long discussion of Professor Eccles' exposition. It will, I hope, be clear that I am not trying to base the existence of human freedom, with all that it involves for the Christian religion, upon the theories of any modern biologist, however eminent, or upon the findings of modern biology as a whole. Professor Eccles himself would repudiate any such endeavour, for he explicitly accepts human freedom as a primary datum of experience, not as the conclusion of scientific theorising.[1]

---

[1] Op. cit., p. 271. I am not convinced by Sherrington's remark (*Man on his Nature*, p. 173): "I have the conviction that I can pick from the bookcase either this book or another. As I do not however know which of them determinism prescribes I cannot tell whether in taking a volume I depart from determinism or do not depart from it." For what I am conscious of is not only that I take this particular book, but also that I am acting freely in taking it. Even if I take the book that determinism would prescribe, determinism is false if in fact I am free in taking it.

It may be added that there is no contradiction whatever between the freedom of the will and the fact that our actions are very largely governed by inherited or acquired habits. To take an exaggeratedly simplified case, suppose that a man's past indulgence in strong drink has so weakened his self-control that on nine occasions out of ten he is incapable of refusing a drink when it is offered him. This does not in any way imply that on any specified occasion he is bound to accept the drink. If he accepted eight times running and refused the ninth, he cannot plead that he is bound to accept on the tenth occasion in order to keep up his average; for he could keep it up equally well by refusing on the tenth occasion and accepting on the eleventh and all subsequent occasions up to the twentieth. Nor is he bound to give way when the eleventh occasion arrives; for the average

It is none the less interesting to see the extent to which scientific theory can find room for the operation of the will within the framework of its system. The point can be made clear by remarking that, if we had been writing in the last century, all we could have said would have been that contemporary physics offered no loophole for the freedom of the will, but that anyhow physics had not the last word in the matter. To-day we can go further and say that, even if physics had the last word in the matter, there would be plenty of room for the freedom of the will. What we should have to say if we were writing in the twenty-first or twenty-second century I do not know.

It also emerges, I think, from our discussion that the physiologists who talk about the problem of the body-mind relation are not talking quite such nonsense as Professor Ryle and Professor Ayer have suggested. It is true that they have a most stubborn tendency to talk about the relation between body and mind in terms of a "gulf" to be "bridged". Thus Professor Eccles writes on the last page of his Waynflete lectures that his theme has been "to show how recent neurophysiological developments make it possible to give in many respects a fairly adequate functional description of the nervous system that is based on physics and chemistry and that gives some clue as to the manner in which the gulf between mind and matter may ultimately be bridged."[1] If bridging the gulf between mind and matter means, as Ayer assumes, finding some kind of third stuff,

could be maintained by refusing then and accepting on all subsequent occasions up to the thirtieth; and so on. In fact, he can go on refusing indefinitely without in any way falsifying the previously established law; though an observer may then be led to doubt whether the law was correctly formulated or to suspect that it has ceased to hold. This last supposition is in fact extremely likely, for it is by just such action as I have suggested within the limits of an existing habit that it is possible for the habit to be changed. When the dipsomaniac says "You know I am obliged to give way nine times out of ten", we can always reply "Yes, but the next time needn't be one of them". And every time that he acts in accordance with this advice it is probable that he is building up a new habit with a lower proportion of acceptances to refusals. Probability has the paradoxical character, which makes it very difficult to set it on a strictly logical basis, that, although we are accustomed to derive probabilities from the observation of sequences of occurrences, even the most wildly improbable sequences are possible; and therefore no postulated probability can be strictly invalidated by any occurrences whatever.

[1] Ibid., p. 286.

neither mind nor matter, in terms of which the action of mind and matter on each other can be made intelligible, he is certainly correct in branding the notion as nonsense. It is, however, clear that in such a passage as that just quoted nothing of the kind is meant. What in fact Eccles has done is to propound a possible way, for which he brings forward a good deal of evidence, in which physical processes in the brain may occur when mentality is involved, to show how these processes differ from those that occur when mentality is absent, and to demonstrate that the laws which present-day physics has derived from non-mental phenomena need no modification when mental activity is present. To have shown this is to have done a great deal, and I do not think that anyone could read such an exposition as that of Eccles without finding it highly illuminating and stimulating. It would, however, be rash to suppose that it represents the last word on the subject or that it has any necessary repercussions in the theological realm.

5. MODELS FOR THE BRAIN[1]

A question that naturally presents itself at this point is whether all mental processes, or only some of them, have their physical counterparts in the brain. It has already been remarked that in recent years a great many of the processes that have generally been considered to be most characteristic of mental activity have been imitated in a very large degree by electronic and other types of computing machines, and that mechanical "tortoises" have been devised, notably by W. R. Ashby, which show in a simplified form an extremely lifelike analogue of animal behaviour. Dr W. Grey Walter has given a fascinating description of these in his book *The Living Brain*. There is the homeostat *Machina sopora*, which "is like a fireside cat or dog which only stirs when disturbed, and then methodically finds a comfortable position and goes to sleep again".[2] There is *Machina speculatrix*, "which behaves so much like an animal that it has been known to drive a not usually timid lady upstairs to lock herself in her bedroom";[3]

---

[1] A very handy popular exposition of the matters dealt with in the following two sections will be found in W. Sluckin's "Pelican" book *Minds and Machines*.
[2] Op. cit., p. 81.   [3] Ibid., p. 82.

this is attracted by moderately bright lights, it is repelled by very bright lights, material objects and steep gradients, it can "recognise" another machine of the same kind or itself in a mirror, and when its battery begins to run down it returns to its stable for re-charging. There is "Cora", the Conditioned Reflex Analogue, which, when grafted on to *Machina speculatrix*, produces *Machina docilis*, a remarkable contrivance which "remembers" and "learns by experience". This striking simulation of intelligent behaviour, so far exceeding that exhibited by even the most life-like automata in the past, has been made possible by the discovery that much of the most characteristic behaviour of animals is due to the cybernetic principle, or principle of "negative feed-back", which is exemplified in the familiar device of the governor of a steam-engine. The essential feature of this is that any divergence of the system from a steady state is reported back to the control-centre and there initiates changes in the energy-supply which counteract the deviation and restore the steady state. It has even been shown by D. M. MacKay that it is theoretically possible to build a machine which would embody an "uncertainty-response" and would thus evince apparently unpredictable behaviour analogous to that which we normally attribute to free volition.[1] It is hardly surprising that some enthusiasts have drawn the con-clusion that animals and human beings are nothing more than complicated machines and that it is only a difference in degree of complexity that separates the humble *Machina docilis* from Aristotle or Einstein. Some representative reactions to this claim may be studied in a series of articles which appeared in the *British Journal for the Philosophy of Science* from 1951 onwards; it is interesting to note the general tone of caution which they exhibit. Mr J. O. Wisdom summarises the situation in the remark that "all that we know at present is that brains are less like levers and gears than like radar and thermostats".[2] Dr D. M. MacKay suggests that "no new philosophical issues are raised by the possibilities so far considered. These artefacts", he writes, "are merely deterministic performers of functions which we ourselves would describe as 'mechanical' were we to carry them out".[3] He

---

[1] Cf. J. O. Wisdom, "The Hypothesis of Cybernetics", *B.J.P.S.*, II, p. 9 (1951); D. M. MacKay, "Mindlike Behaviour in Artefacts", ibid., p. 110.
[2] Ibid., p. 23.   [3] Ibid., p. 109.

denies that there is "any distinction in principle between the observable behaviour of a human brain and the behaviour possible in a suitably designed artefact"; it is therefore all the more significant that he sees in this nothing destructive of human freedom. "The choices of a free man", he asserts,

> are seldom devoid of a statistically-predictable component; someone who knows him well can usually score a significant frequency of success in predicting his choices, though it is most unlikely that they form a stationary time-series. In the same way the choices of the artefact, given a knowledge of the various threshold levels defining transition-probabilities, are statistically predictable on a short-term basis. The suggestion is that the choices of a free man may likewise be governed by statistical distribution-functions which have a physiological representation and are in principle determinate; but that individual choices can be unpredictable in principle, and it is probable that the distribution-functions are indeterminable in practice.

He sums up his conclusion in the following words, which seem to me to be remarkably apt:

> It is suggested that these developments raise no new *theological* issues. This is, of course, a personal view; but the so-called "theological" objection against which Turing tilts in a recent paper [the reference is to an article by A. M. Turing in *Mind*, 1950] appears to be a windmill without an owner among reputable contemporary theologians. Doubtless a full realisation of foregoing implications will have a purgative action on unwarranted speculative accretions in theology, but the central concern of Christian theology at least is framed in terms of the calculus of responsibility, whose categories in the author's view are unaffected by changes in the complementary categories of physical process used to describe brain function. No reputable theologian expects to find physical laws disobeyed in the human brain; and it is difficult to see how elucidation of the particular physical processes which happen to be used can in any way be relevant to the claims (whether admitted or not) which are made by Christianity on the personality whose thought is mediated by those processes.[1]

We ought not to reject the insights of the cybernetic approach simply because some of its proponents have made exaggerated

[1] Art. cit., p. 120.

claims for it. No model ever gives a complete representation of a phenomenon in all its aspects, as we have seen in a previous lecture. R. Thomson and W. Sluckin have pointed out that the great achievement of cybernetics has been to show that teleological or goal-directed activity can be brought about by purely mechanical means: "teleological purposes are controlled by negative feed-back mechanisms: signals from the goal alter the activity after it has been initiated, so that the active system achieves its goal by mechanical reactions controlled from the goal-object or goal-state".[1] What, however, is sometimes overlooked is the fact that while negative feed-back can direct activity towards the goal it does not specify what the goal is to be; Ashby's "tortoises" were designed by Ashby. As Thomson and Sluckin say, "the principal worth of cybernetics is to be found in those writings which confine themselves to what is at the root of the discussion: the negative feed-back hypothesis of neuro-physiology".[2] This seems to be the real point of some criticisms in a review by R. O. Kapp of Ashby's exuberant book *Design for a Brain*. Kapp not only denies that the "memory" evinced by Ashby's homeostat bears any close parallel to the memory of living animals, but also accuses Ashby of neglecting the plain facts of subjective experience.[3] It will be well to recall Eccles' exposition of the way in which the cerebral cortex may be activated by free volition without any interruption of physical laws; for the heart of teleological purpose lies not in the pursuit of the goal, but in its initial choice and its possible subsequent replacement by another.

There is nothing that need disconcert a Christian in the view that our mental processes and events have correlates in our physical bodies; if a human being is a psycho-physical unity, and not simply an angel inhabiting a machine, this is only what we might expect. It may be well to remind ourselves of the extent to which a theologian of such unimpeachable respectability as St Thomas Aquinas stresses the dependence of human mentality

[1] "Cybernetics and Mental Functioning", *B.J.P.S.*, IV, p. 145 (1953).

[2] Ibid., p. 146. Cf. D. Gabor: "Information Theory is not a new name for epistemology, and it is not philosophy. . . . Though Information Theory has a philosophical fringe, its real value is in its hard core of mathematics, and of electronic models" (*Times Science Review*, Spring, 1953, p. 12).

[3] *B.J.P.S.*, IV, p. 169 f. (1953).

upon the bodily organs. For him, all our mental experience so long as we are in this life is, at any rate normally, dependent upon the stimulation of our physical senses: *nihil in intellectu quod non prius in sensu*[1] has become a commonplace of Thomist epistemology. And, although he believes that the soul, when it is separated from the body by death, is still capable of knowledge, he is emphatic that its former and proper mode of knowledge is no longer possible to it and that it knows simply by divine illumination: "the separated soul understands by ideas which it receives from an influx of divine light".[2] Furthermore, he tells us, this knowledge is, as regards natural objects, a very imperfect and confused knowledge indeed,[3] since a disembodied soul, unlike an angel, is in a condition that is unnatural to it. It is even ignorant of what is now going on on earth.[4] St Thomas is equally opposed to Cartesian angelism and to the sentimental modern view that after death the soul, freed from the hindrances of the body, passes into a condition of enhanced and uninhibited activity; for him, the soul between death and the resurrection of the body, if it has died at peace with God, is a loving and willing recipient of the cleansing and restoring activity of its Creator and Redeemer. In the words of Newman's *Gerontius*:

> . . . it lies
> Passive and still before the awful Throne . . .
> Consumed, yet quickened, by the glance of God.

Whether it is impossible in this life for the soul to experience knowledge by infusion of ideas from God himself St Thomas does not seem explicitly to discuss. Certainly he would look upon such knowledge as highly exceptional and abnormal, as belonging to the conditions of "prophecy" and "rapture".[5] Most mystical theologians would say that it occurs in the strictly supernatural and gratuitous gift of mystical experience. But it would be universally denied by all who were in any way in the Thomist-Aristotelian tradition that the soul had any *natural* power of apprehending, imagining or reasoning about material objects that was independent of the intimate collaboration of the body. What

---

[1] *De Veritate*, ii, 3, obj. 19.
[2] *S. Theol.*, I, lxxxix, 3c; cf. 1 ad 3.
[3] Ibid.; cf. 4c.
[4] Ibid., 8c.
[5] *S. Theol.*, II, II, clxxi–clxxv.

scientists have quite recently managed to do—and this demands nothing but gratitude from theologians—is to suggest, in a great deal more detail than was previously possible and with a great deal more experimental evidence to support their suggestions, what the features of that collaboration may be like. But we must never forget the inherent limitations of all "models" and, as we have seen already in other contexts,[1] we must beware of supposing that any model, however exactly it replicates the phenomena under consideration, provides a precise picture of what the physical reality "really is". Thus, the fact that we can store information in a digital electronic computer, in the form of trains of electric impulses circulating in closed circuits, makes it tempting to suppose that we remember things by a similar operation in our brains, especially as the mechanism seems to be there in the shape of neurones, axons and dendrites. But equally the fact that in other calculating machines the information is stored in the form of static patterns of electric charges on the surface of a dielectric, which are scanned by a beam of electrons when required, suggests that perhaps we remember things by some metabolic change in the neurones or their synaptic knobs. It has even been suggested that the former model may hold for our short and transient memories and the latter for the more permanent ones.[2] But it is possible that other models may be devised that are more adequate than these.

6. INFORMATION AND ENTROPY

I shall now turn to an illuminating discussion that has been given in terms of information and entropy in an article by Warren S. McCulloch.[3]

Information is fed into our brains by the stimulation of relays of neurones. Whether it occurs by the repeated stimulation of one neurone, or by the simultaneous stimulation of a number of neurones, or by a combination of these processes, does not matter; the effect upon the memory-store will be the same. Now

[1] Cf. p. 65 f. supra.
[2] Cf. G. M. Wyburn on "Central Cerebral Processes" in *Science News 23*, p. 67 (1952). Cf. J. Z. Young, *Doubt and Certainty in Science*, p. 36.
[3] "Through the Den of the Metaphysician", *B.J.P.S.*, V, p. 18 (1954).

the "amount of information" so communicated, in a mathematically definable sense of this term, is equal to the logarithm to the base two of the reciprocal of the probability of the stimulation-pattern in question, that probability being calculated on the assumption that any relay is as likely to be in a state of stimulation as not.[1] Now this, as McCulloch reminds us,

> has a peculiarly familiar sound. Gibbs had defined entropy as the logarithm of the probability of the state. In Wiener's phrase, entropy measures chaos and information is negative entropy. So, corresponding to the second law of thermodynamics, that entropy must always increase, we can write for any computing machine the corresponding law—*information can never increase*. That insures that no machine can operate on the future, but must derive its information from the past. It can never do anything with that information except corrupt it. The transmission of signals over ordinary networks of communication always follows the law that deduction obeys, that there can be no more information in the output than there is in the input. The noise, and only the noise, can increase.[2]

McCulloch goes on to remark that if we compare the input of information into the nervous system with the output from it there is a reduction in the ratio of a million to one. What, he asks, has become of all that missing information? It has, he replies, been sifted out as a result of the fact that a neurone will "fire" only if it receives two or more impulses practically simultaneously.

> The chief reason for the enormous reduction from afferent signals to efferent signals is the requirement of coincidence along the way. Every such requirement of coincidence, by reducing the *a priori* probability of a signal in the output, increases the assurance which can be placed in any subsequent signal, for that signal must then be due to coincidence in the world impingent upon our receptors. In

[1] It is important to notice that the argument depends on this assumption, which is not self-evident.

[2] Art. cit., p. 21. ("Noise" is here used in the technical sense of random background disturbances arising from within the system.) We might remark that a similar fate overcomes information stored in printed or written books, which become illegible as time goes on for the same reason. That, instead of a page decaying with the passage of time, new information (true or false) should appear on it would be one of those theoretically possible but "astronomically improbable" events that the law of increasing entropy rules out.

short, by throwing away all information that fails to agree with other information, we achieve an immense certainty that what we do observe is due to something in the world.[1]

McCulloch next observes that "the limitation of the information in the output is in large measure determined by the effectors themselves. . . . We habitually think of our sensations, or any knowledge of the world so derived, as an activity going on in those places in which afferent channels end, but we can only demonstrate it by output over some efferent channel".[2] And there are something like ten thousand million neurones in the central nervous system, a number vastly exceeding anything that we can possibly examine. There is clearly room here for a physical counterpart of an enormous range of mental life not manifested in overt actions, and we may surely hold that it is grossly inadequate in view of this to treat statements about mental dispositions in the Rylean manner as being nothing more than symbolic formulas which, by the application of specified rules, can be replaced by statements about overt physical behaviour. This seems to me to be as forced as it would be to interpret statements about bacteria as nothing more than formulas which, by the application of specified rules, could be replaced by statements about the temperature and pulse of feverish patients, the visual patterns seen through microscopes, and so on.

The final part of McCulloch's article deals with the way in which the physical processes of the brain may be co-ordinated with our consciousness of free volition and with awareness of particular or universal propositions (that is, propositions which are not about particular occurrences but about *some* or *all* of the members of a class). The most difficult task in this realm is that of constructing a model for the recognition of universals, of conceiving, for example, how one and the same cerebral process can be produced, however indirectly, by the perception of *any* triangle, whatever its shape or size may be. Traditionally, of course, the abstraction of universals has been held to be one of the essential characteristics of the rational as distinct from the merely sensitive soul, one of the glories that make man superior to the brute beasts; and it is interesting to remark that even

---

[1] Art. Cit., p. 22.   [2] Ibid.

highly trained apes, while developing specific reactions to standard stimuli, seem to be totally unable to abstract the concept of number.[1] Various suggestions have been made of possible types of "scanning" activity in the brain which might produce a uniform response to spatial patterns of a given general geometrical form, and it has been thought that the alpha-rhythm may be connected with this.[2] McCulloch, in his article, suggests that there may be some process comparable to "automatic volume-control" producing a uniform response to all stimuli within a certain group by some kind of negative feedback operation, or, even more ingeniously, that a certain area of the sensory cortex, when stimulated by information corresponding to one member of the group, manufactures the patterns that would correspond to all the other members, averages them out, and then relays the group-average pattern to the next area of the brain. I must confess that I find this last theory extremely difficult to conceive, and I suspect that the patterning of universals in the brain, especially universals that are not just spatial in character, will raise some very difficult problems. But in all this there is nothing that need cause us dismay, so long as we keep our own heads. It would be quite ridiculous, for instance, to interpret McCulloch's reference to information and entropy as meaning that "the Second Law of Thermodynamics has blown up free-will". The status of the Second Law is itself very obscure and it is by no means clear how far living beings fall within its scope; Eddington's attempt to treat it as providing a non-subjective criterion of the direction of time seems by no means free from ambiguity.[3] Again, we ought not to be alarmed by McCulloch's suggestion that the reliability of our information about the external world depends upon the fact that it appears to take more than one impulse to "fire" a neurone. If our information about the external world is not reliable, we have no grounds for

[1] Cf. S. Zuckerman, in *The Physical Basis of Mind*, p. 29.

[2] Cf. Norbert Wiener, *Cybernetics*, ch. vi; Lord Adrian, *Physical Background of Perception*, ch. vi. This does not, of course, mean that the pattern of cortical stimulation would have to be *geometrically* similar to the sensible image correlated with it; it would, however, have to be *relationally isomorphic*. Cf. p. 236 n. 1 supra.

[3] Cf. K. G. Denbigh, "Thermodynamics and the Subjective Sense of Time", in *B.J.P.S.*, IV, p. 183 f. (1953).

supposing that there are any neurones at all or any impulses to fire them. If we are prepared to accept the evidence of our senses, we may subsequently discover quite a lot about the way in which our senses give us evidence. But if we are not—well, that way madness lies. I shall not flog the dead horse of scepticism any more, at least for the time being. I am not sure what McCulloch means when he describes causality as a superstition, especially when he goes on "I humbly submit that it is but a reincarnation of St Thomas' faith that God did not give us our senses to fool us". But I agree with him that "it is enough that this trust in the goodness of God cannot truthfully be denied".[1]

7. CONCLUSION

We might sum up this lecture by saying that the great tradition of Christian theology, in spite of occasional hesitancies and divergences, has steadily taught that a human being is a highly mysterious creature, composed of body and soul, of matter and spirit, interpenetrating each other in the most intimate way, and that modern physiology, while casting a good deal of light upon certain aspects of that interconnection, has certainly done nothing to supersede it. This does not, of course, mean that scientific investigation has proved conclusively everything that Christian theology affirms about the nature of man. It does not, for example, prove that the soul survives the death of the body, or that there is any certain difference in kind between the mentality of human beings and of animals. There are indeed remarkable differences between man and even the highest sub-human organisms as regards the proportion which the brain bears to the body as a whole and still more as regards the proportion which the "silent areas" of the frontal cortex, with which, in spite of the absence of any specific localisation of function, the higher levels of thought seem to be connected, bears to the brain itself. If we are to find any grounds for believing in the immortality of the soul apart from those which come to us from the Christian revelation, we must look for them rather in the nature of the higher operations of the human mind itself than in the structure or the physical functioning of the brain. Nevertheless, the physical facts

[1] Art. cit., p. 31.

themselves are remarkable. "The size of the brain in proportion to the body-weight", writes Professor Le Gros Clark,

> is . . . one of the distinctive features of human anatomy. Its weight is two or three times that of the largest ape, the gorilla, and it seems to have taken a matter of several million years for man to achieve such a prodigious development of his brain. On the other hand, the fossil evidence indicates that the human brain has not appreciably changed in its size for about 200,000 years. There seems to be no evidence that man's brain is undergoing any further evolutionary expansion—or that it is even likely to do so.[1]

I shall be dealing in the next lecture with the question of evolution, and I shall there argue that it provides no necessary ground for supposing that if the souls of the lower animals perish with their bodies the souls of human beings must perish too, or, on the other hand, that if human beings survive bodily death the lower animals must also survive. Here I wish simply to emphasise that Christianity has not only always admitted that body and mind are intimately interconnected but has very emphatically affirmed it. The fact that scientists have in recent years discovered previously unknown and unsuspected facts about the nature of that interrelation is a matter not for dismay but for admiration and joy on the part of Christian theologians. There are no *theoretical* problems for Christian faith, for example, in the remarkable psychological effects of operations such as pre-frontal leucotomy, lobotomy and hemispherectomy, in spite of the difficulty of the practical and ethical issues that they raise. For, if it is true, as the Catholic tradition has maintained, that grace does not destroy nature but perfects it,[2] then the more man knows about his nature the better he will be equipped to utilise and co-operate with grace. As I have said before, in order to exercise our freedom it is essential for us to know what are the limits within which that freedom can be exercised; the more we know about our natural selves the better, whether that knowledge be derived from what psychologists tell us about the unconscious mind or what neurophysiologists tell us about the cerebral cortex. The only caveats are that we should not suppose that the findings of contemporary

---

[1] *The Physical Basis of Mind*, p. 23.

[2] *Cum enim gratia non tollat naturam sed perficiat* . . .(St Thomas Aquinas, *S. Theol.*, I, i. 8 *ad* 2).

science are final or exhaustive and that we should not force the evidence in order to produce premature reconciliations and syntheses. Men are neither machines nor monkeys, though in some ways they are like both. Living on the borderland where matter and spirit overlap, man shares in the life of both realms. In him spirit has found a local habitation, and matter has found a name. And God has taken his nature so that he can partake of God's. "Man", wrote Pascal, "is only a reed and the feeblest reed in nature, but he is a reed that thinks."[1] "What is man, that thou art mindful of him, and the son of man that thou visitest him?" enquired the psalmist; and gave the answer for which Christianity alone provides the justification: "Thou hast made him a little lower than the angels to crown him with glory and worship . . . and thou hast put all things in subjection under his feet."

[1] *Pensées*, vi, 347.

Chapter Seven

MAN'S ORIGIN AND ANCESTRY

Formavit igitur Dominus Deus hominem de limo
terrae, et inspiravit in faciem ejus spiraculum vitae, et
factus est homo in animam viventem.—Gen. ii. 7.

I. THE NATURE AND ORIGIN OF LIFE

THE day is no doubt past when it was possible, as in the famous encounter between Huxley and Wilberforce at the meeting of the British Association at Oxford in 1860, for a prelate of the Church of England to taunt an eminent biologist with the enquiry whether he claimed to be descended from an ape on his grandfather's or his grandmother's side and to receive an answer which, when pruned of its Victorian verbosity, can be reduced to the assertion that it is preferable to be descended from an ape than from a bishop.[1] That evolutionary theory as such is not inconsistent with the Christian Faith would be admitted to-day by all but the most obstinate fundamentalists. Even in the Roman Church, in which as late as the early nineteen-twenties, it was widely believed that the falsity of "transformism" was about to be declared by an official papal condemnation,[2] the recent encyclical *Humani Generis* has explicitly asserted that "the teaching of the Church leaves the doctrine of Evolution an open question, as long as it confines its speculations to the development, from other living matter already in existence, of the human body".[3] Nevertheless there are, I believe, some important questions to be discussed which lie on the borderland between evolutionary theory and theology, and I propose to look at some of them in this lecture.

It is sometimes supposed that Christian theism has a particular

[1] Cf. L. Huxley, *Life and Letters of Thomas Henry Huxley*, I, ch. xiv.
[2] H. J. T. Johnson, "Catholics and Evolution" in *Downside Review*, LXVII, p. 386 (1949).
[3] Trans. by R. A. Knox, C.T.S. ed., p. 20.

interest in asserting that in the evolutionary process there is a
sharp break between living and non-living matter, of such a
character that the appearance of life in the universe can only be
explained by an *ad hoc* intervention of the Deity; and it must be
admitted that some modern Christian apologists have maintained
this position. It is therefore of interest to note that, until the rise
of modern biology, Christians had for centuries believed quite
undisturbedly that animal life could be, and indeed habitually
was, produced by purely natural causes from lifeless materials.
"In ancient and medieval times", writes Sir William Dampier,
"men believed that living things might arise spontaneously from
dead matter. Frogs, for instance, might be generated from mud
by sunshine, and, when the new world was discovered, it was
suggested that perhaps the aboriginal Americans, whose descent
from Adam was difficult to trace, might have had the same kind
of origin."[1] In fact, the abandonment of belief in spontaneous
generation came about as a result of the experiments of scientists,
beginning with Francesco Redi in the seventeenth century, "who
showed that, if the flesh of a dead animal were protected from
insects, no grubs or maggots appeared in it", and culminating in
Louis Pasteur in the nineteenth, who "disproved every known
case of supposed spontaneous generation by showing that the
presence of bacteria could always be traced to the entrance of
germs from outside, or to the growth of those already present".[2]
For scientific materialists this was a somewhat embarrassing conclusion, and its implications were commonly evaded by the
desperate expedient of pushing the problem a stage further back
and adopting Lord Kelvin's suggestion that the first germs of
life might have been borne to the earth "on the moss-grown ruins
of another world". Needless to say, popular apologists, forgetful
of their medieval predecessors, eagerly claimed Pasteur's work as
a deadly blow against the forces of atheism.

Clearly, the general question of the possibility of the non-
miraculous emergence of life from non-living matter is closely
bound up with the question of the fundamental difference between living and non-living beings. This takes us straight into a
famous controversy within the realm of biology itself, the controversy between the mechanists and the vitalists. For the mechanists,

---

[1] *History of Science*, 3rd ed., p. 201.   [2] Ibid., p. 201, 282.

whose totem-ancestor was the great seventeenth-century philosopher René Descartes, there was no essential difference between a purely mechanical system and a living body; the latter was more complicated than the former, but was like it in consisting simply of a collection of material parts moving under the laws of physics and chemistry; if only we could cope with the intricacies of the mathematics involved, we could predict the behaviour of an elephant in the same way as we can predict the motions of the planet Jupiter. The vitalists, on the other hand, maintained that the behaviour of a living organism could be explained only on the assumption that it is directed, in anticipation of its goal, by some mysterious agent or "entelechy" which is fundamentally different from the forces of physics and chemistry. Their leader was the famous Hans Driesch, who was led to his views by his experiments on sea-urchins, which are confirmed by experiments on other animals too. They are described by the distinguished biologist Ludwig von Bertalanffy in the following words:

> In the greenish depths of the sea, the sea-urchins lead a contemplative life, aloof from the problems of the world and science. Yet these same peaceful creatures became the cause of a long-drawn and violent controversy about the essence of life. When a sea-urchin egg begins to develop, it divides first into two, then into four, eight, sixteen, and finally many cells, and in a series of characteristic stages it eventually forms a larva looking somewhat like a spiked helmet and known to science as a "pluteus"; from this the sea-urchin finally develops by way of a complicated metamorphosis. Driesch divided a sea-urchin germ, just at the beginning of its development, into two halves. One would expect that from such a half-germ only half an animal would develop. In fact, however, the experimenter watches a ghostly performance like that in Goethe's *Sorcerer's Apprentice*. . . . Out of each half comes not a half but a whole sea-urchin larva, a bit smaller, it is true, but normal and complete.

Driesch's conclusion was that

> here the physico-chemical explanation of life reaches its limit, and only one interpretation is possible. In the embryo, and similarly in other vital phenomena, a factor is active which is fundamentally different from all physico-chemical forces, and which directs events in anticipation of the goal. This factor, which "carries the goal

within itself", namely, the production of a typical organism in normal as well as in experimentally disturbed development, was called entelechy by Driesch, using an Aristotelian notion.[1]

Now von Bertalanffy, who has a strongly positivistic and "anti-mystical" outlook, rejects Driesch's view as mythological and unhelpful. For him Driesch's "entelechy" is very much the same kind of bogey that Descartes' "mind" is for Professor Gilbert Ryle, and he castigates it with vigour. "The arrangement", he says,

of the superlatively numerous physico-chemical processes, by means of which the organism is maintained and restored even after serious disturbances, and, further, the origin of the complicated "machine" of the organism cannot be explained, according to vitalistic doctrine, save by the action of specific vital factors, whether we call them Entelechy, Unconscious, or World Soul, which interfere, purposely and directively, with physico-chemical events.

At once, however, we see that vitalism must be rejected as far as scientific theory is concerned. According to it, structure and function in the organism are governed, as it were, by a host of goblins, who invent and design the organism, control its processes, and patch the machine up after injury. This gives us no deeper insight; but we merely shift what at present seems inexplicable to a yet more mysterious principle and assemble it into an X that is inaccessible to research. Vitalism says nothing else than that the essential problems of life lie outside the sphere of natural science. If that were so, then scientific research would become pointless; for even with the most complicated experiments and apparatus, it can lead to no other explanation than the anthropomorphism of primitive mankind, who see an elfin intelligence and will similar to their own in the apparent directiveness and purposiveness in living nature. Whether we consider the behaviour of an animal, or the multiplicity of physical and chemical processes in a cell, or the development of organic structures and functions, we always get the same answer—it is just a soul-like something standing behind them and directing them.[2]

I do not know how far all vitalists would accept von Bertalanffy's description of their views. It will, however, be interesting to see how he develops his own outlook, for, while he rejects vitalism, not only as mythological but also as contrary to experimental

[1] *Problems of Life*, p. 5 f.   [2] Ibid., p. 7 f.

evidence,[1] he equally explicitly repudiates mechanism, in the sense that that word has borne in biology.

Von Bertalanffy describes his own view as "the organismic conception", and he asserts that, at least in one realm, that of embryonic development, all modern theories are organismic.[2] "For understanding life phenomena", he tells us,

> it is neither sufficient to know the individual elements and processes nor to interpret their order by means of machine-like structures, even less to invoke an entelechy as the organising factor. It is not only necessary to carry out analysis in order to know as much as possible about the individual components, but it is equally necessary to know the laws of organisation that unite these parts and partial processes and are just the characteristic of vital phenomena. . . .

"In this way", he claims, "the autonomy of life, denied in the mechanistic conception, and remaining a metaphysical question mark in vitalism, appears, in the organismic conception, as a problem accessible to science and, in fact, already under investigation."[3] For him, vitalism is infected with the same error as mechanism; both look upon the body as a machine, but vitalism posits also an entelechy to interfere with it.[4] Both are, in his words, based on the analytical, summative and machine-theoretical principles.[5] He insists that "the organismic conception is not a compromise, a muddling through or mid-course between the mechanistic and vitalistic views".[6] Its aim is the statement of exact laws, but these, owing to the essential characteristic of living organisms, must be *system-laws*.[7] Von Bertalanffy's project, therefore, is nothing less than the reduction of biology to the status of a mathematically exact science, while repudiating the mechanistic assumption that has generally underlain such schemes. He therefore announces his *"claim for a new realm of science"*, which he calls "General System Theory", "a logico-mathematical field, the subject matter of which is the formulation and derivation of those principles which hold for systems in general."[8] It is alleged that, by this method, it is possible to give a rigid and exact definition to notions such as wholeness and sum, progressive mechanisation, centralisation, leading parts, hier-

---

[1] *Problems of Life*, p. 59 f.   [3] Ibid., p. 19 f.   [5] Ibid.   [7] Ibid., p. 21.
[2] Ibid., p. 65.   [4] Ibid., p. 19.   [6] Ibid., p. 20.   [8] Ibid., p. 199.

archical order, individuality, finality, equifinality, etc., which have up till now been no more than vague "metaphysical" ideas.[1] System Theory introduces a hierarchical principle into biology, which manifests itself in a great variety of ways: in the division hierarchy, which is composed of cells and is ordered by the relation "*is a direct cell-descendant of*"; in the spatial hierarchy, which is composed of the complete multicellular organism, with its components and its components' components and so on; in the genetic hierarchy, composed of a fertilised ovum and the succeeding generations of offspring; in Heidenhain's "histo-systems", in which somatic components are incapsulated in others; in the hierarchy of physiological processes; and in the hierarchical segregation which, in embryonic development, brings about the differentiated structure of the complete organism.[2] A characteristic assertion is the statement that "the 'wholeness' manifest in the processes of development is immanent in, not transcendent to, the embryo. The embryo represents primarily a unitary system, not a sum of developmental machines or *anlagen*, which is the common basis of both Weismann's theory and vitalism."[3] Von Bertalanffy appeals to genetics for a further example of his thesis that the biological process can be understood only in terms of the system as a whole. He remarks that, in spite of the success of geneticists in locating genes in the chromosomes, no arrangement of genes can be found which corresponds to the organisation of the animal—he is taking as an example the geneticist's favourite object, the fruitfly *Drosophila*—, that different genes, often in different chromosomes, can produce very similar characters, that the same effect can sometimes be produced by a hereditary gene-mutation or alternatively by a non-hereditary environmental change, and so on. "The *whole* organism", he says, "is produced by the *whole* genome" or gene-system, and "the genome is not a sum or mosaic of independent and self-acting *anlagen*, but a system that, as a whole, produces the organism, the development of which, however, is altered according to changes in parts of this system, the genes."[4] He even quotes Goldschmidt as doubting whether the conception of the gene as a unit of heredity with a separate existence is still tenable.[5]

---

[1] *Problems of Life*, Cf. the outline given by von Bertalanffy in *B.J.P.S.*, I, p. 134 f. (1950). [2] Ibid., p. 37 f. [3] Ibid., p. 60. [4] Ibid., p. 75. [5] Ibid., p. 81.

Von Bertalanffy makes it abundantly clear that he claims, by his organismic conception, to avoid the inadequacies of mechanistic theories while still remaining within the realm of strict scientific method. "It is", he says, "the kernel of the organismic conception that it overcomes the mechanism-vitalism alternative at a higher level",[1] and he devotes an eloquent passage to insistence upon the fundamentally positivistic and anti-metaphysical character of his theory.[2] He attributes extreme importance to the recent work upon the thermodynamics of open systems, that is to say, systems which are free to interchange matter with their environment. We have seen already[3] that it is a characteristic of living bodies that they maintain or increase their own organisation at the expense of a greater *dis*organisation of their environment; von Bertalanffy endorses this point and adds two others. One is that, where quantum processes are involved, a transition to a condition of higher organisation is possible. The second, and to him the more important one, is that the recent development of the thermodynamics of open systems has shown that they are not subject to the Second Law of Thermodynamics and so can pass to states of higher heterogeneity and complexity. To be precise, so far from irreversible processes in open systems leading to a condition of maximum entropy (that is, of maximum disorganisation), the steady state which the system approaches is characterised by minimum entropy-production (that is, of minimum production of disorganisation). There can thus be a spontaneous transition to a state of increased complexity, and von Bertalanffy suggests that this may account not only for the way in which living organisms maintain their organisation but also for the increasing complexity which is so striking a feature of biological evolution.[4] The upshot of all this is to reduce to a purely naturalistic level those characteristics of the living world which have been commonly seen by theistic philosophers as signs of the embodiment of cosmic purposing and as providing strong evidence, if not apodictic proof, of the existence of an intelligent and purposive Creator. Admittedly von Bertalanffy does not declare himself

---

[1] *Problems of Life,* p. 170.   [2] Ibid., p. 171.   [3] Cf. ch. v supra.
[4] Op. cit., p. 113, 125 f., 145, 158. Cf. also R. O. Davies on "Irreversible Thermodynamics" in *Science News 28,* p. 41 f. (1953).

very explicitly on this matter; in his more rhetorical moments he tends to slip into an immanentist monism buttressed by quotations from Goethe. There is, however, little doubt of the main direction of his drift; and it is perhaps significant that the English edition of his *Problems of Life* is published by Messrs C. A. Watts and Company.

I shall turn shortly to the assessment of these conclusions. At the moment it will be convenient to consider a cognate question, that of the sufficiency of natural selection to account for the process of biological evolution. As Darwin first formulated his theory of evolution, it rested upon three chief presuppositions. The first was that of random variations, the second that of natural selection, the third that of the inheritance of acquired characters. The theory has been briefly summarised in the following words:

> All groups of organisms vary and many of their variations are hereditary. More young organisms are produced than live to reproduce in their turn. Those that do succeed in reproducing are on the whole those whose variations best fit them for survival in the struggle for life. The offspring therefore do not inherit all the variations of a preceding generation equally, but there is a selection in favour of the fitter (more adaptive) variations. Long-continued selection of this sort eventually so changes the lineage that it represents a species (or higher unit) different from its ancestry.[1]

Post-Darwinian research has drastically modified the first and third of Darwin's assumptions. So far from random variations being either significant or inheritable, they seem to be neither. On the other hand, much more significant changes occur, which we know as mutations, and they are inherited according to the Mendelian laws. It is nevertheless still a matter of animated dispute among biologists whether mutations *plus* natural selection are sufficient to account for the evolutionary process as it has actually occurred. Von Bertalanffy remarks upon the comparatively minor character of the changes that are produced by mutation. "Apart from some cases occurring in polyploid plants", he writes,

[1] G. G. Simpson, in *Chambers's Encyclopaedia*, V, p. 496, *s.v.* "Evolution".

no new species has ever arisen within the sphere of observation, let alone "macro-evolutionary" changes. Selection Theory is an extrapolation, the boldness of which is made acceptable by the impressiveness of its basic conception. With a less picturesque theory, one would doubtless hesitate to extend cosmically and universally a principle which is controlled experimentally only to a rather limited extent. . . . On the other hand [he continues] for not quite fifty years we have carried out genetical research on some dozens of animal and plant species, the mutations of which never transgressed the limits of the species. It is a bold extrapolation that nothing else has happened in a billion years or so of evolution "from amoeba to man". So the dispute concerns ways of thinking rather than factual evidence.[1]

He also remarks on the extreme adaptability and pliability of the notion of selection, and his final judgment on it is not unlike that of the linguistic empiricists upon theism. "In the case of Selection Theory", he says, "it appears impossible to indicate any biological phenomenon that would plainly refute it."[2]

It must thus be recognised that the sufficiency of natural selection, acting upon genetic mutation, as an explanation of the actual course of evolution is still a highly controverted issue among biologists, and it would be unwise for an outsider to venture an opinion. Only recently there has appeared a large collective work by a distinguished body of supporters of the selectionist view, which has something of the nature of a manifesto.[3] The stock objection to the selectionist thesis is that, in many cases, it is only the simultaneous appearance and combination of a very large number of modifications that would be advantageous, and that the arrival of one or even several of them would be either useless or positively deleterious from the point of view of survival-value. The case which is usually quoted in this connection is that of the human eye, which Darwin himself admitted gave him a cold shudder;[4] nevertheless, if one traces out a representa-

[1] Op. cit., p. 86. The "billion" mentioned is, of course, the American billion, equal to one thousand millions.
[2] Ibid., p. 89.
[3] *Evolution as a Process*, edited by Julian Huxley, A. C. Hardy, and E. B. Ford.
[4] F. Darwin, *Life and Letters of Charles Darwin*, II, p. 273. Cf. C. Sherrington, *Man on his Nature*, p. 104 f.

tive selection of diagrams representing the comparative anatomy of the eye,[1] the transition becomes much more easily imaginable. We pass in succession from the single pigmented light-sensitive cell in the skin of the frog to the multicellular depression in the limpet, thence to the "pin-hole camera" of the squid, thence again to the eye of the snail, in which the whole interior of the "camera" is filled up with a crystalline lens, and finally to the eye of the jelly-fish, in which the lens is restricted to the orifice and the rest of the cavity is occupied by a transparent liquid, in such a way that the general structure of the human eye is anticipated in a simplified form. More difficult from the point of view of the thorough-going selectionist would seem to be a case like that of the cuckoo, upon which Dr C. E. Raven has laid stress in his Gifford Lectures.[2] In order for the young cuckoo to perform the process of ejecting his fellow-nestlings, for which he is notorious and upon which his survival depends, there is required the simultaneous presence of no less than five extremely specialised characteristics, without any one of which the rest would be useless. The cuckoo's egg must be tiny; it must hatch some thirty-six hours before the others; the mother-cuckoo must lay it before the foster-parent begins to sit; the young cuckoo must have a peculiar physical structure capable of ejecting eggs or nestlings; finally it must perform the technique of ejection. There are in fact two closely related questions involved in this discussion. The first is whether modifications on the scale on which they occur can have a sufficiently preferential character to maintain themselves when they have individually occurred; the second is whether, within the time available, they can accumulate to the degree which is necessary to produce the very large differences which distinguish one species from another. In his essay in the symposium to which I have referred Sir Ronald Fisher argues strongly for the second point and presumably, though this is less clear, for the first as well. Arguments based upon probability are, of course, notoriously dangerous, and at this stage of the controversy it would be rash indeed for an outsider to jump to con-

---

[1] E.g. the figure from Starling's *Principles of Human Physiology* reproduced in H. Hartridge's article on "Eye and Vision" in *Chambers's Encyclopaedia*, V, p. 555. Cf. von Bertalanffy, op. cit., p. 89.

[2] *Natural Religion and Christian Theology*, II, p. 137–8.

clusions one way or the other. The whole case of the selectionist rests upon his assertion that, in Fisher's words, "natural selection is a mechanism for generating an exceedingly high degree of improbability".[1]

In spite of the stress which such notable apologists as Dr F. R. Tennant have placed upon the evidence of design which they claim to detect in the universe,[2] I do not myself feel that the theist ought to be much concerned about the issue of this controversy. It is, as I have argued elsewhere, the existence of the universe, rather than its character, which forms the basis of a philosophical approach to Christian theism.[3] Furthermore, if we are to take the apparent evidences of design at their face value, we shall have to recognise the uncomfortable fact that the design is by no means obviously an invariably beneficent one, as for example in the case of the life-cycle of the malaria parasite which has been described so eloquently, and at the same time so uncomfortably, by Sir Charles Sherrington.[4] I shall return to this question later on. At the moment I shall say a little more about the transition from non-living to living matter.

I have already remarked on the fact that, for the greater part of the Christian era, it was assumed quite unconcernedly that living matter could emerge from non-living matter without any action on the part of God beyond his general *concursus* with the natural order. The fact that we no longer believe with Albertus Magnus that worms are generated from dung[5] makes no essential difference. The essential fact is that (leaving over for future consideration the unique case of the human species) the soul of an animal was not conceived as a separate psychic substance temporarily united to the body; it was simply the form in which the body was organised. The fact that an animal was believed to enjoy some form of conscious life did not alter this fact; the consciousness was a consequence of the kind and degree of organisation that the body had achieved. It was not that the body was the integument of a conscious entity; rather, at this stage of organisation the body itself had become conscious in the appropriate way. Although

---

[1] *Evolution as a Process*, p. 5. Cf. von Bertalanffy, op. cit., p. 86 f.
[2] Cf. *Philosophical Theology*, passim.
[3] Cf. e.g., *He Who Is*, p. 177 f.
[4] *Man on his Nature*, p. 265 f.
[5] A. C. Crombie, *Augustine to Galileo*, p. 121.

this view was generally expressed in terms of Aristotelian concepts of form and matter, it was emphasised rather than weakened by its association with the Christian Faith. For in the Christian view the great line of division in the created universe is not between lifeless matter and living creatures, or between plants and animals, but between the realm of matter, living and lifeless alike, on the one hand, and the realm of spirit on the other. This is what gives man his unique position as a dweller in both realms. Certainly neither St Augustine, nor St Albertus Magnus, nor St Thomas Aquinas would have been in the least perturbed by the work that has been done in recent years in the border-line region between lifeless and living matter; but all of them, especially St Albertus, would have been most deeply interested.

No longer is it the case that, when confronted with the question of the origin of life, the scientist has to take refuge in improvisations such as Lord Kelvin's suggestions that life was brought to the earth on the moss-grown ruins of another world.[1] It is at least highly likely that in some members of that extremely miscellaneous collection of substances which are known by the somewhat uncomplimentary name of viruses we have a link between lifeless matter and what was formerly recognised as the lowest level of living beings.[2] From one point of view viruses seem to be simply gigantic protein-molecules, though this fact alone should make us pause when we remember that the same seems to be true of the genes in a living cell. The molecular weight of the tobacco-mosaic virus, for instance, is something like 40·7 millions. They vary in size from about 10 millionths of a millimeter in the case of the poliomyelitis virus, to about 250 in the case of the psittacosis virus. Since the size of a haemoglobin molecule is about 5 of these units and the size of the *bacillus prodigiosus* is about 750, the viruses nicely span the gap between indubitably lifeless and living matter.[3] Now the peculiar charac-

[1] Though it is interesting to note that Hoyle, who holds that the earth was not formed in an entirely molten state but accumulated from a multitude of cold bodies, suggests that the most primitive forms of life came into being before the earth itself (*Frontiers of Astronomy*, p. 103).

[2] Several excellent accounts of viruses are readily obtainable, such as K. M. Smith's *Beyond the Microscope*, and F. M. Burnet's *Viruses and Man*, and *Science News 14* (1949) and *33* (1954). See also the admirable symposium on "The Origin of Life" (*New Biology 16* (1954)).

[3] Cf. Wilson Smith in *Chambers's Encyclopaedia*, XIV, p. 338, *s.v.* "Virus".

teristic of a virus is that, while it will normally remain for an indefinite period in a quite static condition, neither decomposing nor multiplying, when it is placed in some special environment (very often the body, or part of the body, of one particular living creature) it will reproduce itself at an astounding rate. Thus a few hundred molecules of the tobacco-mosaic virus will rapidly infect a whole plant. The polyhedral virus, starting work inside the nucleus of a cell in the body of a caterpillar, will rapidly reduce the whole creature to a skinful of crystals. A preparation of pure bacteriophage particles "shows no evidence of life, or biological activity of any sort, until added to a population of multiplying bacterial host cells. Then it behaves as a lethal poison, destroying the infected cells and at the same time increasing manyfold. The individual phage particle is apparently an organism which can be dead by all the usual tests for 'life' until it gains entry to the host cell".[1] Furthermore, viruses, like genes, can undergo mutations. It may be added that recent work has shown that the bacteriophage particle is not entirely without physical structure but consists of a minute envelope of protein-material, in the shape of a sphere with a short thin tail, containing the active substance nucleic acid.

Now it is, of course, obvious that the viruses which we know cannot be the beings that, in the historical course of evolution, have bridged the gap between indubitably non-living and living matter, if only for the simple reason that they do not exhibit vital phenomena at all unless living beings which are above them in the evolutionary scale are already present to act as their hosts. Nevertheless it may well be that there existed in the past beings with a similar structure which did not need a living host, and it is possible that the present-day viruses are their mutated and specialised descendants. The important fact is that we now know of the existence of structures that in one environment behave as normal lifeless chemical molecules, while in another environment they spontaneously manifest the essential characteristics of life.

Through what precise chemical process the transition was made from lifelessness to life is a matter of acute controversy among those best qualified to speak. The state of the question is entertainingly presented in the symposium on the Origin of Life pub-

[1] J. E. Hotchin, in *Science News* 33, p. 92 (1954).

lished in April 1954 in *New Biology 16*, which is enlivened by
some vigorous interchanges between the disputants.[1] The conclusions reached are largely dependent upon the view that is
held about the origin and the early history of our planet, and this
lets into the discussion cosmologists, physicists and geologists,
as well as biologists. I have already referred to the way in which
some of the main features of animal behaviour can be simulated
by machines of purely physical construction;[2] but none of Mr
Ross Ashby's "tortoises" has yet succeeded in reproducing itself.
In the symposium Professor J. B. S. Haldane mentions a claim by
J. von Neumann to have proved that it is theoretically possible to
construct a self-reproducing machine from a finite number of
parts of about twelve different kinds. No one, he notes, has
calculated the number of individual parts such a machine would
need to have, and he offers some inconclusive remarks on the
question whether, supposing a nucleic-acid molecule was an example of such a "machine" it would be likely to be formed by
chance in a universe such as ours. As the most lifelike molecule
known to us, he instances ATP, or adenosine-triphosphoric acid,
two molecules of which, by interaction with glucose, can ultimately give rise to four ATP molecules; it even manifests something which can be fancifully compared to a sexual process. His
suggestion is that

> various kinds of subvital unit molecules were able to reproduce
> themselves in suitable environments. Any such "sub-life" may have
> lasted for minutes, or for thousands of years. Occasionally such sub-
> lives combined to produce something more complicated. . . . The
> fortunate combination which gave rise to our ancestors may have
> involved the meeting together—the marriage if you like—of a
> number of such molecular races.[3]

"To sum up", writes Haldane,

> I suggest the following hypotheses. Metastable organic compounds
> were formed by the action of solar radiation on the atmosphere
> before it contained much free oxygen. Catalytically active molecules
> which could increase their own number while breaking down these
> compounds came into being. No such molecule is certainly known

[1] The writers are J. B. S. Haldane, J. D. Bernal, N. W. Pirie and J. W. S.
Pringle.
[2] Cf. ch. vi supra.   [3] Op. cit., p. 21.

at present, but adenosine-triphosphoric acid comes near to being one. The long-chain polymers found in living organisms have "back-bones" composed of phosphate, glycine or pentose residues. . . . The critical event which may best be called the origin of life was the enclosure of several different self-reproducing polymers within a semipermeable membrane.[1]

On the other hand Mr J. W. S. Pringle postulates "a much more gradual process than the sudden catastrophic and highly improbable events involved in the ultra-violet light schemes of Haldane and Bernal. . . . It is possible", he says,

to picture a progressive building up of biochemical structure and dynamic organisation in a large volume of water, with a later condensation of the reacting system into smaller regions. The organism as a coherent machine thus emerges from a diffuse system of chemical reactivity and its properties are added step by step by a process akin to natural selection. Life truly evolves from chaos with no moment of special creation to identify its birth.[2]

Such examples as these suffice to show that, while there is virtual agreement among biologists to-day about the central part played by polymers of the protein type in the transition to living organisms, the details of the process are highly debatable. I have already given reasons why in my opinion there is nothing which should worry the theologian in the view that no special divine intervention is involved in the appearance of life on the earth. Unless we are deists, we shall see the whole process as *gesta Dei per naturam*, as conserved and energised by the creative activity of the transcendent God. No doubt there is a real element of mystery about the emergence of mental life, even of the lowest conceivable type, from lifeless matter. Even that dim adumbration of sensitivity which we may suppose to be present in the amoeba or the bacteriophage, seems to be logically irreducible to mechanical and chemical processes. (It is perhaps an implicit recognition of this fact that leads our modern positivists so obstinately and irritatingly to ignore, even when they are discussing human beings, everything other than overt physical behaviour.) Even if we are convinced that every physical organism as a matter of course embodies whatever type of mental life

[1] New Biology 16, p. 26.　　　　[2] Ibid., p. 65.

is capable of correlation with its particular physical structure, we may still find ourselves forced, not on biological but on purely logical grounds, to hold either that some rudiment of mentality attaches even to what we are accustomed to describe as lifeless matter, or else—and this seems to me to make better sense—that when an appropriate degree of physical complexity has been reached in the evolutionary process—for example, to adopt Haldane's hypothesis, when several self-reproducing polymers have become enclosed within a semipermeable membrane—God creates and attaches to it the appropriate mental subject. The equipment of physical structures with their appropriate mental subjects, from the level of the self-reproducing polymer up to that of the hominid, may well be part of God's normal *concursus* with the process of nature. Thus it seems to me that nothing compels us either, on the one hand, to adopt a purely mechanistic view of living beings or, on the other, to attribute the appearance of life to an act which is, in the theological sense of the words, supernatural or miraculous. It may be well to add that the view which I have outlined does not in any way imply that animals have "immortal souls". It does imply that they have souls—*animae sensitivae*, principles of animate life—in the scholastic sense of "soul". Dr C. S. Lewis may be right in his tentative suggestion that domesticated animals can under certain conditions acquire a dependent and participated immortality in relation to their human owners,[1] but, leaving aside this special and abnormal case, nothing that has been said above necessarily implies that the mental subject which God has attached to the physical organism survives the disintegration of the latter. As its sole concern is with the functioning of the organism as a constituent of the physical world, there is no reason why it should. I may perhaps add that this does not mean either that I am not fond of animals or that I think it does not matter how people treat them.

2. HUMAN AND SUB-HUMAN SOULS

But now what about man? Has not Christian theology traditionally maintained that the souls of men are spiritual

[1] *The Problem of Pain*, ch. ix.

entities independent of the body, which survive the body's death and decay? And has not at least a very weighty body of Christian thought held that the soul of the first human being, and indeed the soul of every human being, is produced by a direct and immediate creative act of God? Is this really consistent with what has been implied above? And does it not imply a continual interference in the created order which is hard to reconcile with the view that nature itself is God's instrument and not his opponent? Clearly there is need of a full discussion here.

It is notable that belief in the substantiality and immortality of the human soul has not always come easily to the minds of men. Hindu thought, for example, has rarely risen above the view that human beings are temporary and evanescent crystallisations of a featureless and impersonal psychic material. Again, Semitic thought, at least in its earlier forms, found it difficult to conceive man as very much more than one of the many bits of nature which God had temporarily insufflated with his living breath. Psalm civ, for instance, sees little difference between the ultimate fate of man and the lower animate creation.

> When thou takest away their breath, they die and return
> to their dust.
> When thou sendest forth thy breath, they are created;
> And thou renewest the face of the ground.

And when finally the Jewish people arrived at a full and explicit belief in a future life, it was conceived primarily in terms of bodily resurrection; whether between death and the resurrection the human being could be said to exist at all was dubious. (We may note that some modern theologians, of the school which tends to interpret Christianity primarily in terms of its Old Testament background and is profoundly suspicious of the influence of Greek conceptions upon patristic theology, have spoken of the human being as collapsing at death and being reconstituted at the general resurrection, in a way that has conveniently eliminated all concern with either the saints or the faithful departed.) Now I have emphasised in the last lecture the quite central importance in the Christian Faith of the doctrine that a human being is not just a spirit that is temporarily condemned to inhabit a material garment, but is a highly complicated psycho-somatic unity, in which the body is an essential constituent. And the survival of the Christian Gospel depended upon the Church maintaining the essentially Hebraic basis of its belief, in the teeth of the paganising pressure of Gnosticism. Nevertheless, it was part of the plan of divine providence that the Gospel should be launched, as it was, out of its Hebrew cradle into the intellectual turmoil of the Greco-Roman world. I would thoroughly applaud the late Dr Prestige's defence of the Hellenic element in Christian theology.[1] And indeed, as Bultmann has plainly, if misleadingly, emphasised, the New Testament is itself by no means free of Greek forms of thought.

To return to our point, the doctrine that the human soul, while it is only one part of the twofold body-soul unity of the man, is nevertheless a subsistent entity which survives the death of the body, is central to the Christian tradition; I have previously referred to M. Gilson's remark that the hesitations of some of the early Fathers on this point represented, and were bound to represent, only a passing phase.[2] How much cogency belongs to purely philosophical arguments on the question may be a matter for discussion. St Thomas Aquinas certainly maintained the incorruptibility of the soul on purely philosophical grounds, though, as he did not hold the Greek belief in its inherent divinity, he admitted that it would cease to exist if God ceased to conserve it.[3] But as good a Thomist as Cajetan says explicitly that "no philosopher has yet demonstrated that the soul of man is immortal: there does not appear to be a demonstrative argument; but we believe it by faith, and it is in agreement with probable arguments."[4] This seems to me to be thoroughly sound.

There are in fact two characteristics of the human mind which seem to be different not merely in degree but in kind from anything of which we can see indications in other living beings, and which suggest that it has a concern with something above and beyond the life of the body. The first of these is the capacity for abstract and rational thought, for standing as it were outside the

[1] *God in Patristic Thought*, Introduction.
[2] Cf. p. 210 supra.
[3] *S. Theol.*, I, lxxv, 6, c et *ad* 2.
[4] Commentary on *Ecclesiastes*, cit. F. Copleston, *History of Philosophy*, III, p. 340.

deliverances of the senses and comparing them, classifying them, and making them the starting-point of discursive ratiocination. In view of the somewhat exaggerated significance that has sometimes been placed upon the feat performed by Köhler's chimpanzee Sultan in annexing a previously inaccessible banana by fitting two bamboo sticks together,[1] the following statement by Professor Solly Zuckerman is of interest:

> We all know that animals lack speech and language; they also seem incapable of making number abstractions. Some years ago, two of my students tested this out. They tried in carefully controlled experiments to discover whether monkeys and apes understand what we seem to do by number. But it became more than clear that while they could tell the difference between one and two black circles—or any other set of convenient signs—the animals didn't realise there was a similar numerical quality in the different sets of signs used. Their failure was in isolating the number concept from the perceptual background in which it appeared and in analysing it into its constituent units. The basis of our thinking and reasoning powers is our capacity for such kinds of abstraction and for mastering many kinds of symbolic process.[2]

The second of the characteristics to which I alluded above is the virtually universal institution of religion, with the witness that it bears to a fundamental human intuition that the ultimate reality with which a man has to reckon and the ultimate realm to which he belongs lie behind and beyond the fragile and transient world of sense-phenomena. The force of this consideration is likely to be obscured by the general abandonment of religious practice and the apparently almost complete absence of religious awareness in our modern industrialised civilisations. It is therefore all the more important to emphasise how abnormal a phenomenon in human history this secularist outlook is. Dr F. Sherwood Taylor has pointed out that "before the separation of science and the acceptance of it as the sole valid way of apprehending nature, the vision of God in nature seems to have been the normal way of viewing the world, nor could it have been remarked as an exceptional experience".[3] Now it is, of

---

[1] Cf., e.g., the account in Lord Russell's *Outline of Philosophy*, p. 41 f.
[2] In the symposium *The Physical Basis of Mind*, p. 29.
[3] *The Fourfold Vision*, p. 91.

course, open to anyone to claim that the secularisation of modern man marks his final emancipation from slavery and superstition; though such an objector ought to take account of the fact that the bondage from which man is alleged to have been liberated is in fact one of the most notable features that distinguish him from the beasts, so that the emancipation seems to contain a strong dose of retrogression. Again, the fact that people believe something does not prove it to be true. All this may be admitted; nevertheless, the universal religious consciousness of man is a remarkable fact which, without having coercive argumentative force, is *prima facie* evidence for the reality of its object. We are not concerned here with the bearing of this upon the question of the existence of God; I have discussed that elsewhere.[1] Our present point is that the religious consciousness bears witness to a concern of the human mind with a supra-sensible or, perhaps it would be more accurate to say, a trans-sensible order of reality, with which the mentality of beings lying below the human level shows no concern whatever. This may be dismissed as self-deception, and we may echo Freud's judgment that religion is "the universal obsessional neurosis of humanity",[2] but if we do we shall, I think, need to produce a better account than Freud's of the genesis of the neurosis or we may find that we have sawn off the branch on which we were sitting. In any case, all I am arguing at the moment is that the empirical fact of the virtually universal religious consciousness in man is fully coherent with, and is *pro tanto* a valuable confirmation of, the traditional belief of Christianity that the human soul is not bound up solely with the life of the body and the senses, and that in its own right it survives the death of the body.

We may recall at this point that, even on the physical level, there are striking differences between man and his nearest biological congeners, particularly as regards his brain.[3] Once again, the bearing of this on our question cannot be considered as conclusive. It might be urged that this enormous development of the brain took place by normal evolutionary means, and that it is precisely the fact that he has a more elaborate

---

[1] Cf. *Existence and Analogy*, p. 68 f.
[2] *The Future of an Illusion*, p. 76.
[3] Cf. the remarks of Dr Le Gros Clark quoted on p. 252 supra.

brain than the apes which accounts for man's marked intellectual superiority to them. We may well admit that there would be no point—if we can put it this way—in associating an intelligent subsistent soul with a physical organism unless the physical organism was sufficiently elaborate to serve the soul's needs; unless, for example, it contained enough neural cells and circuits in the cerebral cortex to provide a physical correlate for the discursive ratiocination which the soul was capable of supporting. Our argument was based not upon the soul's capacity to perform complicated reasoning, but upon its intuition of a trans-sensible realm. We may add that Christian tradition has persistently held that the fact that the greater part of our intellectual activity consists of discursive thought, of ratiocination, is directly connected with the fact that we are not bodiless spirits, like the angels, but composite beings, made up of body and soul, of matter and spirit, in a mysterious and intricate unity. So far as the soul is able to transcend its unity with the body, it is able to engage in simple contemplative undiscursive intellectual enjoyment of supra-sensuous and trans-sensible realities, and in particular of the supreme reality which is God; this is its character as *intellectus*. In so far as the soul is operating on the level of the senses, it proceeds by a discursive process of ratiocination *per divisionem et compositionem*; and this is its character as *ratio*. It is fundamental to this point of view that ratiocination is not a purely intellectual process, it is an activity of the whole man, of body and soul acting as a bipartite unity; the Christian tradition will thus welcome as a confirmation of its own doctrine all the evidence that anatomical science and neurophysiology can bring concerning the way in which human ratiocination involves the functioning of the human physical organism and in which it can be deranged by the latter's breakdown. The nature of the traditional doctrine has been largely forgotten as a result of the dominance of the views of Descartes and Kant; the following passage from Josef Pieper's remarkable little book *Leisure the Basis of Culture* may thus be of interest:

> The Middle Ages drew a distinction between the understanding as *ratio* and the understanding as *intellectus*. *Ratio* is the power of discursive, logical thought, of searching and of examination, of abstraction, of definition and drawing conclusions. *Intellectus*, on

the other hand, is the name for the understanding in so far as it is the capacity of *simplex intuitus*, of that simple vision to which truth offers itself like a landscape to the eye. The faculty of mind, man's knowledge, is both these things in one, according to antiquity and the Middle Ages, simultaneously *ratio* and *intellectus*; and the process of knowing is the action of the two together. The mode of discursive thought is accompanied and impregnated by an effortless awareness, the contemplative vision of the *intellectus*, which is not active but passive, or rather receptive, the activity of the soul in which it conceives that which it sees.[1]

It thus seems to me to be thoroughly congruous with the evidence of biology to hold with the tradition of Christendom that the human soul is a spiritual subsistent entity, which for its full and normal functioning needs to be united to a body, but which, even while it is united with the body, is capable of a certain undiscursive contemplation of spiritual realities, and which, even when it is performing discursive ratiocination in reciprocal partnership with the body, infuses into that discursive ratiocination a certain supra-sensory contemplative character.

The point with which we are concerned may perhaps be made plainer by reference to a comparison which is common in the Christian Fathers and is found in that ancient statement of belief known as the Athanasian Creed. "As the reasonable [rational] soul and flesh is one man," we are told, "so God and man is one Christ."[2] In its original context this statement is meant to elucidate the orthodox doctrine of the Incarnation by comparison with contemporary anthropology; it can, however, easily be thrown into reverse. The orthodox doctrine of the Incarnation is that, whereas in every case other than that of Jesus of Nazareth, the human nature of a human individual is organised round, acted through, and experienced by a personal subject which came into existence with the individual nature and is indeed nothing more than a kind of central focus of the human organism, in the unique case of Jesus the human nature is organised round, acted through, and experienced by the pre-existent Person of God the Son, and this without the removal of any constituent of human nature to make room for this pre-existent

[1] Op. cit., p. 33.
[2] *Sicut anima rationalis et caro unus est homo, ita Deus et homo unus est Christus.*

Person. The anthropological parallel will then state that, whereas in subhuman beings the functioning of the physical organism is organised round, acted through and experienced by a psychical subject which is nothing more than a kind of central focus of the physical organism and will cease to exist with the latter, in the case of a human being the functioning of the physical organism is organised round, acted through, and experienced by a subsistent spiritual entity which will survive the body's death. It is, of course, important to be clear about the features in which the comparison fails to apply. There are bound to be differences between a union of the Creator with his creation and a union between two created entities, between something which has happened once in the course of the world's history and something of which there are at the present moment over two thousand million instances on this planet. There are differences between the union of two natures in one Person and the union of two constituents of one nature. There is the difference that God the Son existed before the Incarnation, while a human soul does not exist before the event of physical conception. There is the difference that the union between Godhead and manhood in Christ will never be dissolved, whereas the union between the body and the soul of a man is temporarily dissolved at death. In fact the attempt to press the comparison to the limit leads us straight into heresy, and indeed into several heresies at once. And yet the comparison has a real value. For the truth, and indeed the only truth, which it is concerned to emphasise is that, both in the conception of a human being and in the Incarnation of the Son of God, we have a case wherein an organic pattern of life existing upon one level of being is appropriated by and drawn into the life of a subject existing on a higher level, without any of its own essential functions being ejected or suppressed. The union in Christ of human nature with the divine Person does not in any way mutilate the human activity, although that activity does not condense within itself its own subjective centre, but has as its subject the pre-existent Person who has made it his own; so far from being suppressed, the human activities are ennobled and perfected by the union. So, *mutatis mutandis*, the union of man's body with his soul does not suppress the biological functions which man shares with the brutes, although that activity has as its subject not that purely immanent mentality which is what we mean when we speak of the "sensitive soul" of an animal, but the subsistent spiritual entity which is the rational human soul; so far from being suppressed, the biological functions are ennobled and perfected by their union with the rational soul. The union of body and soul does not maim the body's integrity any more than the union of Godhead and manhood in Christ maims the integrity of the manhood; to suppose so would be to fall into an anthropological error which would be the analogue of the Christological heresy of Monophysitism. But neither, on the other hand, does the distinction of body and soul mean that body and soul lead separate and disconnected lives, any more than the distinction of Godhead and manhood in Christ means that, in Christ, God and man lead two separate and disconnected lives; to suppose that would be to fall into an error analogous to Nestorianism. In each case a lower level of being is taken up into the life of a superior subject without losing its own reality and distinctness; and this is why, in spite of all the cautels with which it needs to be placarded, the comparison which was quoted from the Athanasian Creed is legitimate and useful.

3. THE ORIGIN OF THE HUMAN SOUL

The transcendence and substantiality of the human soul raise an important question about its origin. It is well known that, in the early days of the Church, the opinion was held in certain quarters that the soul was pre-existent to the body, and that its embodied state was a penalty imposed upon it for some pre-natal sin; man was, in fact, to all intents and purposes a fallen angel. This view, the most distinguished supporter of which was the great Alexandrian apologist Origen,[1] obviously has its roots in Greek rather than Judaeo-Christian thought; it savours of the Platonic doctrine that the soul is the real man. Its rejection, which was formally promulgated at the council held at Constantinople about the year 540 and which has been endorsed by the general consensus and tradition of Christendom, involves the consequence that the soul makes its appearance in the body at some

---

[1] Cf. N. P. Williams, *The Ideas of the Fall and of Original Sin*, p. 210 f.

time between conception and birth. This involves two questions: How is the soul produced, and when?

The former of these questions was the subject of the historic controversy between traducianism and creationism. The traducianist view held that the soul, like the body, is derived by generation from human parents; the creationist view held that each soul is a fresh creation by God, infused into the humanly derived body. Both in the East and in the West great authorities can be quoted for either view, but in the Western Church the creationist view finally established itself and was approved by St Thomas Aquinas.[1]

Prima facie there might seem to be much to be said for traducianism. Not only physical but also mental and spiritual qualities are frequently inherited, and it might seem that the easiest way to account for this was to assume that the soul of a new human being is in some way composed of fragments of the souls of the parents. Again, creationism would seem to posit a supernatural and miraculous interposition of the divine activity into something which, however striking it may be, ought surely to be thought of as a purely natural process. Something like two thousand children are conceived each day in Great Britain alone; are we to suppose that in each of these there is involved a strictly miraculous act of God? If so, this particular type of miracle would seem vastly to outnumber all other types. I think, in fact, that these objections rest upon a misunderstanding, that all the points that can be argued in favour of traducianism are congruous with creationism, and that traducianism is really nonsensical. For what meaning can we assign to the statement that the new soul is composed of fragments of the souls of the parents? When we say that the *body* is derived from the parents we know what we mean. We mean that the bodies of the parents produce respectively an ovum and a spermatozoon, that these two gametes physically unite in a way familiar to biologists, that the fertilised cell absorbs nourishment from its environment and divides into two, that the process of nutrition and division is repeated again and again, that differentiation and organisation of the embryonic mass sets in, until in the end we get the fully formed individual. This whole description depends upon the

---

[1] Cf. *S. Theol.*, I, cxviii, 2.

fact that the entities with which we are dealing are material objects which are extended and divisible in space; it becomes simply unintelligible if we try to apply it to a subsistent spiritual entity which is located in space only in the sense that it animates a spatially extended body. When we are concerned with reproduction of living creatures below the human level, traducianism may well be true. For, as we have seen, on the sub-human levels, the soul is a purely immanent principle; it has no concern with anything except the life of the body and presumably cannot exist in separation from it. Indeed it seems hardly accurate to speak of the creature as 'having a body and a soul', if this phrase is meant to imply that the soul is an entity which can be thought of as functioning on its own; it might be better simply to say that 'the body is alive'. How little anything like real individuality is involved in the possession of such a soul is shown by the fact that in many sub-human organisms, some of which have a fairly large differentiation of physical structure, it is possible, by artificial or natural means, to produce the most remarkable combinations and divisions; newts with two heads but only one tail, planarian worms which can be sliced into a score of fragments each of which develops into a new planarian worm, particoloured tadpoles formed by grafting the front half of one species on to the back half of another. "Can we insist on calling a hydra or a turbellarian worm an individual", asks von Bertalanffy,

> when these animals can be cut into as many pieces as we like, each capable of growing into a complete organism? Other experiments with fresh-water polyps also demonstrate the extreme vagueness of the notion of the "individual". It is easy to produce a double-headed polyp by making an incision at the anterior end. Afterwards the two heads compete: if a water-flea is caught, both heads quarrel about the booty, although it does not matter at all which one takes it—in any case it goes down into the common gut, where it is digested and so benefits all parts.[1]

So long as a soul is nothing more than the form of organisation of particular arrangements of matter, there seems no reason why souls should not divide and combine as does the matter of which they are the forms. Centuries ago Aristotle remarked that "in

[1] *Problems of Life*, p. 48.

the case of plants some parts clearly live when divided and separated from each other, so that the soul in them appears to be one in actuality in each whole plant, but potentially more than one".[1] In the case of man, however, the soul is transcendent to, as well as immanent in, the physical organism; it is a subsistent entity round which the life of the physical structure is organised; it does not exist simply in connection with the body, rather the body exists in connection with it. It assumes to itself the body with all its sensitive and vegetative operations in a way which, as we have seen, Christian thought has seen to be analogous to the way in which, at a higher level still, the Person of God the Son has assumed to himself a complete human nature with all the operations, sensitive, vegetative and rational as well, which go to make up a complete human life. And just because the human soul, in its higher levels of activity, in its powers of abstraction, contemplation and so on, has its own sphere of life which is not concerned merely with that material partner which we call the body, it seems impossible to conceive of it as dividing, combining and changing its identity simply in accordance with the vicissitudes of the matter with which it is associated. Creationism seems to be inevitable, but we must not fall into over-simplification or neglect the truths which traducianism was intent on preserving.

If, therefore, we agree with the view which has come to prevail in Christian theology, that each soul is an immediate product of the creative act of God, we must not assume that this act is entirely arbitrary or that the soul will bear no marks of the ancestry from which its physical associate is derived. The soul is made for a body, and each soul is made for the body which it actually receives.[2] Now, since the body is derived from the parents in accordance with the ordinary laws of heredity, the soul with which God unites it will not be a mass-produced article but will be made for the particular body which it is to animate. The infusion of a soul into a foetus which it did not "fit" would produce not a human being but a monster. Thus, while holding that the *soul* is a fresh creation, we can still hold that the *human being* is continuous with the past history of the

---

[1] *De Anima*, II, ii, 413 b.

[2] Cf. St Thomas Aquinas: *Haec enim anima est commensurata huic corpori e non illi, illa autem alii, et sic de omnibus (S.c.G.*, II, lxxxi).

race, and there is nothing to prevent us from supposing that mental characters, like physical ones, are registered in the gene-structure of the chromosomes. Creationism thus not only admits but requires the general principle and laws of physical heredity. But we must beware again of over-simplification.

For since the soul is the supreme and governing principle of the human being it cannot be simply passive to the inherited character of the body to which it is united. From the moment of union it will begin, in however primitive and inchoate a way, to mould the life of the body. It must indeed fit the body at the start, and it will itself develop and extend its potentialities *pari passu* with the development of the body. But the body will be subject to the soul, not of course in the sense that the soul will be entirely independent of the limitations that existence in a body, and in that particular body, imposes upon it, but that, working within those limitations, it will control the future life of the whole psycho-somatic unity which is the living man. There should be no particular difficulty about this notion, though it is not easy to put it succinctly into words. We are all of us familiar with the fact that the soul does govern the body, although, in doing this, it has to respect the limitations that the body imposes; it can under normal conditions decide whether the body shall sit down or stand up, it cannot decide that the body shall run at sixty miles an hour or sprout daffodils. And although in its beginnings the life of the human foetus will be extremely rudimentary, this intimate combination of a real subordination of the body to the soul with an equally real restriction of the soul by the body, and a development of the soul *pari passu* with the body, will be present from the moment of animation.

We have still, however, to consider the objection that the creationist doctrine postulates a strictly miraculous act of God in the conception of each human being. Now this objection is valid and serious if we hold a deistic doctrine of God's creative activity, but not if we hold the traditional orthodox Christian view. From the deistic standpoint, *any* activity of God within the universe, subsequent to the act by which he created it at the beginning and set it in motion, is strictly miraculous. In its day-by-day functioning the world is able to get on perfectly well on its own by making use of the powers with which God long ago endowed it. From the orthodox standpoint, on the other hand, the creative activity of God is present to any being throughout its existence. As I emphasised in a previous lecture, when discussing the creation of the universe,[1] the first moment of a creature's existence in no way differs from any other, except from the standpoint of the creature. Whether we are considering the world as a whole or an individual human soul, the creative act by which God conserves it is outside time, and posits the creature and its temporal span together. The trouble about creationism is the word itself, which, applied as it is to the beginning of the soul's existence in abstraction from its subsequent development, can only too easily carry a suggestion of deism with it. In an orthodox setting, however, creationism in no way posits a strictly miraculous act of God at the conception of each human soul; it is a statement about the nature of the human soul, rather than about the creative activity of God. It says that the human soul is something that cannot be made out of pre-existing components and that it can therefore only be understood as something whose temporal span of existence is bounded by a first moment; no more than in the case of the beginning of the world is it supposed that this first moment marks a change in the creative activity of God. Furthermore, the way in which God is concerned with the origination of the soul is part of his ordinary *concursus* in nature. I have in an earlier lecture[2] raised the question whether, in view of our knowledge of quantum phenomena, we have to hold that in the individual microscopic events of the physical world, as distinct from the statistically averaged macroscopic effects, the primary causality of God must be conceived as operating without the conjunction of secondary physical causes. Whatever may be the answer to that question, there is not, in the light of what I have just been saying, any relevant difference between the activity of God in ordinary physical and biological processes and in the origination of a human soul. God acts by respecting and concurring with the secondary causality with which he has endowed his creatures, not—except in strictly miraculous interventions—by suppressing it or superseding it. We might indeed sometimes find ourselves reflecting, if the thought might be allowed without irreverence, that it would be

[1] Cf. ch. iv supra.   [2] Cf. ch. v supra.

a good thing if God interfered a little more in the process of human conception than he does; certainly his *concursus* in the process might seem sometimes to involve a remarkable connivance with human acts that are positively against his will. This is, of course, only a special case of a very pervasive problem, the problem of God's extreme forbearance with human perversity and his extreme respect for human freedom; it does not differ in essence from the question why God did not strike Hitler dead or why he doesn't "stop the atomic bomb". This is not the place for its discussion. I have mentioned the matter only to emphasise the point that the creationist view of the origin of the human soul does not involve a suppression of the natural order by a miraculous intervention on the part of God.

I shall touch more briefly upon the other matter which I mentioned in this context, that of the moment of animation of the human foetus by the soul. Here it is obviously impossible to speak with confidence. The general medieval view, which was held by St Thomas among others,[1] was that conception and animation are not simultaneous, but that animation takes place later than conception, probably at the moment when the first stirrings of the embryo are perceptible in the womb. This view is much less common among theologians to-day. As Dr Herbert Doms has pointed out, and as indeed is notorious, the medieval view of conception rested upon a very inaccurate acquaintance with the physiological facts.[2] We need not pursue the topic further than to remark that at the present day most theologians who have considered the subject incline to hold that the rational soul is infused into the physical organism at the moment of fertilisation of the ovum by the spermatozoon;[3] this does not, of course, mean that the exercise of rationality is immediately apparent. As has been already emphasised, the soul always fits the body; it follows that when the body is extremely rudimentary the soul will be extremely rudimentary too. It *is* a rational soul, for one day it will exercise rational functions, but at the start those functions are entirely potential. The life of the human being will

---

[1] *S. Theol.*, I, lxxvi, 3 *ad* 3; cxviii, 2 *ad* 2.

[2] *The Meaning of Marriage*, p. 69 f.

[3] It would be difficult to suppose this in the cases of human "monsters", and there is some evidence that in these cases the abnormal development is due to influences *after* conception; cf. M. Abercrombie in *New Biology 17* (1954).

gradually develop from the vegetative to the sensitive and finally to the rational level, and the soul will successively operate on these levels also. Observation of very young children might lead one to doubt whether, even by the time of birth, the life of the soul has yet got beyond the sensitive level; but that does not prevent it from being a rational soul.

A few words may not be out of place at this point about that mysterious and distressing condition known as "multiple personality", in which the behaviour of the person afflicted is almost as if the body was inhabited alternately, or even simultaneously, by two or more individual subjects. We must always be on our guard against taking abnormal phenomena as a canon for the interpretation of normal ones; this is a tendency to which psychiatrists, with their professional concern with pathological cases, are inevitably exposed. From the point of view of our previous discussion, with its stress on the way in which mental characteristics are influenced by and registered in the physical organism, there is no difficulty in admitting that in certain cases part of the organism may begin to function as a relatively autonomous whole; that, for example, a certain section of the brain should operate as a comparatively self-contained system, so that the soul is in the painful condition of being the subject of two more or less isolated mental lives. This is a matter for investigation by psychologists and neurophysiologists; all that needs saying here is that multiplicity of mental lives is quite consistent with unity of the rational soul which is their subject.[1] Of course, it is conceivable that sometimes there may be a genuine multiplicity of *subjects*; that is a case not only for the psychologist and the neurophysiologist, but also for the exorcist. The two cases may be very difficult to distinguish, and the difficulty may be enhanced by their occurring together in the same patient. As the treatment needed will be markedly different, the danger that attaches to a false diagnosis is obvious. The annals of psychopathology and of ascetic theology show striking examples of this lamentable fact. But in principle I think the distinction is clear.

There has been in recent years a good deal of speculation about

---

[1] Dalbiez categorically states that there is not the least reason for asserting a break in the metaphysical unity of the individual (*Psychoanalytical Method and the Doctrine of Freud*, II, p. 14; cf. ch. i passim).

the possibility of using human genetic material for biological experiments. From time to time rumours have circulated of experiments in the crossing of human beings with apes, although definite information is difficult to obtain. Up to now the theme has mainly been one for imaginative novelists, though it ought to be remembered that the imaginative novelist is sometimes remarkably successful in forecasting the trend of scientific achievement. In his novel *Moscow 1979* Mr Erik von Kühnelt-Leddihn introduces two quasi-human haploid monstrosities, produced by the fertilisation of human ova with chemical substances. Mr Olaf Stapledon, in his *Last and First Men*, has given his imagination even freer rein. I am not at the moment concerned with the morality of such manipulations as these, but with their theological aspects. Some people will no doubt think that their mere possibility is in conflict with the Christian view of man and that therefore the theologian ought, in defence of the Christian Faith, to denounce them as ridiculous and unrealisable. I cannot see that this is so. What we should think about creatures of the type I have described will depend upon whether their physical organism is united to a rational soul, and this will depend simply upon the decision of God. They might be simply animals, or they might be something more. That the human body is capable of giving rise to organisms living a relatively independent life on some sub-rational level is in fact true. Blood-corpuscles provide one instance, spermatozoa another, and the human embryo in its early stages (unless we hold that animation and conception are simultaneous) provides a third. It would, I suggest, be highly unwise, as well as theologically quite unnecessary, for us to deny the possibility of even stranger phenomena, though I doubt whether in fact anything can be very much stranger than the way in which the general creative activity and *concursus* of God, the desires and passions of human beings, and the normal process of the physical world are interrelated in the conception and birth of an ordinary human child. I suspect that it is only its unfamiliarity that makes Mr Stapledon's book seem more fantastic than any matter-of-fact treatise on human genetics and embryology. The moral aspects of this question will depend largely upon the place that we believe the human species to have in the designs of God; I shall say something about this in the next lecture. I shall leave the matter here for the time being, and shall return to the point from which I digressed, namely the appearance of man as a rational being in the course of the evolutionary process.

4. THE UNITY OF THE HUMAN RACE

If the union of the soul and body in each individual man is to be conceived as I have suggested, the human species has, at least so far as this planet is concerned, a unique and exalted status; I have discussed in a previous lecture the possibility of the existence of rational beings in other parts of the universe.[1] It is thus a matter of some interest to enquire whether the whole of the human species is descended from one pair of primitive rational ancestors, or whether, on the other hand, the different branches of mankind have independent origins, in which case the hypothetical common ancestors of all mankind, if indeed there are such, will have to be sought in some pre-human and sub-human species. Theologians have very commonly assumed that the Christian Church has a particular interest in maintaining the former view; for only so, it has been felt, can we account for the universal infection of the human race by that highly mysterious taint which theology knows as original sin. Thus, for example, in the encyclical *Humani generis* of 1950, immediately after the passage already quoted, in which the physical evolution of man is explicitly declared to be an open question, the Pope goes on to say:

There are other conjectures, about polygenism (as it is called) which leave the faithful no such freedom of choice. Christians cannot lend their support to a theory which involves the existence, after Adam's time, of some earthly race of men, truly so called, who were not descended ultimately from him, or else supposes that Adam was the name given to some group of our primordial ancestors. It does not appear how such views can be reconciled with the doctrine of original sin, as this is guaranteed to us by Scripture and tradition, and proposed to us by the Church. Original sin is the result of a sin committed, in actual historical fact, by an individual man named Adam, and it is a quality native to all of us, only because it has been handed down by descent from him.[2]

[1] Cf. ch. i supra.   [2] Trans. by R. A. Knox, C.T.S. ed., p. 21.

This pronouncement upon a matter which is primarily the concern of biologists seems to me to be very unfortunate, even though it has not the character of an infallible definition. As is shown in the late Dr N. P. Williams's great work on the subject,[1] original sin is an extremely difficult and obscure conception, however certain we may be of its reality. I have mentioned before the amusing, and presumably apocryphal, story of a Russian Orthodox priest who was also an experimental geneticist, who was convinced that he had located upon one of the human chromosomes the gene that carries original sin and who was hoping by irradiation to produce an allele by making use of which he would breed a mutated human line which would be free from this lamentable defect.[2] I do not of course suspect Pope Pius XII of so crude a view, but I think that since the days of St Augustine theologians have shown from time to time a tendency to conceive the transmission of original sin too much from a quasi-biological standpoint.[3] Two things, as I have already suggested, need to be remembered. First, original sin is a negative principle of incoherence, rather than a positive taint; it is propagated not, as it were, by some specific mechanism which exists for the purpose, but rather by the absence of a principle of unity which would maintain the human race in unity and integrity. As I have written elsewhere:

> If the chief effect [of the Fall] is a destruction of unity . . . no mechanism is needed to transmit the *absence* of something. It is presumably original righteousness rather than original sin that would require a *mechanism* for its transmission; and since the Fall that mechanism is no longer there.[4]

Indeed, the term "mechanism" can only be used in a highly analogous sense, even to describe the transmission of original righteousness, and this will lead on to my second point. The unity of the human race, which is implied in the notion of original righteousness, and which has been lost as a result of sin, is not fundamentally a physical or biological unity, even though its presence or absence may have consequences in the biological

[1] *The Ideas of the Fall and of Original Sin* (Bampton Lectures, 1924).
[2] Cf. ch. i, p. 34 supra.
[3] Cf. N. P. Williams, op. cit., p. 327 *et al.*
[4] *Christ, the Christian and the Church*, p. 156.

realm. It is metaphysical, or it would perhaps be better to say *theological*; and it is none the less real for that. Original sin is thus the common property of all men, not in virtue of their physical descent from Adam but of their membership of the human species. However repugnant this notion will be to positivists, it must be emphasised that both our fallenness and our redemption are communicated to us not by physical inheritance from our parents, but through our participation in the common nature of humanity. (I will anticipate protests by hastening to add that this common nature of humanity is a very remarkable thing, and is quite unique. I have argued elsewhere that it altogether transcends the various traditional doctrines of the philosophical schools about universals and particulars.)[1] The consequence is that sin occurring anywhere in the human race will make itself felt throughout, not just as a tendency to evil-doing but as an interior dislocation of man's relation to God in the ontological roots of his being. If, therefore, God has arranged things in such a way that the essential nature of humanity has been embodied independently in different branches of a pre-hominid stock, I cannot see that this in any way weakens the doctrine of original sin.

Having said this, it may be well to add that the general weight of opinion among present-day anthropologists seems fairly strongly to agree with the Pope, though on different grounds from his, in rejecting the polygenistic theory. Thus Mr I. W. Cornwall writes:

An uncommonly human-like simiid (*Proconsul*) lived in East Africa in the Lower Miocene. It seems, then, that the original separation of the human and simian stems may have taken place in Africa at least as early as this. . . . It is possible, of course, that the Hominidae [that is, the zoological Family that consists of the one genus *Homo*] could have arisen independently from two or more distinct forms of ape, at different periods and in different parts of the world; but the human family is found, even at its earliest appearance, to be basically so homogeneous that it is generally concluded that such parallel evolution cannot have played so important a part in its first emergence. This does not exclude the play of parallel evolution among the Hominidae at a later stage.[2]

[1] *Existence and Analogy*, p. 58 f.; *Corpus Christi*, p. 11.
[2] *Chambers's Encyclopaedia*, IX, p. 32, *s.v.* "Man, Evolution and Antiquity of".

It remains to add that all that anthropology can investigate is the emergence of a creature which has the *physical* characteristics of a human being. Whether it was the divine plan to infuse a rational soul into the first animal whose cerebral and other bodily characteristics were sufficiently complex to provide an adequate physical correlate, or whether there was a period when there existed sub-rational beings that were physically indistinguishable from men, is a matter that we can decide for ourselves in accordance with our several ideas as to what it was fitting for God to do; but I cannot see any way of settling the question decisively apart from a direct revelation from heaven.

This has been a somewhat diffuse discussion in which we have reached only few and tentative conclusions. That was to be expected and we ought not to be disappointed. It has been my fundamental conviction throughout these lectures that, whereas there are a good many useful and important things that can be said about the borderline where science and theology overlap, we cannot look to either of those disciplines to settle the other's problems. When all is said and done, the truth remains to which the book Genesis testifies, that, however long the process may have been and of whatever unimaginable complexity, the Lord God has formed man of the dust of the ground and breathed into his nostrils the breath of life; and man has become a living soul.

Chapter Eight

THE PURPOSE OF CREATION

Colligite quae superaverunt fragmenta, ne pereant.—
Johan. vi. 12.

I. THEISM AND HUMANISM

IT has been my object in these lectures to give a reasonably
full discussion of a small number of selected questions
bearing upon my subject, rather than to attempt a broad, and
therefore necessarily more superficial, survey of the whole realm
of the relations between Christian theology and natural science.
This has inevitably resulted in little or no attention being given to
some quite interesting and important matters. I have, for example, said nothing about the large and impressive mass of work
that has been done in recent years in the field of parapsychology,
in the experimental and statistical investigation of the alleged
phenomena of telepathy, clairvoyance, precognition and psychokinesis. I must confess that I very much doubt whether this
particular branch of research, even if its findings are as well
founded as its proponents maintain, is of quite as much importance for the human race, in either its theoretical or its
practical aspects, as some of them believe. I do not myself think
that the Central Question about Man is exactly what Professor
Rhine thinks it is, or that parapsychology is as capable of solving
it as he asserts.[1] Nevertheless, other things being equal, it would
no doubt be better to discuss parapsychology, or any other
science, than to ignore it. I frankly admit that my main reason
for avoiding it is my incompetence to form any reliable opinion
about the correct interpretation of phenomena about which, in
spite of certain notable conversions from scepticism to belief,
there is still very animated dispute. For much the same reason I
have said nothing about spiritualistic and mediumistic pheno-

---

[1] Cf. J. B. Rhine, *The Reach of the Mind*, ch. i, "The Central Question about
Man".

mena. It would, I am sure, be very unwise, as well as quite unnecessary, for a theologian to build his main case for the freedom of the will or the subsistent reality of the human mind upon parapsychology, or for human survival upon spiritualism. Some of my other omissions are due simply to plain straightforward ignorance; I have thus made no reference to the voluminous and fascinating material provided by the social anthropologists. It may provide some slight excuse for this to point out that even scientists themselves are very often remarkably ill-informed about scientific matters lying outside their own immediate field of work. Anyone can test this for himself by asking a chemist a question about comparative anthropology, or even by asking a nuclear physicist a question about astrophysics. This fact implies no slur upon the scientists; but it does witness to the extreme specialisation and technicality which characterise twentieth-century science, and to the grave perils which beset anyone, and not least the unwary theologian, who is so rash as to wander unaccompanied through such a vast, varied and rapidly developing countryside. At best he is in danger of losing his bearings and wandering round in circles; at worst, of sinking slowly into a bog or suffering sudden and violent destruction from unsuspected representatives of the local fauna. However, as I pointed out in the first of these lectures, I have had no intention of answering all the questions or tying up all the loose ends of my subject. What I have tried to do is to show, by discussing a certain number of matters in which both theology and science have an interest, that it is possible to be an orthodox Christian without either ignoring or repudiating the discoveries and theories of present-day science. This is a task which no one could hope to perform even imperfectly without a good deal of assistance, and I am happy to acknowledge the help that has been given me, sometimes unwittingly, by various scientific colleagues, while they are not, of course, responsible for my mistakes. What I have been trying to do is to open up a field of discourse between theologians and scientists which has for too long had its gates locked on both sides. Whether I have managed to undo the locks it is not for me to decide, and whether anyone else will want to enter the field remains to be seen. In any case, I am sure that I have myself profited by my flounderings, though that is perhaps insufficient justification for occupation of the Bampton Lecturership.

Having said this, I shall now in this last lecture make some attempt to see my subject in its wider aspects. We are sometimes told at the present day that the choice between a theistic and a humanistic interpretation of the universe is one that cannot be made at the rational level, but requires an existential engagement (blessed phrase!) of the whole man. If this means that it is impossible simply to argue someone into theism as you might argue him into accepting Green's theorem about volume and surface integrals, I agree; for, though I believe that the traditional approach of natural theology to the existence of God is valid, its acceptance appears to depend upon an attitude of mind which, however authentic it may be, modern industrialised man has been conditioned not to possess.[1] Again, I would agree that mere intellectual assent, necessary as it is to a rational religion, is sterile and futile unless it leads to a personal commitment of one's life to God. I cannot, however, agree that the choice between Christian theism and humanism rests upon an act of blind choice without any intellectual content. Such an act would be simply immoral, for one has no right to commit oneself to an interpretation of the universe and of human life unless one is convinced that that interpretation is true. The relation between the intellect and the will in the act of Christian faith may be very mysterious; one could hardly read Gardeil or Farrer or Trethowan[2] without admitting that. The ability of the human mind to see God in his works may be weak and clouded, and the evidences of God's purpose in nature may be disquieting and ambiguous; Christian theology agrees, and has an explanation why this is so. The process by which any particular person arrives at belief in God may involve the convergence of a great many different indications derived from experiences of very diverse types; presumably no two persons travel along precisely the same path, and the amount of conscious ratiocination that is involved may in some cases be very small. Furthermore, there is in the spiritual biographies of some persons an agonising stage

---

[1] Cf. my *He Who Is*, p. 80; *Existence and Analogy*, p. 69, 80. Cf. p. 272 supra.
[2] A. Gardeil, *La Crédibilité et l'apologétique*; A. M. Farrer, *Finite and Infinite* and *The Glass of Vision*; I. Trethowan, *Certainty*.

of doubt which is only resolved by the almost desperate decision to commit oneself, on the ground that only by such commitment can that clearer knowledge of God be attained by which (if there is a God) the doubt will be ultimately dissipated. All this is true, and yet the fact remains that the state which is finally achieved must include an intellectual acceptance and not consist merely of a reiterated act of naked choice. And if it includes an intellectual acceptance, then the question whether there are any rational grounds for such an acceptance can hardly be by-passed. Nobody —or at least only a person who was either pathologically sophisticated or else a complete moron—could commit himself to the service of God in complete indifference as to whether there was a God or with the conviction that there was not.

This may all seem to be very obvious, but in fact a good deal of play has been made in recent years with the idea that the difference between Christian theism and humanism is simply the difference between two attitudes to life, and that the decision whether to be a theist or not is like the decision whether to eat jam or honey. The word "existentialism" is very useful here. But, strangely enough, one finds the same position being taken up in practice by many people who would claim to be following the severest dictates of reason. Fifteen years ago Dr C. H. Waddington wrote a book which received a good deal of atten-tion, entitled *The Scientific Attitude*. The title is significant and, except for the fact that "humanistic" would be a more exact adjective than "scientific", it accurately describes the contents of the book. For what the book expresses is not a rationally argued position but an attitude, namely the outlook upon life and the universe which looks to science to provide all that a man or woman can need. There is no *argument* for the truth of scientific humanism; yet its truth is clearly not taken to be indifferent. It is in fact taken as being too obvious to need argument; and the fact that the great majority of civilised twentieth-century people assume that it is true is taken as an implicit proof of its truth.

2. THE PURPOSE IN THE PROCESS

I have, I hope, already made it clear that I do not hold that scientific arguments, as such, can decide between theism and atheism. There is, I would maintain, an approach to the world which can make this decision, but it is a metaphysical and not a scientific one. Admittedly, many proponents of natural theology in recent years have claimed that the knowledge of the universe which has been achieved in the last three centuries shows it to be the theatre in which a great purpose is gradually unfolding itself and that this fact provides at least presumptive evidence for the existence of a great Designer. Dr F. R. Tennant's great work *Philosophical Theology*, which was published in the late twenties, provides one of the most monumental examples of the argument from "cosmic teleology". Nevertheless the approach seems to me to be a very ambiguous one.

It is, I think, significant that the only form of teleological argument which occurs among the "Five Ways" of St Thomas Aquinas is one which makes no reference to large-scale teleology at all. The *Quinta Via*[1] is based upon the assertion that every process, however minute it may be, must have a final cause of some kind. Any attempt to base belief in the existence of God upon the design that is alleged to be found in nature comes straight up against the problem of evil. The occurrence of evil presents, indeed, a serious problem even for a theism which is based upon metaphysics; but there it is the problem of how its existence is to be reconciled with the existence of God, not the problem whether evil disproves his existence. The metaphysical approach, which is based upon the *existence* of the world will, of course, carry no weight with the positivist, but if its validity is accepted it is conclusive. The argument from cosmic teleology, on the other hand, is based upon an examination of the world's empirical characteristics. It claims to argue from the nature of the world's plan to the nature of the planner, and the nature of the planner will depend on the nature of the plan. And when the plan is examined it does not seem at all points to be the sort of plan that a beneficent deity would put into operation. If the argument from design proves anything at all, it might well seem to prove that the designer, if there is one, is either malicious, quixotic or incompetent. And modern science seems to enhance, rather than to dispel, this suggestion, for some of the things that it has discovered about the universe are very strange indeed.

[1] *S. Theol.*, I, ii, 3c.

We ought not to be too much disturbed by those features of the universe which are merely aesthetically displeasing. Most of us, I imagine, feel a faint sensation of disgust on first hearing about the domestic arrangements of the marine worm *Bonellia*, in which the female is an inch or two long, while the male is a minute parasite which lives inside the reproductive organs of the female. If we had been arranging the process of evolution, we feel, we should hardly have thought of that. Zoologists, however, rapidly accustom themselves to arrangements like this and can indeed admire them for their beauty. It is clear that the aesthetic sense, like most other faculties, requires training if it is not to ignore or reject some of the objects which it is meant to apprehend; and, while the fact that we appreciate beauty in some things is *prima facie* evidence that they are beautiful, the fact that we find some things ugly and distasteful need mean nothing more than that our aesthetic sense is very largely untrained. The positive evidence of the man whose eyes are open is worth very much more than the negative evidence of the man whose eyes are shut. The amazing variety of the modes under which life is lived on this earth, a variety which seems to be greater than anything that is demanded by the variety of its environments, may indeed repel the economical mind of the bourgeois, who feels that one or two simple and efficient methods of living ought to be enough for any planet and indignantly inquires, like the disciples in the gospel, "To what purpose is this waste?" To God, however, whose resources are infinite, such prudential considerations may be altogether irrelevant. This astounding collection of living creatures, with their amazing, and perhaps quite unnecessary, diversity of methods of nutrition, locomotion and reproduction may simply be a witness to the exuberance and versatility of God, who never gets tired of making something new and is glorified no less by the marine worm than by the gazelle. No one, I think, could fail to be fascinated by the stories of animal behaviour in Konrad Lorenz's book *King Solomon's Ring*. It has been remarked that the Victorian business man, while he was repelled by the prodigality of nature, which seemed to him to be thoroughly wasteful, approved of natural selection and the survival of the fittest, which seemed to be simply the application in the biological realm of something with which he was quite familiar in the realm of commerce. I suggest that the reverse is in fact the truth; that the prodigality of God is something which we ought to expect and in which we ought to rejoice, while on the other hand there are features of the biological struggle which pose serious, if not unanswerable, questions for theism and which suggest that, even if the world as God's creation is good, something has gone very seriously wrong with it.

It is, of course, important not to exaggerate here. Dr C. E. Raven has reminded us[1] that the cruelty of nature, "red in tooth and claw", has been often misconceived. In the absence of a brain with a highly developed frontal cortex, the chief ingredients of suffering—memory, imagination and anticipation—could be present, if at all, only in a very rudimentary form. Dr C. S. Lewis's description, in his novel *That Hideous Strength*, of the mental life of the brown bear Mr Bultitude, whose "mind was as furry and as unhuman in shape as his body",[2] is perhaps as far as we can get in sympathetic understanding of the consciousness of a sub-human creature. "Pain", Dr Raven tells us, "does not take a major part in the experience of any organism below the human level; and . . . the life of wild creatures far from being spent in constant fear is active, rhythmic and, if such a word be allowed, joyous."[3] We may admit all this and nevertheless feel troubled by examples such as those given by Sir Charles Sherrington of the life-cycle of the liver-fluke and the malaria parasite. The fascinating and at the same time rather horrible stories are told, as only Sherrington could tell them, in his Gifford Lectures *Man on his Nature*: I shall summarise them briefly.

The liver-fluke starts life from the egg as a small pond-worm which bores its way into the lung of a water-snail and turns into a bag which feeds on the snail's blood. There its cells become separate individuals, which bore their way out into the body of the snail and live upon it, skilfully preserving their food as long as possible by starting with the less vital parts. They breed in the body of the dying snail, and finally the young ones bore their way out and settle down in an encysted form among the green leaves at the edge of the pond. They are swallowed by a browsing

---

[1] *Natural Religion and Christian Theology*, II, p. 116. Cf. ch. i, p. 35 supra.
[2] Op. cit., ch. xiv.   [3] Loc. cit.

sheep or ox, the cyst is dissolved in the animal's stomach, and the liver-flukes thus released swim from the stomach to the liver, where they suck the animal's blood and mature. The animal is then suffering from "sheep-rot". After three months the mature flukes produce eggs, which pass down the animal's liver-duct and escape to the wet pasture; thence as free larvae they reach the pond and look for another water-snail. And then the whole story begins afresh. "It is", says Sherrington, "a story of securing existence to a worm at cost of lives superior to it in the scale of life as humanly reckoned. . . . The example taken is a fair sample of almost countless many."[1]

Well, we may reflect, it is only a question of one sub-human being against another, and did not Dr Johnson say that there is no settling the point of precedency between a louse and a flea? Here, then, is Sherrington's second story, and it is one in which we ourselves are directly concerned. I shall somewhat amplify his account, for research conducted since he wrote has shown the process to be even more elaborate than he recognised.

The gnat *Anopheles* lives by stabbing our skins with a conveniently shaped organ and extracting a drop of human blood. So far, so good; we have plenty of blood to spare, and the dose of poison which the gnat injects in order to increase the flow of blood to the spot, while it is irritating does us no real harm. Sometimes, however, the gnat's poison-gland is swarming with the sporozoites of a microscopic parasite, *Plasmodium*. When injected into the human bloodstream with the dose of poison which the gnat administers, these parasites are carried to the liver, where they enter the parenchyma cells. Such a parasite will then multiply by asexual division until it has formed some thousands of minute "merozoites". The cell bursts and the merozoites are set free. Some of them will enter fresh liver-cells and repeat the process, but others will attack the red cells of the blood. Each of these settles down, eats out the inside of the cell, grows and splits up into a family of young. The cell bursts, the young escape into the blood stream, where each one attacks a red cell as its parent did, and eats up the cell in turn. As the life cycle of these

[1] Op. cit., p. 265. We could, of course, start the story at any point of the cycle. Dr H. A Baylis, in his article in the *Encyclopaedia Britannica* (14th ed., XXII, p. 451, *s.v.* "Trematodes") begins with the fluke in the liver of the sheep.

parasites lasts three or four days, millions of infected cells will break down simultaneously about twice a week, disgorging the enclosed parasites and, with them, poisons which are highly injurious to the human host and which cause a paroxysm of fever. Furthermore, this army of parasites in the blood will be periodically augmented by reinforcements arriving from the liver. This is the story of the terrible scourge known as malaria, but it does not end here.

A stage arrives at which, instead of continuing as before, the parasite prepares for a sexual stage of existence. In each red cell, instead of dividing asexually, the parasite turns into an immature male or female form which, instead of bursting the cell, settles down and waits. It waits until another gnat comes along and bites the human sufferer; the blood which the gnat draws into her stomach contains many red cells inhabited by these patiently waiting immature sexual forms. In the gnat's stomach these latter rapidly develop into mature sperm-cells and ova. Fertilisation occurs, each fertilised ovum subdivides into hundreds of cells which break off as separate individual parasites and swarm in the gnat's blood. They swarm especially in the poison-gland in the gnat's head, where they are ready, next time the gnat bites, to infect a fresh human being. Here are Sherrington's reflections on the process:

> This parasitic animal scourges with misery and death entire regions of Earth's surface which might but for it be happy places. A poet who had seen much of it called it "million murdering", and that is true. Its life is the destroying of other lives, and it infects nearly one-third of Earth's human population. It is a product of evolution. Evolution has adapted it, complexly, delicately and effectively to kill other lives. Since it requires man for its slaughter it would seem an evolution of recent date. Its hideous cycle has overcome with "ingenuity" great obstacles to perpetuate itself. For instance, from within the gnat's stomach it must win its way to the poison-gland. How does it know the poison-gland? Perhaps a chemotactic principle directs it thither.[1]

There are, of course, as Sherrington points out, many ways in

---

[1] Op. cit., p. 269. The complete story, including the more recently discovered subsidiary cycle in the liver, is given by H. E. Shortt in *The British Medical Bulletin*, VIII, p. 7 f. (1951). I have confined myself in the text above to the briefest outline.

which such a story may be interpreted. The naturalist and the physician naturally lapse into language that supposes mentality on the part of the plasmodium: "each merozoite tries to enter a red cell", and so on. But, says Sherrington,

> we can take another line of thought. We may say the creature which benefits by the scheme is but expressing a purpose, not of its own conceiving, but of the Design which runs traceably through Nature. With attribution of that kind to Design runs attribution likewise of infinite Knowledge and infinite Power.[1]

We might, of course, with the positivists, take a third course and say simply that this is the way things happen, and that is all that is to be said about the matter. For the Christian theist this last course is not open. He believes that the whole process is under the ultimate control of God, and stories such as that of the malaria parasite raise a question of which he is bound to take note. Two questions at least force themselves on his attention. How has this kind of thing come about in a world which is the creation of a good and almighty God? And what, if anything, is God doing about it?

3. EVOLUTION, EVIL AND THE FALL

With regard to the former of these questions, I must take up again a point touched on in my first lecture. Christian theology has not waited for the researches of micro-biologists before asserting that something has gone very badly wrong with God's world. The doctrine of the Fall and its effects has been part of its teaching from the start. The act by which, at the beginning of his history, man broke away from the God who is the source of his being—the first case, presumably, of rebellion against God's ordering of the world originating from within the material order —has traditionally been seen as introducing disorder and disorganisation into the whole of man's nature and all of his relationships. Not only have his spiritual faculties been impaired, but his bodily life and his relation to the rest of the material universe have been thrown out of joint. It has been widely held that, while bodily death is natural and proper for an irrational being whose mental life never rises above the affairs of the body, the

[1] *Man on his Nature*, p. 271.

union of the body with a rational soul would, if man had not sinned, have made the body capable of receiving from God a transformation into a glorified and immortal condition analogous to that which we see in the transfiguration and the ascension of the perfect man Christ our Lord. From this point of view, then, man's mortality and his liability to physical disease are consequences of his failure to make that joyous and loving acceptance of the will of his Creator in which he would have found not only spiritual and mental, but also physical beatitude. In the metaphorical imagery which is its proper instrument of communication, the book Genesis sees the Fall of Adam as involving his exclusion from the tree of life, and his expulsion from a paradise where all things were subject to him into a land where the soil bears thorns and thistles and where he can maintain himself only by the sweat of his brow. It is important to stress that it is not the mere *existence* of parasitic organisms that raises problems for theodicy; many parasites are perfectly harmless to their hosts. The evil lies in the unbalanced condition in which the parasite can survive only at the expense of its host's life or happiness. And many of the organisms which are harmful to man, whether they are as elaborate in their structure and life-history as *Plasmodium* or as simple as the viruses, seem to have evolved into their existing forms subsequently to man's appearance.

It thus does not seem extravagant to suggest that a great deal at least of the suffering which human beings undergo may be attributed to the disorder that man has introduced into his world by his rebellion against God. We must remember also that the fact that man experiences his suffering as an evil is very largely due to his alienated condition. We have seen already that beneath the level in the evolutionary scale at which rationality appears the most distressing accompaniments of pain are probably lacking, in consequence of the absence of imaginative anticipation based upon conscious memory. With the appearance of rationality, there arrives also the possibility of anxiety and apprehension as we know them, with all the intensification of suffering that they bring. But only the possibility; for it is also possible for one who is entirely convinced of the love of God and fully surrendered to his will to accept pain, at its most intense, as something for which God can be thanked and which can become a means of

sanctification both for the sufferer and for those on whose behalf
he accepts it. Such a positive use of pain can be seen in countless
heroic lives. And if the sufferer himself sees no contradiction
between pain and the love of God, why should anyone else?
Admittedly, this does not remove the problem of those who
suffer without making use of their pain in this way. But it does
make it plain that the ultimate evil of pain lies not in the fact that
God allows it to exist, but in the fact that so many of us fail to
use it positively and profitably; that the real root of the problem
lies not in the world around us but in our own selves. We have
thus a further reason for accepting the traditional view that
physical evil, in the only sense in which it raises a real problem
for faith, is a consequence of the Fall of Man.

It may be objected, however, that, in spite of all that has been
said about the comparative absence of suffering in the sub-human
realm, it is impossible to interpret the course of pre-human
evolution as free from distortion and deviation. Even if Nature
is not as red in tooth and claw as Tennyson believed it to be
when he wrote *In Memoriam*, it may well seem to be redder
than we should expect it to be if it was the creation of a beneficent
and omnipotent God. It is therefore well to recall that while,
so far as we know, the first human sin marked the first rebellion
against God that originated within the material world—the first
occasion on which a material creature contravened the will of
God by its own choice—it did not mark the first rebellion against
God within the whole created order. Angels—pure spirits—
had sinned before man; and although man was perfectly free not
to sin, his own sin was provoked by suggestions from the fallen
spiritual realm. And the result of angelic sin may well have been
to introduce into the material realm a disorder which has manifested itself in a distortion of the evolutionary plan. As Dom
Illtyd Trethowan has written in a recent book:

> Sin, then, started with the angels. They refused to *accept* grace—
> that is, the supernatural knowledge and love of God for which they
> were created. They preferred to remain as they were—God was not
> to be allowed to come into the foreground of their intelligences, to
> encroach on their self-sufficiency. Some of the Fathers put it like
> this: that the angels wouldn't stand for the Incarnation, for the
> putting of human nature above themselves. We don't really know

how it ought to be put. Anyhow the sin which the angels committed must have been a sin of pride—a refusal to toe the line. We can't think of any other sin for a pure spirit to commit. One of the results, we may suppose, was a disorganisation of the material universe over which, according to a reasonable theory, the angels had charge. It is a reasonable theory, because it seems to be a general law that the lower orders should be governed by the higher ones, that God's creatures should be arranged in a hierarchy, with a certain dependence of those below on those above.[1]

This suggestion is the more compelling because the doctrine of an angelic fall was certainly not originally postulated in order to account for the existence of evil in the material world before man. It was in fact generally believed that all the evil in the material world was the direct consequence of human sin, even if one of the consequences of that sin was that the world had largely fallen under the domination of the fallen angelic powers.[2] It is

[1] *An Essay in Christian Philosophy*, p. 128.

[2] This is perhaps the most convenient point at which to make some remarks about the demonology of the Bible. It is often asserted that the whole of the New Testament doctrine about Satan and evil spirits must be rejected as being the product of a discredited theory according to which such disorders as insanity and epilepsy were due to possession by demons. I do not think this rejection can be justified. The New Testament does not teach, as many people apparently think it does, that the world is under the undisputed dominion of its Creator with the exception of a few unhappy human beings who are inhabited and controlled by demons. What it does teach is that the whole world lieth in the evil one; that is, that to a greater or less degree the whole created order is under the power of the rebellious forces of evil. This being so, the places where this diabolic rebellion will be most devastating and destructive will be those places where, possibly by taking advantage of some congenital or acquired mental weakness, it has achieved a specially firm grip upon the personality of a rational being. Those whom the New Testament describes as possessed by devils are not the only beings in God's creation who have fallen under the influence of the evil powers, but they are, as it were, the strong points of the revolt. It is for this precise reason that our Lord singles them out for direct and frontal attack; he strikes the rebellion where it is strongest and where it is most harmful. If the demonic powers can be routed in the key positions where they are most firmly entrenched, they are in principle already defeated. It is therefore only to be expected that, after his first successful encounter with Satan in what we somewhat misleadingly describe as Christ's temptations but might perhaps better describe as the devil's first trouncing, our Lord launches his main assault upon the strongholds in which the diabolic forces have acquired exceptional control over the minds of human beings. If we approach the question from this standpoint, I think we shall agree that, in spite of their admittedly imperfect medical knowledge, the New Testament writers were not fundamentally mistaken in their understanding of Christ's attitude to both mental and physical disease.

therefore striking that the twin beliefs that the angels had charge over the material world and that many of them had fallen away from God before the commission of the first human sin were, so to speak, stored away in readiness for answering a problem as yet unthought of, namely that of a possible distortion and deviation in pre-human evolution.

I do not claim that the above discussion clears up every single obscurity in a matter that is more than usually obscure. I have, for example, said nothing about the perennial problem as to why God should allow his creatures to rebel against him and why he should not take immediate action to annul the consequences of their revolt. This, however, is not a specifically scientific question, but rather a theological or philosophical one, and I do not think that I have very much to add to the standard discussions. What I hope I have shown is that the traditional doctrine of the origin of evil in the world is, in its essential features, fully compatible with what science has discovered in recent years; and I do not think that there is any need for us to take refuge in such theories as that which the late Dr N. P. Williams so eloquently expounded in his Bampton Lectures of 1924, of a pre-cosmic fall on the part of a hypothetical World-Soul or Life-Force. "The World-Soul", he wrote,

> ... was created good; but, our theory must continue, at the begin-ning of Time, in some transcendental and incomprehensible manner, it turned away from God and in the direction of Self, thus shattering its own interior being, which depended upon God for its stability and coherence, and thereby forfeiting its unitary self-consciousness, which it has only regained, after aeons of myopic striving, in sporadic fragments which are the separate minds of men and perhaps of superhuman spirits.[1]

And the results of this catastrophe?

> We can at least feel sure that this interior self-perversion, which we have hypothetically attributed to the collective Life-Force which was God's primal creature—this orientation away from God and in the direction of ruthless self-assertion—would necessarily manifest itself in a development of organic life permeated through and through with the spirit of selfishness, manifested in ferocious competition and in a bloodthirsty struggle for existence. It might

[1] *The Ideas of the Fall and of Original Sin*, p. 526.

a priori have been expected to appear in the cruelty which ravages the animal world, in the unknown maleficent factor which hindered the due development of herd-instinct just when the anthropoids were becoming men, and in the mysterious ebullitions of pure fiendishness which, within the sphere of responsible human action, are known as "criminality". If, in harmony with later Jewish and primitive Christian thought, and with the consensus of those who are known as "spiritual experts" in every age of the newer dispensation, we are prepared to admit the existence of evil discarnate intelligences, it would doubtless follow that the malevolent nature of such beings was to be regarded as the outcome of the pre-mundane Fall of that World-Soul, of which they, equally with men and beasts, would be the offspring.[1]

For all its ingenuity and the persuasiveness of its presentation, I find this theory very difficult to render intelligible and, for the reasons which I have given above, I do not believe that we are in fact constrained to make such a drastic departure as it involves from the main body of Christian tradition.

4. GOD'S METHOD WITH EVIL

So much, then, for the origin of the world's evil. What is God's reply to it?

There is a natural and understandable impulse on the part of the human mind to say that God, if he had the power, ought to have intervened at the moment when the first sin was committed and have forcibly cut off its consequences at their root. In its crudest form this impulse is embodied in the remark which one heard at intervals during the Second World War, "If there is a God, why doesn't he strike Hitler dead?" Natural as this reaction is, it is doubtful whether those who give way to it fully understand its implications. For if I demand that other people should be struck dead or paralysed in the commission of their sins, I must also demand that I should be struck dead or paralysed in the commission of mine; the obvious reply that, however nasty they may be, my sins are not as far-reaching in their consequences as Hitler's, will seem clearly sophistical to anyone who has

[1] *The Ideas of the Fall and of Original Sin,* p. 527. In expressing disagreement with Dr Williams on this point, I do not wish in the least to belittle the extraordinary brilliance and value of his treatise as a whole.

fully realised the gravity of sin as such, the inherent malignance
of even the least rebellion of a creature against its Creator.
Christianity at least is clear that, even at the cost of appearing
to be helpless or to be conniving at the consequences of sin, God
will not destroy its effects by destroying the freedom of his
creatures. It is in fact one of the supreme manifestations of God's
love for us that he prefers the intermittent and half-hearted
homage which we offer him by the exercise of the mutilated
freedom which we still possess, to the infallible and automatic
service which he could exact from us if he was content to destroy
our freedom and reduce us to the condition of machines. The
Christian view of the way in which God undoes the effects of
evil, by the Incarnation, Passion and Resurrection of his Son
and by the incorporation of men and women into the Church
which is Christ's Body, is bound to appear unnecessarily complicated and fantastically devious to anyone who has not realised
this; it will also appear to involve a quite callous acquiescence
in human suffering while this long and tortuous process is
going on. Christian faith is, however, sustained by two convictions. The first is that God can afford to deal so patiently and
gently with human perversity because his ultimate victory is
certain, and he therefore has no need to make sure of results by
taking short cuts. The second is that God's ultimate rewards are
so entirely satisfying that even those who have gone through
the depths of pain and degradation—even the victims of Belsen
or Hiroshima—will in the end see of the travail of their soul and
be satisfied. Without Christian faith we can only encourage
ourselves with the pagan's reflection that nothing can last for
ever:

O passi graviora, dabit deus his quoque finem.[1]

The Christian, on the other hand, is confident of an end which
will make the previous pain amply worth while and to which the
pain itself will have mysteriously contributed.

A woman when she is in travail hath sorrow, because her hour
is come: but when she is delivered of the child, she remembereth no
more the anguish, for the joy that a man is born into the world.[2]

[1] Virgil, *Aeneid*, I, 199.   [2] John xvi. 21.

To the Christian these words are of cosmic significance; and even while he is in the depths of suffering he can receive a dim, but nevertheless genuine, participation in the glory that shall be hereafter.

To follow up this line of thought in detail would take us outside our present subject into the realm of dogmatic theology in the strict sense. We cannot, however, avoid it altogether. For the doctrine of the Incarnation, while fully compatible with all that science has found out about the world, bestows upon the world's history a purpose and a direction which science left to itself is powerless to discern. There is a respectable body of Christian thought, of which the chief medieval representatives were the school of Duns Scotus, which holds that even if man had not sinned, God the Son would nevertheless have become incarnate, in order to bring the created world to a peak of splendour and glory which it could in no other way have achieved. And even those, such as the theologians of the Thomist tradition, who have felt that such speculation goes beyond the bounds of solid and reliable argument, have maintained that, whatever would have been the case if man had not sinned, the actual fact is that the Incarnation has not only redeemed man from his fallen state but has also conferred a supreme dignity upon his human nature. Liberal theologians have sometimes viewed Jesus of Nazareth as simply the culmination of the evolutionary process, maintaining, as one of them has said, that "what is *ex hypothesi* potential in all men—that is, the complete union of the human with the divine— was actualised in" Christ,[1] but this seems to me to claim both too much and too little for human nature. Too much, in that it exaggerates the inherent powers of fallen human nature and belittles the extent to which the evolutionary process is distorted; too little, because the dignity that has been conferred upon human nature by its assumption by God the Son as the *instrumentum conjunctum* of his divine Person vastly exceeds anything that even unfallen human nature could have attained by its own natural powers. The Incarnation, as orthodox theology conceives it, is the result of a direct intervention of God into the created world; but it is an intervention which does not suppress nature but exalts and perfects it. Thus the Incarnate Lord is *both* true God *and* perfect

[1] J. F. Bethune-Baker, *Journal of Theological Studies*, XX, p. 187 (1919).

man. If we wish to see the place that God has assigned to man in the history of the universe, it will not do simply to examine the physical and mental characteristics of man and compare them with those of the higher apes, impressive as the results of such an examination may be. Man's primacy is not indicated adequately by the fact that his brain is two or three times as heavy as that of the gorilla, or his lasting importance by the fact that it has not appreciably changed in size for two hundred thousand years. From the purely biological point of view there seems to be no reason why man should not advance to a higher stage of physical development, with correspondingly enhanced mental abilities. Nor is there any scientific reason why, somewhere else in the universe, such more highly developed beings should not exist already. Man's crowning dignity consists in none of this, but in the fact that in his nature the Son of God has become incarnate. I raised in the first lecture of this course the question whether it is conceivable that, in addition to his assumption of human nature, God the Son might assume the nature of some other rational creature or creatures as well. If the answer to this highly speculative question should be in the affirmative, man's position in the universe would not be unique, but our present point would be unaffected. It is that the supreme privilege which God has conferred upon the human species comes from without and not from within the order of nature, though nature is glorified and transfigured by it.

5. THE VIRGIN BIRTH: A DIGRESSION

It is the failure to appreciate this point that has caused so many discussions of the virginal conception[1] of our Lord to be confused and pointless. That Jesus of Nazareth was born from his mother by the operation of the Holy Ghost and without the agency of a human father, is part of the age-long tradition of the Church and is enshrined in the Church's creeds. However, the essence of the Incarnation is not the virginal conception but the hypostatic union, the assumption of human nature by God the Son. Liberal theologians have shown a curious and revealing

[1] This phrase is more strictly correct than the commoner phrase "the virgin birth", which I have used in the heading of this section.

indecision about the virginal conception. It is, of course, fundamental to their position that nothing supernatural or miraculous, nothing that would make him different from us except in degree, must be allowed to attach to Christ. But they have shown a tendency to waver between the view that the virginal conception is impossible and therefore cannot have occurred, and the view that it is quite possible but of no special significance. The tendency among the earlier liberals was, of course, to deny it altogether. Later on, as science has become more and more familiar with parthenogenesis in many types of living creatures, a tendency has shown itself to suggest that the virginal conception may well have occurred as a rare but purely natural example of parthenogenesis in the human species. The late Dr E. W. Barnes, in his Gifford Lectures of 1927-9, wrote, in a somewhat inconclusive paragraph, as follows:

> I have, personally, little doubt that biological research will in due course prove a human virgin birth to be possible. Probably the individual so produced would be haploid, with but half the normal number of chromosomes, and the chances are that its sex would be male. But whether haploid or normal, male or female, it would vary little from the normal mental and emotional make-up of the human race.

After a somewhat sneering remark about "breaking the entail of sin", Dr Barnes continued:

> . . . there is no reason to believe that a human being produced by parthenogenesis would lack normal appetites and passions. Biological parallels indicate that, if haploid, such an individual would probably be of subnormal physical development. I do not personally think that such development could be regarded as "congruous with" the Incarnation, though Rendel Harris in an ingenious investigation has adduced some evidence to show that Jesus of Nazareth was below normal height. It may be added that, if the story of the Virgin Birth be rejected, Jesus will remain, as St Mark implies, the son of Joseph and Mary. We should then know of nothing in his ancestry to explain the moral ascendancy and religious genius which were undoubtedly his. These qualities might be held to result from a dominant mutation: and if all mutations are to be regarded as manifestations of the creative activity of God, the

spiritual excellence of Jesus would be from God. As these lectures clearly show, I personally do not doubt that God acts in and through the evolutionary process; and between such a mode of divine action and the assertion of the divinity of Christ I see no necessary opposition.[1]

The one thing that clearly emerges from this passage is Dr Barnes's determination to eliminate the supernatural from the Incarnation and to interpret what he calls the "divinity" of Christ in terms simply of human moral excellence. But it is of interest for the absence of the assumption, made by earlier liberals, that the virginal conception of Christ can be dismissed out of hand.

Some remarks from a very different angle are to be found in a small book by a Roman Catholic scientist, Dr F. Sherwood Taylor's *The Fourfold Vision*. It is there argued that, so far from human parthenogenesis being an impossibility, there is some evidence bearing in the contrary direction. He instances an account published in 1939 by Reimann and Miller, who claimed to have caused an unfertilised human ovum to commence development by mechanical stimulation in human blood-serum containing a trace of ethyl acetate. He also gives an example of fully successful, artificially produced parthenogenesis in a creature as high up the evolutionary scale as the rabbit; this is striking, because the examples of natural parthenogenesis that are known to naturalists are confined to worms, flies, insects and other sub-mammalian organisms. Dr Sherwood Taylor even goes so far as to suggest that natural parthenogenesis may occur regularly, if infrequently, in human beings. "There is", he says,

> no evidence that in the normal course of nature, one conception in 10,000 or more is not a virgin conception; for were it to be so we would be very unlikely to discover it. There is at present the small positive evidence that girls of good character are occasionally known to allege this occurrence in their own cases (I know of two instances). They are, of course, disbelieved; but only on grounds of analogy, not of positive proof. Such proof might, of course, be supplied by examination of the chromosomes of the children. In the case of unmarried women of loose morals, or married women, no abnormality would even be suspected.[2]

[1] *Scientific Theory and Religion*, p. 458.   [2] Op. cit., p. 48.

Dr Sherwood Taylor remarks, quite rightly, that these cases have "no real bearing on the case of our Lord's birth, for the essence of that event was its supernatural character." The point is, however, of interest as showing the extreme difficulty of deciding what events are possible and what impossible, even on the natural level. A parallel case is provided by the phenomenon of stigmatisation. It was the general practice until recently among Protestant writers to reject the accounts of stigmatisation of Catholic mystics as fabrications; the occurrence and the careful investigation of contemporary cases has, however, produced a tendency, among both Protestant and Catholic writers, to look upon them as genuine occurrences, but not as essentially supernatural.[1]

Very few theologians, even among those who are most convinced of the truth of our Lord's virginal conception and of its centrality in the corpus of Christian dogma, would be prepared to argue that it would be in the strictest sense *impossible* for the Incarnation to have taken place through the instrumentality of an ordinary act of procreation by two human parents; it is never wise to set limits to the power of God. Nevertheless, we can maintain without any colour of paradox that a virginal conception was far more *congruous* to the requirements of the case. For the Incarnation does not mean, as any normal act of human procreation means, the beginning of the existence of a new human person; it means the giving of a new nature, a human nature, to a divine Person who already existed and had existed from all eternity. We ought not, in strict speech, even to say that the Holy Ghost played the part of a human father—to say that would be to assimilate the Incarnation to the pagan legends in which women bear sons to gods—for what the Holy Ghost did was to make Blessed Mary into a virgin-mother, and that is a very different matter. In the Incarnation there is both continuity and discontinuity. There is continuity, because the human nature which the Son of God united to himself was taken from a mother who was a member of the existing human race; what God became was *man*. There is discontinuity, because something happened in the Incarnation which had never happened before; he who became man was *God*. For the Incarnation to have taken

[1] Cf. H. Thurston, *The Physical Phenomena of Mysticism*, ch. ii.

place through an ordinary act of human intercourse would in fact have involved a greater interference with the normal working of nature than for it to have taken place by a virginal conception; for in the former case there would have been the whole causal framework which normally issues in the production of a new personal subject, and God would have had to withhold his concurrence at the last moment, as it were, in order to prevent these causes from having their natural and normal effect. In the provision of a human nature from a virgin-mother for a divine Person who already existed, there is no such interference with the existing causal framework; a unique type of causal constellation is producing a unique effect. I think it would be found on investigation that most of the people who hold, in the words of a celebrated Report, that "a full belief in the historical Incarnation is more consistent with the supposition that our Lord's birth took place under the normal conditions of human generation"[1] have a view of Christ that is much closer to adoptionism or Nestorianism than to orthodoxy. If we believe that Christ was a purely human being who was at some stage of his life elevated into a relation of sonship to God, or that in him there were two persons, a divine and a human, side by side, the statement just quoted would seem perfectly true. But it seems to be very difficult to justify if, in Jesus of Nazareth, God had become man. As to whether his chromosomes were haploid or diploid it would, I think, be hazardous to speculate.

6. EVOLUTION AND THE INCARNATION.
THE END OF THE STORY

We must now return, after this long but not perhaps irrelevant digression, to the point from which it began. That point was that, in becoming incarnate in human nature, God has conferred upon the human race a dignity that exceeds anything that follows simply from the place that man holds in the evolutionary process. This seems to me to be particularly relevant in view of the power that man is now acquiring over his own physical and mental equipment. In the earlier days of the scientific movement man was

[1] *Doctrine in the Church of England* (1938), p. 82. The signatories of the Report did not, as a body, commit themselves to this view.

standing over against Nature and learning how to manipulate her for his own ends. It was no doubt true, in the words with which Sir William Dampier prefaced his *History of Science*, that Nature could be conquered only by obeying her;[1] still, it was believed that by obeying her she could be conquered. Man stood over against Nature as the artist stands over against his materials. Now, however, man has begun to realise with a shock that he himself is a part of the Nature which he studies and with which he experiments, and that by scientific techniques he can bring about changes in himself.[2] The effects upon human character of leucotomy and lobotomy are by now well known; so are those of psychological manipulation, whether in the comparatively humane forms of educational programmes and highly organised propaganda or in the brutal police methods of the totalitarian states. In their different ways, George Orwell, Arthur Koestler and C. S. Lewis have given vivid and terrifying expression to the present achievements and the future potentialities of these techniques.[3] Still more disquieting are the possibilities of deliberate or accidental interference with the genetic material of the human species, consequent upon the highly detailed knowledge which we are now acquiring about the relation of physical and mental characteristics to the mechanical and chemical structure of the chromosomes in the germ-cells. It is, of course, never easy to discriminate between changes in human conditions which will make men more fully human and those which will tend to dehumanise them; the history of the industrial revolution provides ample material for thought on this question. It does look, however, as if in the fairly near future our knowledge of genetics may be such as to face us with the choice between trying to make man more fully his real self and trying to change him into a different (and, no doubt, from the point of view of the manipulator, a superior or at any rate a less troublesome) species. The

[1] *Natura enim non nisi parendo vincitur.*

[2] A striking expression of a scientist's own anxiety on this point will be found in C. F. von Weizsäcker's *The World View of Physics*, p. 204 f. And, quite apart from any attempt to bring about substantial changes in the human species, the development of such techniques as artificial insemination, transplantation of ovaries and the like raises extremely difficult social and moral questions.

[3] G. Orwell, *Nineteen Eighty-four*; A. Koestler, *Darkness at Noon*; C. S. Lewis, *That Hideous Strength*.

prospects are truly terrifying, and I do not think a Christian can evade them by saying that God would not infuse a rational soul into the products of these manipulations and that the most that could be produced from human beings by such methods would be purely animal offspring. It may be so, but, as we saw previously, God does co-operate to a remarkable extent in the consequences of human generative acts, even when the acts themselves are sinful. And, quite apart from this particular aspect, the question remains whether such attempts to change the fundamental characteristics of the human species are legitimate or desirable. If we answer in the negative, this does not imply any desire to restrain the laudable curiosity of the scientist; it simply means that there must be limits to it somewhere. I do not suppose that anyone would feel that it was, for example, an act of obscurantist tyranny to prevent a scientist from infecting a whole town with cholera in order to satisfy his scientific curiosity about some point in bacteriology. To return to our point, I do not think there is any doubt about the answer which a Christian will give. It is that, in spite of all the folly and misery in which the human race involves itself, he would rather be the kind of being which God has become in the Incarnation than some species alleged to be biologically superior.

We are in fact faced with the question what the next step in the evolutionary process is to be. This question has indeed always been implicitly present ever since the appearance of man on the earth, and man has, in the course of his history, interfered pretty extensively with the evolution of other living creatures. Dr Julian Huxley has made this very clear in his essay on "The Evolutionary Process" which opens the symposium to which I have previously referred.

> Before man could develop the cortical structure by which he achieved undisputed biological dominance, his ancestors had first to become brachiating arboreal creatures, a small and unimportant group confined to certain types of forest, and then to descend from the trees and free their hands by becoming bipedal. But once the critical point was passed at which conceptual thought and true speech could develop, a new method of evolution became possible— the method of cultural transformation, based upon the cumulative transmission of experience. . . .

Thus man is not only the latest dominant type to be produced during geological time, but also the only one now capable of raising the upper level of evolutionary performance, the sole potential vehicle of further evolutionary progress for life. And with man, a new method of evolutionary transformation has come into being, as different from the purely biological method of the natural selection of self-reproducing variants as that was from the methods of inorganic cosmogony. . . .

The new phase of evolution thus opened up was characterised by a new relation between the organism and its environment. The human type became a microcosm which, through its capacities for awareness, was able to incorporate increasing amounts of the macrocosm into itself, to organise them in new and richer ways, and then with their aid to exert new and more powerful influences on the macrocosm. And the present situation represents a further highly remarkable point in the development of our planet—the critical point at which the evolutionary process, as now embodied in man, has for the first time become aware of itself, is studying the laws of its own unfolding, and has a dawning realisation of the possibilities of its future guidance or control. In other words, evolution is on the verge of becoming internalised, conscious and self-directing.[1]

In view, then, of this alarming power which man has acquired over his own future, what do we want the human race to become? What do we want man to be? I have already said that the Christian, remembering that God himself has become man, can only reply that he wants man to be man. This may sound a somewhat unadventurous and uninspiring answer, but it is in fact nothing of the sort. Christianity does not believe that God became man simply in order to bring human history to a full stop and to reduce man to the status of a divinely certificated fossil. The Incarnation did not only set upon man the seal by which God guarantees man's imperishable importance and inalienable dignity; it brought into the world a new thing and inaugurated a new era of human history. The human organism which the Son of God took from his Virgin Mother and in which he died and rose from the dead was not destroyed by his resurrection and ascension; it was transfigured and glorified and made accessible to men. By baptism a man or woman is incorporated

---

[1] *Evolution as a Process*, pp. 11–13.

into this glorified humanity of the Word-made-flesh and is made one with those others who have been likewise incorporated, thus becoming a member of the Church which is Christ's Body. By the new birth of baptism he becomes a member of the restored human race, whose first member and head is Jesus Christ, as by his natural birth he became a member of the fallen human race, the race of the sons of Adam. His further progress is then not progress within the natural order, but within the supernatural order of grace and redemption, though within the supernatural order the natural order will itself be fulfilled and transfigured. And what is God's will for individual human beings is his will for the human race. Dr Huxley was speaking more truly than perhaps he realised when he wrote that with man a new method of evolutionary transformation has come into being, though "evolutionary" is too weak a word to use. It is the method of incorporation into Christ's body and of being transformed into his likeness. What secularised man may do with his newly acquired power over himself it would be hazardous to predict. Quite conceivably he may be carried away into more and more daring genetical experiments, producing from human stock creatures with two heads and with eyes in the ends of their tails, until finally the human race will have modified itself to such an extent that it will have lost the power to modify itself any longer and will perish by a kind of experimental suicide. In a less spectacular way than I have just suggested, we can see this process at work in more than one part of the world to-day. The Christian has a different ideal, the building of human beings as living members into the organism of the Body of Christ. This is a task in which science, like every other human activity, can play its part, but only if it is determined that men are to be men. "He gave some to be apostles, and some prophets, and some evangelists, and some pastors and teachers, for the perfecting of the saints, unto the work of ministering, unto the building up of the Body of Christ; till we all attain unto the unity of the faith, and of the knowledge of the Son of God, unto a full-grown man, unto the measure of the stature of the fullness of Christ."[1] For Christian faith, the ultimate term of human evolution is the Total Christ, consisting of Head and members in intimate union sharing a

[1] Eph. iv. 11–13.

common supernatural life, as "one mystical person",[1] in that
final transfiguration of the whole created order which theology
knows as the resurrection of the body for the life everlasting.
Into what grisly and fantastic blind-alleys man may be led by his
waywardness we cannot surmise, nor how God will bring even
the consequences of folly and sin within the ambit of his final
purpose, the summing up of all things in Christ, both the things
in the heavens and the things upon the earth.[2] Whether the
establishment of God's sovereignty over his creation will have
as its prelude the gradual conversion of the world to Christ or
an almost total apostasy is a question about which Christians
have always differed and about which God has not seen fit to
enlighten us. Men's minds have tended to be swayed by the
condition of the world as they have known it. Whether man will,
by the grace and mercy of God, subdue to his own true interests
the tremendous physical power that now lies in his grasp or will
use it for his own destruction we do not know. The recent advances in intra-atomic physics have led more than one Christian
writer or speaker to suggest that the *solvet saeclum in favilla* of the
medieval hymnodist may be realised by nuclear fission or fusion.
Where we know so little, it is legitimate to speculate but unwise
to come to conclusions. *Hora novissima, tempora pessima sunt*—
perhaps. In any case, *vigilemus*. However the end may be attained,
about the end itself there is for the Christian no doubt at all. God
the Son has become man in Christ, in order that in Christ men
may become the sons of God. "We have begun to be some great
thing", wrote Augustine of Hippo, when the world of his day
was falling about his ears, "Let no man despise himself. We were
once nothing, but we are something. . . . We have said 'Remember
that we are dust'; but out of the dust he made man, and to dust
he gave life, and in Christ he hath brought this dust to the kingdom of heaven, he who made heaven and earth."[3] He who brings
the world out of nothing will not desert his creation. For the
Son of God came to gather into one the children of God that
were scattered abroad, and he will gather up the fragments that
remain that nothing may be lost.

[1] Cf. St Thomas Aquinas, *S. Theol.* III, xix, 4c: [*Christus caput totius Ecclesiae*]
cui omnes uniuntur sicut capiti membra, ex quibus constituitur mystice una persona.
[2] Eph. i. 10.   [3] Quoted by Alfred Noyes, *The Unknown God*, p. 251.

Appendix

A RECENT WORK BY DR SMETHURST

Dr A. F. Smethurst's recent book *Modern Science and Christian Beliefs* has appeared too late for discussion in the text of the present volume; it is an important work by a priest who was for some years engaged in chemical and biological research. His approach is somewhat different from mine, and he covers a wider field in less detail; the place where our discussions to some extent overlap is in his second part, in which he deals with problems arising out of the relation of individual sciences to Christian doctrine. His chapter on the physical sciences is brief and somewhat inconclusive, though he is more confident than I am about the theological implications of modern physics. "The doctrine of Creation", he writes, "cannot be opposed except by postulating that the universe has existed from eternity. . . . But in the light of the subsequent development of physical science and of the conception of entropy, this belief in the eternity or everlastingness of the universe becomes incompatible with one of the most fundamental laws of physical science. Thus the conception of entropy and the Second Law of Thermodynamics seem to supply an exceedingly direct piece of evidence of the truth of the Christian dogma of creation" (p. 92). I have given in Chapter IV above my reasons for rejecting this view; and Dr Smethurst himself refers to the steady-state cosmological theories, though he strangely claims them also as providing evidence for theism. He goes into more detail in the chapter on the biological sciences, and there is very little here with which I would disagree. But perhaps his most valuable discussion is that of the nature of human character, in which he makes detailed use of the discoveries of biochemistry, endocrinology and neurophysiology, as well as of the theories of the various schools of psychology. He stresses very impressively the concern of Christianity with the material side of human nature; though I think, both on theological and on scientific grounds, that he goes too far when he proposes to reject altogether the notion of the soul and asserts that, in teaching the resurrection of the body, St Paul, and the Christian Church after him, maintained that the survival of self-conscious personality was unthinkable apart from a body. This view has presented obvious attractions to modern Protestant writers; I must refer to Chapter VII above for my reasons against it. All these matters are dealt with in the middle section of Dr Smethurst's book; it is preceded by a discussion of such general problems as the presuppositions of modern science and the relation between the Christian virtues and the attributes of a good research scientist, and it is followed by an investigation of the problems presented to the scientist by miracles and creeds. There is in all these chapters much of the greatest interest and importance, but I cannot help feeling that, in attempting to cover so much ground in three hundred pages, Dr Smethurst has set himself an almost impossible task. In only too many cases he drops a theme just when it is becoming interesting and leaves his argument hanging in the air. But in saying this I am perhaps merely voicing the natural sentiments of one who, in his own treatment, has deliberately chosen to discuss a small number of questions exhaustively rather than to give a less intensive survey of a wider field. Dr Smethurst has shown an expert grasp of the outlook and technique of modern scientific research that is all too uncommon in books on this subject, and I am only sorry that his book was not published early enough for me to refer to it in detail at the relevant points of my own argument.

BIBLIOGRAPHY

(The editions mentioned are those made use of in the preparation of this book; in many cases other editions, of earlier or later date, are available. Standard works existing in many editions have not been generally included.)

ADRIAN, LORD (E. D.). *The Physical Background of Perception*. Oxford Univ. Press, 1947.

ALFVÉN, H. *On the Origin of the Solar System*. Oxford Univ. Press, 1954.

ALLERS, R. *The Successful Error*. London: Sheed & Ward, 1941.

ASHBY, W. R. *Design for a Brain*. London: Chapman & Hall, 1952.

BAILLIE, J. *Natural Science and the Spiritual Life*. Oxford Univ. Press, 1951.

BARNES, E. W. *Scientific Theory and Religion*. Cambridge Univ. Press, 1933.

BARNETT, A. *The Human Species*. London: MacGibbon & Kee, 1950.

BARTSCH, H. W. (ed.). *Kerygma and Myth*. London: S.P.C.K., 1953.

BERGSON, H. *L'Évolution Créatrice*. Paris: Alcan, 1927.

BEVAN, E. *Symbolism and Belief*. London: Allen & Unwin, 1938.

BONDI, H. *Cosmology*. Cambridge Univ. Press, 1952.

BORN, M. *Experiment and Theory in Physics*. Cambridge Univ. Press, 1943.

—— *Natural Philosophy of Cause and Chance*. Oxford Univ. Press, 1949.

BRAIN, SIR W. RUSSELL. *Mind, Perception and Science*. Oxford: Blackwell, 1951.

BRAITHWAITE, R. B. *Scientific Explanation*. Cambridge Univ. Press, 1953.

BRIDGMAN, P. W. *The Logic of Modern Physics*. New York: Macmillan, 1927.

BURNET, F. M. *Viruses and Man*. London: Penguin Books, 1953.

BURTT, E. A. *Metaphysical Foundations of Modern Physical Science*. London: Kegan Paul, 1932.

BUTTERFIELD, H. *The Origins of Modern Science 1300–1800*. London: Bell, 1949.

CALDIN, E. F. *The Power and Limits of Science*. London: Chapman & Hall, 1949.

COLLINGWOOD, R. G. *The Idea of Nature*. Oxford Univ. Press, 1945.

COPLESTON, F. *Aquinas*. London: Penguin Books, 1955.

—— *History of Philosophy*. Vol. III. London: Burns, Oates, 1953.

CROMBIE, A. C. *Augustine to Galileo*. London: Falcon Press, 1952.

DALBIEZ, R. *Psychoanalytical Method and the Doctrine of Freud*, 2 vols. London: Longmans, 1941.

DAMPIER, SIR W. C. D. *A History of Science and its Relations with Philosophy and Religion*. Cambridge Univ. Press, 1942.

DARWIN, F. (ed.). *Life and Letters of Charles Darwin*. London: Murray, 1887.

DE BROGLIE, L. *The Revolution in Physics.* London: Routledge, 1954.
DE TONQUÉDEC, J. *Questions de Cosmologie et de Physique chez Aristote et Saint Thomas.* Paris: Vrin, 1950.
DINGLE, H. *The Scientific Adventure.* London: Pitman, 1952.
—— *The Sources of Eddington's Philosophy.* Cambridge Univ. Press, 1954.
Doctrine in the Church of England. London: S.P.C.K., 1938.
DOMS, H. *The Meaning of Marriage.* London: Sheed & Ward, 1939.
DRAPER, J. W. *The Conflict between Religion and Science.* London: H. S. King, 1874.
DUHEM, P. *Essai sur la Notion de Théorie Physique de Platon à Galilée.* Paris: Hermann, 1908.
—— *Le Système du Monde.* 5 vols. Paris: Hermann, 1913–17.
ECCLES, J. C. *The Neurophysiological Basis of Mind.* Oxford Univ. Press, 1953.
EDDINGTON, SIR A. *Fundamental Theory.* Cambridge Univ. Press, 1946.
—— *New Pathways in Science.* Cambridge Univ. Press, 1935.
—— *Relativity Theory of Protons and Electrons.* Cambridge Univ. Press, 1936.
—— *The Expanding Universe.* London: Penguin Books, 1940.
—— *The Nature of the Physical World.* Cambridge Univ. Press, 1928.
—— *The Philosophy of Physical Science.* Cambridge Univ. Press, 1949.
FARRER, A. M. *Finite and Infinite.* London: Dacre Press, 1943.
—— *The Glass of Vision.* London: Dacre Press, 1948.
FLEW, A. G. N. (ed.). *Logic and Language.* Vol. I. Oxford: Blackwell, 1951.
FREUD, S. *The Future of an Illusion.* London: Hogarth Press, 1928.
GAMOW, G. *The Creation of the Universe.* New York: Viking Press, 1952.
GARDEIL, A. *La Crédibilité et l'Apologétique.* Paris: Gabalda, 1928.
GEORGE, W. *Elementary Genetics.* London: Macmillan, 1951.
GILSON, E. *God and Philosophy.* New Haven: Yale Univ. Press, 1941.
—— *Le Réalisme Méthodique.* Paris: Téqui, n.d.
—— *Réalisme Thomiste et Critique de la Connaissance.* Paris: Vrin, 1939.
—— *The Spirit of Medieval Philosophy.* London: Sheed & Ward, 1936.
—— *The Unity of Philosophical Experience.* London: Sheed & Ward, 1938.
HALL, A. R. *The Scientific Revolution 1500–1800.* London: Longmans, 1954.
HESSE, M. B. *Science and the Human Imagination.* London: S.C.M. Press, 1954.
HOYLE, F. *Frontiers of Astronomy.* London: Heinemann, 1955.
—— *The Nature of the Universe.* Oxford: Blackwell, 1950.
HUME-ROTHERY, W. *Atomic Theory for Students of Metallurgy.* London: Institute of Metals, 1947.
HUXLEY, A. *The Doors of Perception.* London: Chatto & Windus, 1954.
HUXLEY, J., et al. *Evolution as a Process.* London: Allen & Unwin, 1954.
HUXLEY, L. *Life and Letters of Thomas Henry Huxley.* 2 vols. London: Macmillan, 1900.
JEANS, SIR J. *The Growth of Physical Science.* Cambridge Univ. Press, 1947.
JEFFREYS, H. *Scientific Inference.* Cambridge Univ. Press, 1937.
JOHNSON, M. *Time, Knowledge and the Nebulae.* London: Faber, 1945.

JONES, SIR H. SPENCER. *General Astronomy.* London: Arnold, 1923.

KALMUS, H. *Genetics.* London: Penguin Books, 1948.

KIMBLE, G. H. T. *Geography in the Middle Ages.* London: Methuen, 1938.

KOESTLER, A. *Darkness at Noon.* London: Cape, 1940.

LASLETT, P. (ed.). *The Physical Basis of Mind.* Oxford: Blackwell, 1950.

LEWIS, C. S. *Miracles.* London: Geoffrey Bles, 1947.

—— *That Hideous Strength.* London: John Lane, 1945.

—— *The Problem of Pain.* London: Geoffrey Bles, 1940.

LINDSAY, J. (ed.). *The History of Science: Origins and Results of the Scientific Revolution.* London: Cohen & West, 1951.

LORENZ, K. Z. *King Solomon's Ring.* London: Methuen, 1952.

McLAUGHLIN, P. J. *Modern Science and God.* Dublin: Clonmore & Reynolds, 1952.

McTAGGART, J. E. *Philosophical Studies.* London: Arnold, 1934.

MARGENAU, H. *The Nature of Physical Reality.* New York: McGraw-Hill, 1950.

MARITAIN, J. *Quatre Essais sur l'Esprit.* Paris: Desclée de Brouwer, 1939.

—— *Redeeming the Time.* London: Sheed & Ward, 1943.

—— *Religion and Culture.* London: Sheed & Ward, 1931.

MASCALL, E. L. *Christ, the Christian and the Church.* London: Longmans, 1946.

—— *Existence and Analogy.* London: Longmans, 1949.

—— *He Who Is: A Study in Traditional Theism.* London: Longmans, 1943.

MATTHEWS, W. R. *God in Christian Thought and Experience.* London: Nisbet, 1930.

MELLOR, J. W. *A Comprehensive Treatise on Inorganic and Theoretical Chemistry.* 9 vols. London: Longmans, 1922–9.

MILNE, E. A. *Modern Cosmology and the Christian Idea of God.* Oxford Univ. Press, 1952.

MITCHELL, O. M. *The Orbs of Heaven.* London: Ingram, Cooke, 1853 (4th ed.).

MONCRIEFF, M. M. *The Clairvoyant Theory of Perception.* London: Faber, 1951.

NOYES, A. *The Unknown God.* London: Sheed & Ward, 1934.

NUTTIN, J. *Psychoanalysis and Personality.* London: Sheed & Ward, 1954.

ORWELL, G. *Nineteen Eighty-Four.* London: Penguin Books, 1954.

PIEPER, J. *Leisure the Basis of Culture.* London: Faber, 1952.

POLLARD, W. G. *The Cosmic Drama.* New York: The National Council of the Episcopal Church, 1955.

PRESTIGE, G. L. *God in Patristic Thought.* London: S.P.C.K., 1952.

PRICE, H. H. *Some Aspects of the Conflict between Science and Religion.* Cambridge Univ. Press, 1953.

PTOLEMY. *The Almagest. Books I–V.* Eng. Trans. Chicago: Encyclopædia Britannica, 1948.

RAMSEY, I. T. *Miracles: an Exercise in Logical Mapwork.* Oxford Univ. Press, 1952.

RAVEN, C. E. *Natural Religion and Christian Theology.* 2 vols. Cambridge Univ. Press, 1953.

READE, W. H. V. *The Christian Challenge to Philosophy*. London: S.P.C.K., 1951.

REICHENBACH, H. *Philosophic Foundations of Quantum Mechanics*. Berkeley: Univ. of California Press, 1946.

RHINE, J. B. *The Reach of the Mind*. London: Faber, 1948.

RITCHIE, A. D. *Reflections on the Philosophy of Sir Arthur Eddington*. Cambridge Univ. Press, 1948.

RUSSELL, LORD (BERTRAND). *Outline of Philosophy*. London: Allen & Unwin, 1927.

RYLE, G. *Dilemmas*. Cambridge Univ. Press, 1954.

—— *The Concept of Mind*. London: Hutchinson, 1949.

SCHRÖDINGER, E. *Nature and the Greeks*. Cambridge Univ. Press, 1954.

—— *What is Life? The Physical Aspect of the Living Cell*. Cambridge Univ. Press, 1944.

SHERRINGTON, SIR C. *Man on his Nature*. Cambridge Univ. Press, 1951.

SIMPSON, J. Y. *Landmarks in the Struggle between Science and Religion*. London: Hodder & Stoughton, 1925.

SLUCKIN, W. *Minds and Machines*. London: Penguin Books, 1954.

SMART, W. M. *The Origin of the Earth*. Cambridge Univ. Press, 1951.

SMETHURST, A. F. *Modern Science and Christian Beliefs*. London: Nisbet, 1955.

SMITH, K. M. *Beyond the Microscope*. London: Penguin Books, 1943.

STAPLEDON, O. *Last and First Men*. London: Penguin Books, 1937.

STEBBING, S. *Philosophy and the Physicists*. London: Methuen, 1937.

STOKES, SIR G. G. *Natural Theology*. London: A. & C. Black, 1891.

SULLIVAN, J. W. N. *The Bases of Modern Science*. London: Penguin Books, 1939.

TAYLOR, F. SHERWOOD. *The Attitude of St Thomas to Natural Science*. Oxford: Blackfriars, 1944.

—— *The Fourfold Vision*. London: Chapman & Hall, 1945.

TENNANT, F. R. *Philosophical Theology*. 2 vols. Cambridge Univ. Press, 1928, 1930.

THORNTON, L. S. *Revelation and the Modern World*. London: Dacre Press, 1950.

THOULESS, R. H. *Authority and Freedom*. London: Hodder & Stoughton, 1954.

THURSTON, H. *The Physical Phenomena of Mysticism*. London: Burns, Oates, 1952.

TOULMIN, S. *The Philosophy of Science*. London: Hutchinson, 1953.

TRETHOWAN, I. *An Essay in Christian Philosophy*. London: Longmans, 1954.

—— *Certainty*. London: Dacre Press, 1948.

TRIMMER, S. *An Easy Introduction to the Knowledge of Nature, and Reading the Holy Scriptures, adapted to the Capacities of Children*. London: Rivingtons, 1817.

UREY, H. C. *The Planets*. New Haven: Yale Univ. Press, 1952.

VERRIÈLE, A. *Le Surnaturel en nous et le Péché originel*. Paris: Bloud et Gay, 1932.

von Bertalanffy, L. *Problems of Life*. London: Watts, 1952.

von Kühnelt-Leddihn, E. M. *Moscow 1979*. London: Sheed & Ward, 1946.

von Weizsäcker, C. F. *The World View of Physics*. London: Routledge, 1952.

Waddington, C. H. *The Scientific Attitude*. London: Penguin Books, 1941.

Walter, W. Grey. *The Living Brain*. London: Duckworth, 1953.

White, A. D. *A History of the Warfare of Science with Theology in Christendom*. New York: Appleton, 1897.

White, V. *God and the Unconscious*. London: Harvill, 1952.

Whitehead, A. N. *Adventures of Ideas*. Cambridge Univ. Press, 1933.

—— *Process and Reality*. Cambridge Univ. Press, 1929.

—— *Science and the Modern World*. Cambridge Univ. Press. 1926.

Whitrow, G. J. *The Structure of the Universe*. London: Hutchinson, 1949.

Whittaker, Sir E. *A History of the Theories of Aether and Electricity*. 2 vols. London: Nelson, 1951, 1953.

—— *Eddington's Principle in the Philosophy of Science*. Cambridge Univ. Press, 1951.

—— *From Euclid to Eddington*. Cambridge Univ. Press, 1949.

—— *Space and Spirit*. London: Nelson, 1946.

—— *The Beginning and End of the World*. Oxford Univ. Press, 1942.

Wiener, N. *Cybernetics*. New York: John Wiley, 1948.

Williams, N. P. *The Ideas of the Fall and of Original Sin*. London: Longmans, 1927.

Wittgenstein, L. *Philosophical Investigations*. Oxford: Blackwell, 1953.

Young, J. Z. *Doubt and Certainty in Science*. Oxford Univ. Press, 1951.

INDEX